Remodeling Your Temple

Restoring Your Physical And Mental Well-Being To Glorify God

PART 2

Laurie K. Dahle

I AM F.E.D.

ISBN-13: 978-1-7323946-1-2

Library of Congress Control Number: 2018906506

Scripture references are from the following sources:

Scripture quotations marked (NIV) are taken from THE HOLY BIBLE, NEW INTERNATIONAL VERSION®, NIV® Copyright © 1973, 1978, 1984, 2011 by Biblica, Inc.® Used by permission. All rights reserved worldwide.

Scripture quotations marked (NLT) are taken from the Holy Bible, New Living Translation, copyright © 1996, 2004, 2007, 2013, 2015 by Tyndale House Foundation. Used by permission of Tyndale House Publishers, Inc., Carol Stream, Illinois 60188. All rights reserved.

Cover and Temple Diagram Designed by Andrew Dahle
Photograph of Temple by Laurie Dahle
Bible verse on cover from NIV

I am honored that God had the confidence in me to write these books. He never gave up on me even when I was discouraged or felt overwhelmed. God has shown me that when I trust Him, He will show me His glory and can do amazing things in my life. God can use my weakness to show His power.

Thank you Dr. Brenda Miano for sharing your love of God and nutrition with me. The information you have shared with me is invaluable. Thank you for being a consultant on the nutrition chapters of this book.

Thank you Andrew Dahle for all your work in designing the cover and temple drawings as well as all the support you gave me as I undertook this project.

Thank you Mary Ann Chase and Lisa Ulrich for helping with editing this book and all your encouragement.

*** Disclaimer: All information contained within this book is for reference purposes only and not intended to substitute the advice given by a pharmacist, physician, or any other licensed health-care professional. Every person needs to be responsible for his or her well-being; therefore, they should research all advice or information so they can make an informed decision as to how they are going to enhance their lifestyle. Although the author has made every effort to provide accurate and complete information we assume no responsibility for errors, inaccuracies, omissions or any inconsistencies herein.

TABLE OF CONTENTS

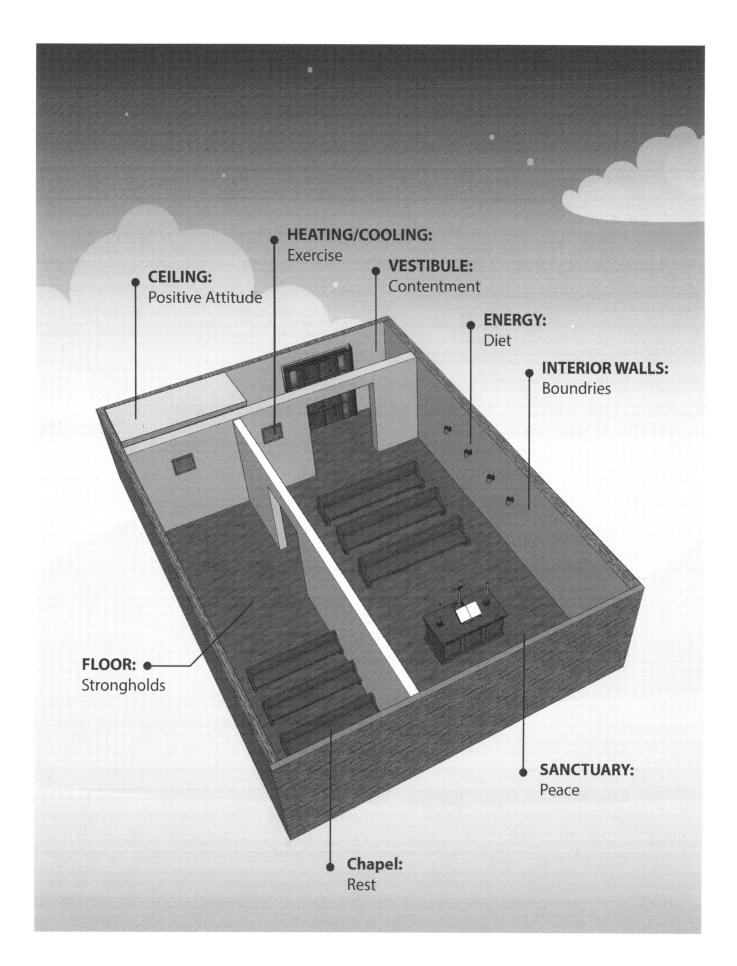

CEILING:
Positive Attitude

HEATING/COOLING:
Exercise

VESTIBULE:
Contentment

ENERGY:
Diet

INTERIOR WALLS:
Boundries

FLOOR:
Strongholds

SANCTUARY:
Peace

Chapel:
Rest

Bible verses for Remodeling Your Temple

Blueprints: *For God is working in you, giving you the desire and the power to do what pleases him.* (Philippians 2:13 NLT)

Trusting The Architect: *Moreover, we have all had human fathers who disciplined us and we respected them for it. How much more should we submit to the Father of spirits and live!* (Hebrews 12:9 NIV)

Walls (Boundaries): *Fearing people is a dangerous trap, but trusting the Lord means safety.* (Proverbs 29:25 NLT)

Ceiling (Attitude): *A cheerful heart is good medicine, but a crushed spirit dries up the bones.* (Proverbs 17:22 NIV)

Sanctuary (Peace): *I pray that out of his glorious riches he may strengthen you with power through his Spirit in your inner being, so that Christ may dwell in your hearts through faith. And I pray that you, being rooted and established in love, [18] may have power, together with all the Lord's holy people, to grasp how wide and long and high and deep is the love of Christ, and to know this love that surpasses knowledge—that you may be filled to the measure of all the fullness of God.* (Ephesians 3:16-19 NIV)

Floor (Strongholds): *Now I stand on solid ground, and I will publicly praise the LORD* (Psalm 26:12 NLT)

Vestibule (Contentment): *For the Kingdom of God is not a matter of what we eat or drink, but of living a life of goodness and peace and joy in the Holy Spirit.* (Romans 14:17 NLT)

Chapel (Rest): *Whoever dwells in the shelter of the Most High will rest in the shadow of the Almighty.* (Psalm 91:1 NIV)

Energy source (Diet): *Then God said, "Look! I have given you every seed-bearing plant throughout the earth and all the fruit trees for your food.* (Genesis 1:29 NLT)

Heating and cooling (Exercise): *Dear friend, I hope all is well with you and that you are as healthy in body as you are strong in spirit.* (3 John 1:2 NLT)

Preface

Commitment To God And Self: Deuteronomy 13:4, 1 Chronicles 28:20, Psalm 139:23-24

Additional verses: Joshua 22:5, 1 Samuel 12:24, 1 Chronicles 28:9, Jeremiah 7:23, Zechariah 6:15, John 15:10, 1 Thessalonians 4:1, 2 Timothy 2:22, Titus 2:12-13

Day 1 of each week let God's Word prepare you for the study. Let His Word give you the insight as to the changes you need to make to improve your life and the strength to make these changes.

Make cards out of the Bible verses and use them throughout the week to help you on your journey as you rebuild your temple.

There are 3 highlighted for each section and then additional ones if you choose to use them or as a reference at a later time. To prepare yourself for the weeks study use these verses to pray to God for guidance and strength to make changes in your life.

COMMITMENT TO GOD AND SELF

My eyes will be open and my ears attentive to every prayer made in this place. For I have chosen this Temple and set it apart to be holy—a place where my name will be honored forever. I will always watch over it, for it is dear to my heart. 2Chronicles 7:15-16 (NLT)

Welcome back. Are you ready to remodel the inside of your temple? Making changes and seeing results can be exciting. God created you with a specific purpose in mind. He has plans for your life and wants you to live your life to the fullest. You were not created to live a mediocre life. Unfortunately, many people let their physical and emotional health become run down and this hinders their living a life that is pleasing and glorifies God. It is essential that both the external and internal structures of the temple be maintained. For some people, their outside of the temple (spiritual) can be structurally sound but the inside (the physical and/or emotional components) of the temple is in disarray.

I hope you had a chance to appreciate all the hard work you have done to rebuild the outside of your temple and now are ready to tackle the remodeling of the inside of your temple. I pray that you are seeing God more active in your life and have an increased dependency on Him. By building a strong external structure, you trust that God can and will give you the strength and willpower to make the changes necessary to live a healthy lifestyle. If you did not do the first part of this study, I hope that after completing this one you will find the time to do it because faith and a relationship with God are essential to living a healthy life. We cannot make the changes on the inside of our temple if the outside is falling down. Faith and trust in God are the keys to changing and living productive lives. As I have said before, we can have healthy physical bodies by eating a nutritious diet, and we can be physically strong, but we are still not completely healthy until we have a strong faith and bask in the love of our Father.

In this book, we are going to tackle our diet and exercise after we look at many of the emotional factors that can affect how we live our lives to their fullest. How we perceive things can change how we react to various situations as well as to how we worship and honor God. Many times our eating habits can be affected by how we deal with stress, our contentment with our lives and feelings of self-worth. We need to seek God's help and trust Him so that He can make us aware of and correct some of the underlying factors that keep us from remodeling our temple. God can give us the strength to overcome our strongholds. Until we seek Him, we will continue to fight the same battles.

When I initially started writing these books, I thought I was going to address mainly diet because I felt that it was the most crucial part of healthy living. As I stated in the first book, when I began my journey on improving my lifestyle, diet was my primary focus followed by exercise. My most significant changes came after I allowed God to take over my life and He became my primary focus.

God and I battled when I started teaching classes about healthy living because I wanted to address diet first. Most of the people that joined my classes were coming for the nutritional information. Each week I wanted to tackle nutrition and God wanted me to address faith first. God kept telling me that although many of the participants may already have a great faith foundation, they had not completely surrendered this area of their life to Him. Living a healthy lifestyle is not only about having the knowledge as to proper nutrition and exercise but also having the ability to utilize it. This includes surrendering this aspect of our lives entirely to God. How many people do you know who preach healthy living, yet are overweight, have illnesses that are worsened or caused by poor diet, or have cigarette, food or alcohol addictions? For many this is because they lack the willpower or have an inability to surrender this aspect of their life to God? We will address nutrition in depth once we address other areas that may affect diet.

I would like for you to review how you rebuilt the outside of your temple and the significance of each part of the temple. You have to have faith (footings) to develop a relationship with God (foundation). Jesus Christ is the cornerstone of your faith. The Holy Spirit (rebar) enlightens you and helps you understand scripture. The Holy Spirit can guide you in prayer (bolts) to keep you connected to God. By building a relationship with God, you can experience His love. When you know God's love, your external walls are structurally sound. The more secure you are in God's love, the better you will be able to love yourself. When you know you are loveable, it is easier to make changes in your life because you see yourself as worthy of change. Christian fellowship (grout) supports you and can hold you accountable for your actions and sharpens your faith. God's Word (roof) is what allows you to build your faith, know God's love and help you stay strong against temptation. Knowing you have a purpose and calling in life (the door) gives you a reason to want to change and to see the necessity for having a healthy body, mind, and spirit. Shame and guilt (windows) can leave you feeling as if you are in a dark place, suffocating, and unworthy of God's love. This can hinder your ability to make changes. Unforgiveness (stairs) blocks your entrance into seeing all God can do in your life. Forgiveness and repentance help you draw closer to God and restores peace and joy. Accepting God's gift of grace (bells) lightens the load you carry throughout life, and you can improve all the other components of your temple. The final piece of the outside of your temple is salvation (steeple). Knowing that you have an eternity in Heaven makes all the struggles and battles you face on earth worth fighting. Now that you have the outside structure of the temple erected, it is time to attend to remodeling the inside of your temple.

At the beginning of the first book, I asked you to make healthy living your hobby. Hobbies are things we enjoy. We want to spend time enjoying hobbies and will often let them take over our lives. Spend as much of your free time as you can on this new hobby, allowing God to help you improve your skills and habits. At first, this may take extra effort to pull yourself away from unhealthy habits that have controlled your life. With the help of God, these patterns will be replaced. You will see that living a healthy lifestyle is a joy and will draw you closer to God.

Spending a mere thirty minutes a day on your new hobby will not allow you to develop new habits and change your lifestyle. This study addresses many areas of healthy living and takes additional commitment if you are going to see life-changing results. Therefore, you need to be willing to incorporate what you learn throughout your day. Your dedication to this study will be well worth it. The effort you put into it will have a direct correlation to the outcome you will see. For some of you, this is your first attempt at making healthy changes in your life. Just reading the material may be the place for you to begin. We all have to start somewhere. I hope that once you become familiar with the material, you will revisit the chapters and utilize the information to make healthy changes.

Making changes in your life requires that you first obtain the necessary information, process it, and finally, apply it to your life. These applications have to become habits. Therefore, you have to spend time re-establishing the norms of your life. It also requires you to be honest with yourself, be willing to look at your life with an open mind, and have a desire to change the unhealthy areas.

Six years ago, God began working in my life to make many of the changes I have addressed in these books. At first, it was not easy, but as I got more comfortable with my relationship with God I learned to trust that He could and would help me change. I then began to enjoy the journey. It has since become my passion. My life has become more fulfilling, and I have found the peace and joy that only God can give. I hope that you too will allow God to work wonders in your life.

I am asking you to commit these next seven weeks to God. Tell Him you are His willing and obedient servant. Let Him know you are willing to do what it takes to not only build a stronger relationship with Him but also to make changes in your life so you can better serve Him.

As I wrote these books, God spoke very clearly to me. He told me that His Word is the most crucial part of this study. Unless you know and live by His Word, your trying to live a healthy life will be very difficult. You may be able to clean up some areas, but until you completely surrender to Him and use His Word as your footings, you will continue to miss the most critical part of healthy living. It is crucial that you have a relationship with your Father and know His love. God created you and therefore understands every aspect of your complex and wonderfully made life. When you surrender to Him and accept His love, you will find you can live your life the way He envisioned for you. It is then you will reap the benefits, and see all areas of your life improve.

In the first book, I asked readers to become more aware of their diets, eating habits and toxins that they encounter. I have included these same questionnaires in the back of this book for you to review. If this is the first study you are doing, you can answer them over the next few weeks so when you begin the diet sections, you are more aware of some of your habits.

For you created my inmost being; you knit me together in my mother's womb. I praise you because I am fearfully and wonderfully made; your works are wonderful, I know that full well. My frame was not hidden from you when I was made in the secret place, when I was woven together in the depths of the earth. Your eyes saw my unformed body; all the days ordained for me were written in your book before one of them came to be. *(Psalm 139:13-16 NIV)* God has given each one of us a plan to live a healthy and productive life. He has a specific calling for each one of us. However, you must be willing to follow His plan if you want to live the life He has intended for you. Your body is a beautifully constructed temple that was designed to be able to fulfill your calling on earth. In doing so, you honor God, your Creator. To live the life God has specially designed for you, you must be willing to keep your temple in good shape. Healthy living is so much more than just eating a clean diet and exercising. I have addressed many of these issues in this study. Over the next seven weeks, you are going to study God's Word and learn how it can help you to lead a healthy, spiritually based life.

These books contain information that you can immediately begin utilizing in your daily life. Sometimes, people join a healthy living group or read a book on this topic because they feel it is going to give them all the answers and not require much work. Although many of us like to think we can make these changes quickly, the reality is that change takes time and hard work. It is not something we can wish to happen and then reap immediate benefits. I have made the material in these books user-friendly by giving the basic information to get you started on this journey. I recommend that if something is not clear or you do not feel you have enough information, research it in more depth. There is plenty of literature out there on all the topics I have covered in these books. I have highlighted each specific option so you can easily find the information and can scan the book when trying to locate a subject. Read the book slowly, so you can take time to digest it.

No two people will travel along the same path. We are all unique individuals who have different needs, levels of determination, financial resources and abilities. As I researched each topic, I have shared the things that I found most valuable for my journey, and I have given different options that have worked for others. Know that you too will have to pick and choose what works best in your life. You, like me, will have to experiment with how you can incorporate what works best in your life. You, like me, will have to experiment with how you can incorporate healthy living into your lifestyle. It will take time to find and become comfortable with a routine that works for you. Don't be hard on yourself when you struggle or make a mistake. Instead, enjoy the journey, and know this is all part of growing and improving your life.

I feel nutrition is essential to living a healthy life. The food we eat determines whether or not our bodies will receive the proper nutrition, maintain a healthy body weight and give us the energy to fulfill our callings. Therefore, I have three weeks dedicated to nutrition. Food plays a vital role in our society. For many, it is a way to socialize. People get together and share a meal. Eating is also a way people mask their emotional pain. When a person cannot quiet their mind, eating diverts the attention. Eating helps to combat boredom and loneliness, which can lead to poor habits and addictions. Our brains begin to associate food with comfort. Eating can bring us pleasure as well as fill many voids in our lives. For some, food has become a crutch to avoid addressing unhealthy matters in their lives. If food is a crutch, a person cannot remove the crutch until there is healing. Before we can make nutritional changes, we have to address issues that may be causing us to overindulge or eat poorly. I have chosen to address nutrition later in the book so that readers can first identify any other factors that may hinder their making changes in the diet so they can be more successful. By allowing our hunger to be for our faith and God, it will help us to break our addiction to food and change our dietary habits.

- Before beginning each chapter, pray that God guides your thoughts and gives you the wisdom to be able to improve your life. Pray that you grow physically, emotionally and mentally as well as spiritually. This growth will enable you to draw closer to God as you go through this journey called life.

- Although this study is divided into weeks, there may be some sections you need to spend extended time to address issues and make changes. Take the extra time you need so that you can improve your life.

•   To start each section, I have given you a list of Bible verses to review. The first several sections pertain to a greater number of subjects, so there are more verses. During the nutrition sections you will not have as many new verses, so use the time to review the other cards. I suggest you write out the verses on index cards. I have highlighted 2-3 verses per subject. Write these out; I have also given you extra verses you can use if you choose. You can then place the cards that pertain to a specific topic together. (I have used loose-leaf binder rings to hold mine together.) If you have a different ring for each subject, you can pull the subject that you are struggling with and read those cards. Use the cards frequently to help you make the necessary changes in your life. You CANNOT make these changes on your own. You must stay in God's Word if you are going to make the changes in your life. God's Word is the ultimate truth, and He can give you strength to help you break strongholds that prevent you from living the life He intended for you to live. There are days when you need to pray, and yet the words do not come. These cards can act as conversation starters with your loving Father. The verses can also be prayers to God, asking Him to help you in a specific area. Use the scripture to remind you of God's promises. Use God's Word to open your heart and mind in preparation to do the homework. By seeking God's Word first, He can reveal things to you that you would otherwise wish to keep buried or not address.

•   Each chapter begins with a Nugget. The Nuggets are part of a ministry that God has called me to do, which I call Nugget of the Day. Each night God gives me a Bible verse and something to contemplate in regards to the verse. Often before I begin a chapter in one of my books God gives me a nugget, which pertains to the subject I am going to address that day.

•   Take time to answer the questions throughout the chapter. The questions will help you to understand the material better and give you direction as to where you need to make changes in your life. Some of the questions have been repeated throughout the study. As you make alterations to your lifestyle, your answers may also change, and you will be able to answer the questions more thoroughly.

•   You will be asked to set goals, and by doing so, you will be able to establish a game plan. Without establishing goals your time will be spent jumping from one idea to another. By having to think about and write the goals you are setting, you are telling yourself that you are ready to make a change. You also need to make sure the goals you set are realistic and attainable. By making short-term goals as well as long-term goals, you will be able to see progress and keep a positive attitude. It is easy to get discouraged and quit when you set unrealistic goals. Spend some time thinking about your goals and being honest with yourself. Don't ignore challenges that are causing you pain or hindering you as you set these goals. You will have to address these concerns if change is to occur.

•   I recommend you use a journal as you read this book. After each chapter record your thoughts. Write your story on these pages. These notes may be something you can look back on and realize how far you have come on your journey. They can also help you design your game plan. It may one day serve as a testimony as to how much you have grown in your faith. Include God moments so you can see just how active He is in your life during this time. In my story, in the next chapter, I share some of my God moments. Write down subjects you want to further research and new things you want to try and implement in your life. Include your feelings, good things that have occurred and struggles you have had. I found that by writing things down, it helped me put into words what I was thinking. It also helped me to address questions I had as I learned new information. It helped me to see how I was growing. I was able to remember the changes that I had forgotten. When I was struggling, I could look back and see the effort I was putting forth was making a difference.

•   On the first day of the section, there is an assignment to start incorporating healthy lifestyle changes into your daily routines. For some, it may be a small thing to do, but this little step puts us in control of making improvements in our lifestyles. For others, it may be a significant change and difficult to find the time to implement. Give your best effort to try and complete these assignments. When you get to the diet chapters, there is a lot of information, and it can be overwhelming if you think you need to make all the changes at once. By becoming more aware of your diet and environment, it will help you to start incorporating small changes, which will lead to the bigger ones. There are also a few bonus assignments.

- Conclude each chapter with a prayer, asking God to help you understand what you have just read. Prayer will empower you to make the changes necessary to help you incorporate healthy living into your current lifestyle.

- At the end of this book, I have referenced books and Bible studies I felt were useful in my journey. You can use these resources when you are ready to delve deeper into a subject you find interesting and want to learn more.

This study requires a commitment of your time to make changes in your life. This commitment is no easy task, and you must be willing to do your homework if you are going to see the results and adopt a healthy lifestyle. I have tried to give you tools to help you make these changes. You will have to decide which means you can use. Please know that it is all right if you cannot do everything in this book. Small changes will eventually lead to more significant changes. Do what you can at this time, and as you begin to make progress, you may want to try to add more changes to your life.

As you work through these books, realize that with God's help, you can take control of your life. Your choices will affect your outcome. I pray that you build a stronger relationship with our loving Father. Additionally, I pray you see God's blessings and experience God's glory as you embark on this journey. If you keep your eyes fixed on our loving Father, He will not disappoint you.

GOD'S WORD
(DAY 1 OF EACH WEEK)

Spend time in God's Word on Day 1 of each Section. Let God prepare your heart so that you are ready to study His ways in which to improve your life. God created you. He knows all about you and has given you the gift of His Word. Hold onto His Word as you muddle through this world. Familiarize yourself with how His Word instructs people to live a healthy lifestyle. God's Word is what gives strength and helps us to get through difficult or trying times. Let His Word guide you so that you make the changes necessary to live a life that serves God and is very fulfilling. Let God's Word become part of you so that it goes deep into the marrow of your bones and is the first defense when life throws you a curveball. Let His Word be the first thoughts that awake you each morning and the last thoughts that bid you a good night. When God becomes first in your life, you will reap the rewards that He has promised you, and you will see His glory.

At the beginning of each week, take the time to look up the highlighted verses in the section you are going to study. Write them on index cards and keep them in a place where you can access them quickly. Use these verses to pray and ask God to give you strength and to help you adopt the healthy lifestyle you long to live. The first several weeks have more Bible verses to go with the week of study. During these first few weeks, it is imperative that you lean into God and ask Him to direct you and to give you strength to meet the challenges you will encounter when making changes in your life. Only God can provide you with insight, reveal the things you need to change, and give you the strength to do so. Along with the highlighted verses, I have given you some extra verses you can use if you like to make more cards to use to let God's Word help you find the strength to make the changes or when you struggle in a particular area. If you do not have the time or energy to write the verses out, just read them. The purpose of this assignment is not to add more work to your life, but to give you help so you can achieve your goals. This study is just the beginning of a lifelong journey to maintain a healthy lifestyle. These cards can help you whenever you face a challenge or need assistance to overcome temptations.

Week 1

Day 1: Review Bible verses
Day 2: The Blueprints
Day 3: Trusting The Architect
Day 4: The Interior Walls
Day 5: The Ceiling

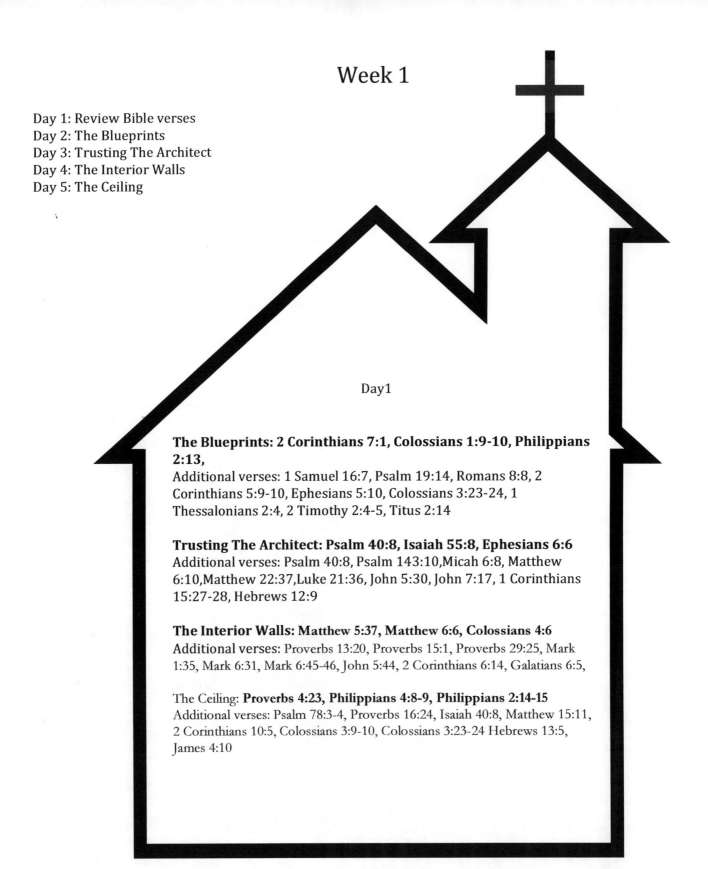

Day1

The Blueprints: 2 Corinthians 7:1, Colossians 1:9-10, Philippians 2:13,
Additional verses: 1 Samuel 16:7, Psalm 19:14, Romans 8:8, 2 Corinthians 5:9-10, Ephesians 5:10, Colossians 3:23-24, 1 Thessalonians 2:4, 2 Timothy 2:4-5, Titus 2:14

Trusting The Architect: Psalm 40:8, Isaiah 55:8, Ephesians 6:6
Additional verses: Psalm 40:8, Psalm 143:10,Micah 6:8, Matthew 6:10,Matthew 22:37,Luke 21:36, John 5:30, John 7:17, 1 Corinthians 15:27-28, Hebrews 12:9

The Interior Walls: Matthew 5:37, Matthew 6:6, Colossians 4:6
Additional verses: Proverbs 13:20, Proverbs 15:1, Proverbs 29:25, Mark 1:35, Mark 6:31, Mark 6:45-46, John 5:44, 2 Corinthians 6:14, Galatians 6:5,

The Ceiling: **Proverbs 4:23, Philippians 4:8-9, Philippians 2:14-15**
Additional verses: Psalm 78:3-4, Proverbs 16:24, Isaiah 40:8, Matthew 15:11, 2 Corinthians 10:5, Colossians 3:9-10, Colossians 3:23-24 Hebrews 13:5, James 4:10

Assignment: Give up food that has sugar, sugar substitutes or high fructose corn syrup for two days. Sugar can be hard to give up, but is essential to do, if you want to clean up your diet. By doing it for a short period at first, it can encourage you to be able to do it for a more extended period of time. Doing this in the middle of the week may be easier when there may be less temptation to eat junk food. If you have medical restrictions, do not do without consulting your doctor.

THE BLUEPRINTS
(ESTABLISHING A PLAN FOR THE REMODEL)

A blueprint is a technical drawing or plan designed by the architect to show how to build the temple. It is a vision with which to set your goals so that you can achieve them. Just as we established a blueprint to rebuild the outside of our temple, we now have to develop one for the inside.

Nugget of the day: In his grace, God has given us different gifts for doing certain things well. So if God has given you the ability to prophesy, speak out with as much faith as God has given you. If your gift is serving others, serve them well. If you are a teacher, teach well. If your gift is to encourage others, be encouraging. If it is giving, give generously. If God has given you leadership ability, take the responsibility seriously. And if you have a gift for showing kindness to others, do it gladly. (Romans 12:6-8 NLT)

Sometimes people spend so much time admiring other people's gifts, that they do not appreciate their own custom designed gift. God handpicked each one of us to fulfill a particular role in the body of Christ. He did not randomly give us talents and dreams. God chose each one of them, and carefully placed them in our hearts. God selected these gifts for us before our conception. We often let these gifts or talents go unappreciated or don't think they are as important as someone else's gifts. When we do not utilize these gifts to the best of our abilities, there is a hole in the body of Christ. Even though a job that may seem small or of little importance to people, it is significant to God. He did not give us our skills based on salary or prestige. He handpicked them determined on how we could best further His Kingdom.

My prayer is that you take the time to appreciate the gifts and talents God has given you. He has entrusted you with the responsibility of using these gifts to further His Kingdom and to bring others to Christ. Spend some time thanking God for believing in you and allowing you to be His ambassador. It is an honor to serve God. Ask the Holy Spirit for guidance so you can use these gifts to make a difference in this world. Can you imagine how much better this world would be if we all used our gifts and talents to further God's Kingdom and to honor God?

****

How often do you try and impress people with your appearance or behaviors? When you go to work, do you make sure you have a nice outfit, comb your hair, and do your makeup correctly? What about your first date with someone? Do you repeatedly try on different outfits until you are satisfied with the look, right down to the last detail? People are very conscious of their outward appearance and how others perceive them. Many of us also have a different way of acting when we first meet someone. We let them see our "good side." We speak kinder, we act happier, and we do things we know will please this person. We love to make good first impressions because we know that is often the image a person will have of us. As time goes on though and we get more comfortable with the person, we often let our guards down. We spend more time in comfy clothes and even let people see us with our "hair down." After a married couple is together for a while, they no longer try and impress one another by dressing up. They are used to the other person seeing them in their sweats and tee shirts. They also no longer feel as if they have to let the other person always see their good side. At times, they grumble about things more and find fault with what is happening in their home. They save their good side for when they go out in public.

This is often true with our relationship with God as well. God is the driving force of our behaviors and our emotional well-being. When we first get to know God, we spend a lot of time in His Word, make time for prayer, are excited to go to a place of worship, and spend time with other believers. We try to live by the commands of the Bible and take to heart the Words that Jesus spoke. Then time goes on, we get comfortable with our faith and let other things take over as a priority in our lives. Before long, the Bible is not opened as often, or might even be covered with dust. We miss Sunday service more frequently. We justify it by saying we had a long week and sleep is more important than going to service. The more lenient our attitude, the more careless we become with our inner and outer appearance before God. Before long we find we are struggling to find the peace and joy that only God can give us in our lives. Now it is time to make the changes and spruce up our lives, so we present to God a temple that is pleasing and worthy of housing the Holy Spirit.

Just as you did in book 1, I am asking you to review the following areas that you are going to address in this book. In the areas you struggle, I am asking you to write down the struggle and then a goal as to how you want to change this area in your life. It helps to make both a short-term and long-term goal so that you can see the progress you are making. Feel free to come back to these goals and add to them as the Holy Spirit reveals more changes to you. Writing out these goals will give you something tangible to work toward and use as a reference. When you need a reminder, you can look at the goals. Not all these areas will pertain to you. Skip the ones that are not causing you any struggles in your life. Research has shown that people who write down their goals have a much higher rate of achievement.

Before you tackle this job, spend some time in prayer and ask God to reveal to you changes you can make. Be open to listening to God. He has your best interest at heart and will help you to find a greater joy and peace in your life when you trust Him to help you make these changes. God has created you with a specific purpose in mind. When you rely on Him to help you grow and make changes in your life, you will see how much more productive your life will become. Remember that God already knows what areas you need to work on; He is waiting for you to approach Him so He can help you. God wants to show you His glory and let you see how He can transform your life when you trust Him.

If you are doing this study in a small group, you may be able to use your strengths to help those who are weak in areas that you are strong and vice versa.

Example: Rest struggle: I tend only to get 5 hours asleep a night and fall asleep at work frequently.
Short-term goal: I will prepare my lunch and get my clothes ready the night before so that I can sleep later in the morning.
Long-term goal: I will get to bed earlier at night and get 7-8 hours of sleep.

Trusting God struggle:
Short-term goal:
Long-term goal:

Strongholds struggle:
Short-term goal:
Long-term goal:

Boundaries struggle:
Short-term goal:
Long-term goal:

Attitude struggle:
Short-term goal:
Long-term goal:

Stress struggle:
Short-term goal:
Long-term goal:

Contentment struggle:
Short-term goal:
Long-term goal:

Rest struggle:
Short-term goal:
Long-term goal:

Diet struggle:
Short-term goal:
Long-term goal:

Exercise struggle:
Short-term goal:
Long-term goal:

Toxic chemicals you are in contact with on a regular basis (Includes health and beauty, cleaning supplies, work environment) struggle:
Short-term goal:
Long-term goal:

TRUSTING THE ARCHITECT
(SUBMITTING TO GOD)

When we hire an architect, we do so because we trust him and want his advice. If we do not follow our architect's guidance, we will still not build a temple that is solid and capable of fulfilling its purpose.

Nugget of the day: And we know that God causes everything to work together for the good of those who love God and are called according to his purpose for them. *(Romans 8:28 NLT)*

It is a human trait to want to control everything. At times, this is a strength, but for the majority of the time, it is a weakness. Our trying to control everything causes much stress. To control everything in our life, it often requires us to attempt also to control other people's lives. Many times, the person we are trying to control is also fighting to be in control. It becomes a vicious cycle. If we heed God's advice and allow Him to be in control, our lives would be less hectic. We find that when God is in control, miracles happen. We have a choice: we can trust that God knows what we need to do to improve our quality of life or believe we know what we are doing and attempt to make changes on our own. When we accept that God has plans, then submit to Him: life becomes less stressful. Doors will open, and we will see dreams become a reality.

My prayer is that you ask the Holy Spirit to give you the ability to commit your life to God and let Him take command. Rather than trying to control situations, put your needs in prayer and let God guide you. He sees the big picture. He can change hearts, break addictions and remove obstacles that are out of your control. God will far exceed your dreams and expectations. With God in charge, He will bring peace and joy. Giving up control is no easy task. Spend some time asking the Holy Spirit for guidance and strength. Let God do what He does best, lead His children.

****

As Christians, we have hired God as our Architect. We need to trust that He has a plan to help us live healthy and productive lives. Jesus came to teach us how to live, and we must trust He knows the answers. When we do not follow His advice, our temple will never be a place we can de-stress and rest. Let's study how Jesus handled stress, so we too can build a room where we can find peace.

"Come to me, all you who are weary and burdened, and I will give you rest. Take my yoke upon you and learn from me, for I am gentle and humble in heart, and you will find rest for your souls. For my yoke is easy and my burden is light. *("Matthew 11:28-30 NIV)* We can easily forget that before Jesus ascended into Heaven, He walked the face of this earth as a man. He faced many of the struggles and temptations that we face in this world. He understands how we feel. Jesus not only came to save us but to help us relate to Him. Jesus personally invites us to find rest by coming to Him. He knows what it is like to live in this world. Even though He is the Son of God, He was not exempt from the struggles of life. Jesus spent His life sacrificing for others. He had people continually needing His attention and had to set boundaries. He was mocked and ridiculed. He was belittled and beaten. Then hung on a cross and died for our sins though He was sinless.

Before Jesus was crucified, He literally sweats blood. He prayed, asking God to take away the cup He was about to be served. *"Father, if you are willing, please take this cup of suffering away from me. Yet I want your will to be done, not mine." Then an angel from heaven appeared and strengthened him. He prayed more fervently, and he was in such agony of spirit that his sweat fell to the ground like great drops of blood.* *(Luke 22:42-44 NLT)* Hematidrosis is a medical condition that occurs when a person is under extreme stress. The capillary blood vessels that supply the sweat glands burst and cause blood to be excreted in the sweat. [1] The Son of God was in such extreme emotional distress that it caused Him to sweat blood and it was no coincidence that Luke, the physician, recorded this.

Notice how Jesus dealt with the stress. Jesus went to His Father. He left the disciples and went to be alone with His Dad. Jesus knew where His strength came from and He knew that only God could get Him through such a difficult time. Have you ever thought about what would have happened had God answered His prayer and stopped the crucifixion? We all would have been lost. We would have only known Jesus as a historical figure. Instead, Jesus listened to His Father. He went through the trials of this earth, died on a cross, rose from the dead and ascended into Heaven to spend eternity with His Father. Because of Jesus' death and resurrection, the whole world has the opportunity to spend eternity with Him.

We all have our struggles in this world. While we are going through these trials, we often miss the blessings. We get wrapped up in our problems. We let stress overcome us. We look for all kinds of outlets and try many solutions. Rather than prayer being our first defense, we often exhaust all other options before turning to prayer.

What if prayer is our first line of defense? The moment we face adversity, we get down on our knees and pray without ceasing. Our outlook would be different. Prayer helps us to cope with pain and suffering. It gives us the strength to face the trials that lie before us and changes lives.

God, in His infinite wisdom, knew from the beginning of time that we would need to experience struggles to draw close to Him. God knows that it is in trials that we will seek Him and build a relationship. God has also proven time and time again that when we remain faithful, we will enjoy His blessings. Who would have believed that God could part the Red Sea for the Israelites? Who would have thought Daniel would emerge victorious from the lion's den? Who would have guessed David could slay Goliath? Without these trials, these bible greats would not have witnessed God's glory.

In the book of Philippians, Paul speaks of holding onto our faith to get us through tough times. He reminds the Philippians to keep their eyes on Heaven. If they lose sight of their ultimate goal, they will experience distress and less peace in life. The same is true for us. When we don't keep our eyes firmly fixed on God and surrender to Him, we will experience unrest.

Read Philippians 4:1-9

What is Paul's command in verse 1? _____

What should we always do? _____

Write verse 6 in your own words. _____

What will your reward be for obeying verse 6? _____

As you are changing your lifestyle, know our Lord is walking with you every step of the way. Know that His ways have a divine purpose. *For my thoughts are not your thoughts, neither are your ways my ways, declares the Lord. (Isaiah 55:8 NIV)* He has a plan for your life. If you allow Him, He will use your trials to show you His glory. Don't be afraid to go to our Lord and tell Him how you are feeling. Share your fears with Him. He understands. Remember, He is fully human and fully God. Lay it all out before Him. You do not have to be afraid of sharing your innermost thoughts. He already knows what they are. Share with God what changes are hard for you and where you need guidance. Then, trust Him.

How often do we tell other people to let God be in control? He knows what He is doing. God sees the big picture. Yet, when it comes to our own lives, we somehow think differently. We need to follow our own advice. Once we give God our problems, we need to trust that He will get us through difficult times. We need to leave our struggles at the cross.

The only way we can relinquish control is to submit ourselves to the Lord. Submission can be a scary word. At times, we think submission means losing control. In actuality, when we submit to God, we allow Him to take charge of our lives. We admit God knows what He is doing and can help us improve our lifestyle. This allows us to be freer. We no longer have to fight to change what is happening in our world. We can accept it and trust God will get us through the challenges we face. God will give us the strength we need to fight the battles. *For the Lord your God is the one who goes with you to fight for you against your enemies to give you victory." (Deuteronomy 20:4 NIV)* Our Lord will provide us with the peace to be able to think clearly and heed His direction. *The Lord gives strength to his people; the Lord blesses his people with peace. (Psalm 29:11 NIV)*

How do you describe submission? _____

_____

Read the following verses and paraphrase them.

James 4:7 _____

Job 22:21 _____

1 Peter 5:6 _____

After reading these verses, do you see how submitting to God is a blessing? _____

Why? _____

    Faith is powerful when we utilize it. This is why our footings must be firm. By having firm footings, we can erect a stable foundation by building a relationship with God, our Father that helps us to trust and believe His Word. God knew that we could not face the challenges of this world alone and He knew there would be times when we would be at a loss as to how to pray to our Father. He gave us a secret weapon to combat our doubt and fears. He gave us the Holy Spirit as our anchor bolts. These bolts strengthen our faith, enabling us to build a stable relationship with our Lord. This relationship allows us to submit our lives to Him. *And the Spirit of the LORD will rest on him--the Spirit of wisdom and understanding, the Spirit of counsel and might, the Spirit of knowledge and the fear of the LORD. (Isaiah 11:2 NLT)* Most of us do not utilize the Holy Spirit in our lives. We have heard sermons about His power, and yet, we do not allow the Spirit to help us take control of our lives. The more we know our God, the more we know of His love. Our external walls are then sturdy to help us deal with the challenges of life. Knowing God loves us, supports and wants the best for us, gives us the strength to make changes. The more time we take to make sure the outside of our temples are solid, the better our quality of life will become. When our outside is secure, we will find the strength to remodel the inside of our temple se that we are able to live a healthier life emotionally, physically and spiritually. It all starts with the footings.

    Changing your lifestyle can cause stress. You have disrupted your routine to establish a new one. When challenged, choose to look to God. God will restore your peace. Your stress level will decrease when God is in control. At times fear may get the best of you, but when you give your worries to God, He will get you through. Many unexpected blessings will be given to you. *Be joyful in hope, patient in affliction, faithful in prayer. (Romans 12:12 NIV)* Once you start investing time and effort into building a relationship with God and Jesus, you will experience peace and joy amidst the trials. *And this righteousness will bring peace. Yes, it will bring quietness and confidence forever. My people will live in safety, quietly at home. They will be at rest. (Isaiah 32:17-18 NLT)*

Food for thought:

1. How does prayer help you deal with fear and anxiety?

2. Do you turn to prayer as your first line of defense? If not, what do you do first when you are worried?

3. What Bible verses give you comfort during these times?

4. Think about your journey so far. What blessings have you seen? (Take some time to think about this. There

may have been some blessings you have overlooked because you allowed stress to control your life.) I urge you to keep a diary of these blessings. One day you may want to share them with others who are struggling.

5. How can you use this time to bring others to Christ?

6. Do you see how your temple is coming together?

Journal your thoughts

Day 4

THE INTERIOR WALLS
(BOUNDARIES)

Walls within a building set the boundaries of each area. The sanctuary is separated from the vestibule by the walls. Depending on the placement of the wall, it can be load bearing or non-load bearing. A load-bearing wall is part of the structure of the building and offers support. A non-load bearing wall is only a partition. Walls can provide security when a person is within the confines of the room.

Nugget of the day: Dear brothers and sisters, if another believer is overcome by some sin, you who are godly should gently and humbly help that person back onto the right path. And be careful not to fall into the same temptation yourself. Share each other's burdens, and in this way obey the law of Christ. If you think you are too important to help someone, you are only fooling yourself. You are not that important. Pay careful attention to your own work, for then you will get the satisfaction of a job well done, and you won't need to compare yourself to anyone else. For we are each responsible for our own conduct. (Galatians 6:1-5 NLT)

While studying this verse, I gained more insight as to the true meaning of carrying one another's burdens. We often get so wrapped up in trying to help someone else; we lose sight of our responsibilities. We try and change a person or try and solve the problem for them. This is not what we are supposed to do. We need to allow each person fight their own battles and solve their problems. It is often these situations that draw us closer to and teach us to rely on God. When we try and step in and be the "savior" we can deter the person from looking to the real Savior. We are to be a support system for people. We can help point them in the right direction, and we can let them know when they are going down the wrong path. We all have our challenges in life, and when we assume someone else's, it can be overwhelming.
We can lose focus in our lives and not complete our callings and solve our problems.

My prayer is that you realize we are not responsible for other people's problems or actions. You have enough trouble fixing your own issues; you should not assume another person's problem. I pray that when you encounter someone who needs assistance or is going down the wrong path, you first go to God in prayer to determine your role in helping him or her. God can give you the insight you cannot get on your own. We are to assist one another, but we cannot fix them. I also pray that you release yourself from any guilt you carry from not "fixing" another person's problem. When faced with helping another person, point them in the right direction and help them to look to the One who can help them. Be careful to not place your burdens on another person. Instead of looking forward to others to fix your life, look up to our Lord and Savior who can heal you, guide you and help you to succeed. If you have trouble letting go of another person's struggles go to God tonight and ask Him to give you clarity as to how to deal with the situation. Release the other person to God. It is exhausting trying to be someone we cannot be. We have enough on our plate just dealing with our own lives.

****

The walls of your temple establish boundaries, so you do not become overwhelmed by other people's problems, take on jobs that are not yours to accept, lose your own identity or frustrate yourself trying to control things you cannot change. There are two types of walls in our temples: load-bearing and nonload-bearing.

The load-bearing walls are our responsibilities and needs that have to be met. Sometimes these responsibilities include taking care of us, a family, assisting aging parents, running a household, holding down a job, and being a good spouse. We cannot remove the load-bearing walls or our temples will fall.

The non-load bearing walls are the needs and responsibilities of others or extra responsibilities we add to our lives. At times these responsibilities can be delegated to others or even eliminated. It is imperative we maintain our load-bearing walls first and then address the issues of the nonload-bearing walls. Often, this is not what happens. We frequently assume responsibility for things that we should not address. We feel pressure from family members, coworkers, friends or organizations. We feel as if we say no or wait until our needs are met to help others, we are not good parents, friends or coworkers. People have a way of making others feel guilty when they say no to a particular task or do not accept a volunteer job. There are times we put other people's needs ahead of ours and in doing so cause chaos in our lives. Family members know how to make us feel guilty when we need alone time, go out with friends or want to spend time on a hobby. For many, being able to admit we cannot volunteer for or take on another job is difficult. It may make us feel weak or not a team player. We can feel cruel or uncaring by not stepping in to help someone else or when making time for ourselves. Therefore, we do not set boundaries.

At times, not being able to say no limits your ability to fulfill your role in the body of Christ. Without setting boundaries, people can take advantage of you and add so much pressure on your life that you cannot accomplish your own work or handle your problems. We all have, or have had people in our lives who want us to fix everything for them or to do their job. Even when they see that we are busy taking care of our business, they want us to stop and help them. Sometimes their requests are legitimate, and they need our assistance. There are times we must step in and help another person, be a support for them or get them through a difficult time. Other times, they are avoiding the task, or they are too dependent on us to take on their own responsibilities. At these times, our stepping in enables them. You must recognize when a person truly needs your help or when they have an unhealthy dependency on you. Many of us know when we need to step in and help someone and when we should step back and let him or her handle the situation. Therefore, it is essential to build boundaries into our temples. We need to know it is okay to say no when we are overwhelmed or need a break. It is okay to tell someone else that their responsibilities are not your responsibilities.

We too can overstep our own boundaries. There are times we put too much pressure on ourselves. Being a parent, working a job, being involved in extracurricular activities can cause chaos in our lives. Trying to keep up with the neighbors or another parent can put unrealistic expectations on us. Accepting that we are not supermoms or dads, our job is not our entire life, or that we do not have to volunteer for every job at our church, work or school can be very freeing. It is healthy for you to recognize your limits and know when you cannot take on another responsibility. It is also all right for you to have quiet time when you are not doing anything or for you to do something you enjoy and leave the children with a sitter. It is essential for family members to see that your life is valuable and sometimes you come first. If you do not establish boundaries for yourself, others will continue to take advantage of you.

Parents have an added burden not only to try and help meet the needs of their spouse but also their children. Without clear boundaries with our children, we interfere too much, prohibiting them from growing into responsible young adults. We can teach them to be dependent on us rather than realize they can be in control. Rather than teaching them to pray and seek God, we try and handle all their problems. As adults, these children will continue to be needy and emotionally drain the parents. Your children will not recognize that you too have a life and need help every once in awhile. Parents need to know it is all right to say no to their children. Their children need to know parents have needs and responsibilities that also need to be met. This also teaches the children how to transition into adulthood and set their boundaries. We do our children a disservice by letting them think they are the most important people in the family. As they grow into adulthood, they will often continue to put themselves first and not acknowledge yours or others wants and needs. They will continue to demand attention even when they are capable of doing things for themselves. Not teaching children to turn to God in prayer for guidance, takes away from them developing a relationship with God.

Spouses can learn helplessness when we do not relinquish some the responsibilities of our household to them. Initially, saying no to unrealistic demands or asking for help when needed is difficult. After the first few times, when you see how it frees you up to meet your needs and to take care of your responsibilities, you will be more confident in saying no when appropriate.

To live a healthy life, you need to establish boundaries for yourself as well as for others.

Do you acknowledge you have needs and set boundaries with your spouse and children? Explain

_____

Eating right, getting adequate sleep, relaxing and exercising are essential to you staying healthy and requires an investment of your time. You will not see improvements in these areas if you do not make the time to deal with them. Even though you know you need to address your needs first, you may still find yourself trying to take on the responsibilities of others. This added responsibility is not fair to the other person or you. Not only will you fail at trying to make your changes; you will also add undue stress to the other parties' lives when you cannot meet their expectations, or they do not learn to handle their problems. It can also cause resentment towards them.

Instead of enabling another person, you should try to empower them. Encourage them to address their problems. Give them examples or demonstrate how you handle situations. If their needs are beyond your scope, direct them to a pastor, counselor or someone who is equipped to help them. By doing so you do not take on the responsibility of making their changes, but you are a support system.

You must remember that your strength does not come from yourself, but from God. The best way to find the strength to deal with your problems is to pray for guidance. You can ask the Holy Spirit to let you know when to intervene with another person and when to step back. Recognize that your job is to please God. In pleasing God, you may not always have the approval of another person, and that is all right. You have a role to fulfill, and God will help you do this. Lean on God as you learn to be assertive and set your boundaries. There is nothing wrong with doing this.

Just as you had to learn to lean on God, it is imperative others do too. The best way to help another person make changes in their life is to pray for them and guide them toward God. We can thank God for putting them in our lives, acknowledge their struggles, ask God to guide them, and help them find the strength to improve their lives.

In what areas do you have trouble setting boundaries? _____

How does this hinder following your calling or improving your lifestyle? _____

_____

Who do you feel responsible for in your life and how is this feeling standing in the way of you changing your lifestyle? _____

In what areas do you need to release this control of others? _____

Giving too much of ourselves to others can burn us out so that we are not helpful to anyone or ourselves. The work we do becomes sloppy and incomplete. Instead of trying to help everyone and assume everyone else's responsibility we need to release this control to God and let Him help him or her in the manner He sees fit. After all, He knows His children and He knows how to help them much better than we do.

How can you relinquish the control of others to God? _____

When you try and control another person, or make changes for them, you can become a hindrance in their life. When they rely on you to give them advice or do their work, they never find their inner strength and more importantly, you hinder their relationship with God. They become dependent on you rather than God.

How does your support for this person limit them from becoming the person they could become?
_____

Take some time to pray for this person now and ask God to help you encourage them. By letting go of the co-dependency, you can continue to grow and make healthy changes in your own life.

Just as we cannot control another person, we should not let someone else control us. We often allow those we love to influence how we handle our circumstances and the way we see and address various issues. This influence is often a major deterrent when we try to make healthy changes in our lives. People interfere for several reasons. People feel threatened when we make changes, and they don't. They are afraid that if we make changes we will become more independent and they will lose any control they think they have over us. Some people cannot find happiness, so they like it when others are just as miserable as themselves. For others, when they see us living unhealthy lifestyles, it helps them to justify their unhealthy habits. Using the following verse, we need to examine the motives of someone who appears to be trying to control us. *Love is patient, love is kind. It does not envy, it does not boast, it is not proud. It does not dishonor others, it is not self-seeking, it is not easily angered, it keeps no record of wrongs.* *(1 Corinthians 13:4-5 NIV)*

I often hear people tell me that they cannot make changes in their lives because family members are unwilling to make changes in theirs. This is going to be the case a lot of the time. Most family members will not buy into your new lifestyle. Although they do not choose to make these changes now, it does not mean our loved ones will not follow this path later in life. At this time they are just not ready. After they witness the changes in our lives, they might see how much healthier we are and how much better we feel. It is at this time that they may decide that they too want to live a healthy lifestyle.

How do family members control your life or influence your decisions and how are they doing it?

_____

_____

How does this keep you from living the lifestyle you know you should be living? _____

_____

_____

How does their control contradict 1 Corinthians 13:4-5? _____

You must come to the realization that you do not need the approval of others. When someone does compliment you, it feels good. However, you cannot allow this to be the driving force behind your behavior. Once you realize it is God you need to please and not people, it frees you to live up to your full potential.

How has criticism limited your ability to change your lifestyle? _____

We all see things from a different perspective, so what might be good for one may not work for another. God, on the other hand, knows His children and He knows what they need. When you finally realize it is God alone you should want to please, you take pressure off yourself. Trying to please others can be tiring. No one can please everyone all the time. Every person has different expectations as to what pleases them. God is consistent. When we know His Word, we know His expectations.

I have realized this in my job. Trying to please many supervisors can be tiring. They each have different

21

expectations and they also each have their flaws. To satisfy each supervisor, I would have to change how I perform my job at each location. When I finally came to the realization that I work to please God, this took the pressure to please each supervisor off of me. I know God's expectations, and I know what is morally and ethically the right way to work. When I am doing my best to please God, I am trying to adhere to a higher standard because I enjoy doing my Father's will. *For none of us lives for ourselves alone, and none of us dies for ourselves alone. If we live, we live for the Lord; and if we die, we die for the Lord. So, whether we live or die, we belong to the Lord. For we will all stand before God's judgment seat. It is written: "'As surely as I live,' says the Lord, 'every knee will bow before me; every tongue will acknowledge God.'" So then, each of us will give an account of ourselves to God.* (Romans 14:7-8,11-12 NIV)

There is an inner peace that comes when you no longer live for another person's approval. This peace enables you not to take their criticism personally. You can spend more time focusing on the positive comments rather than the negative ones you hear. It's ironic that often when a person does a great job on a project, the only thing they focus on is the one negative comment. You do yourself a grave injustice when this happens because you never truly appreciate your accomplishments or enjoy your success.

You need to evaluate a comment and determine if it is a suggestion rather than a negative comment. When you hear a negative comment, look for any truth in the response and use that piece to better your life and release the hurtful aspect.

When you are going to offer someone else advice, be mindful of how you speak to him or her. Words have power, and they have the ability to build up or tear down. Try to model your life after Christ. Before saying anything, determine whether or not your words will help or hurt. A good guideline to use is Galatians 5:22-23. If your words align with this teaching, you can make a difference in this world. *But the fruit of the Spirit is love, joy, peace, forbearance, kindness, goodness, faithfulness, gentleness, and self-control. Against such things there is no law.* (NIV) Speaking your mind often feels right at the moment, but later these same words may come back to haunt you long after they are spoken, causing much regret and anxiety.

Jesus knew to set boundaries. He knew when He needed to retreat to spend time with His Father. (Matthew 6:6) Jesus made sure His needs were met first so that He could better serve God and His followers. When Jesus faced the pressures of this world, He sought God's advice. He recognized that God was the One He needed to please. (John 5:44) Jesus stood up for what He believed and did not let others dissuade Him from going about His business. (Matthew 16:23)

How does knowing Jesus set boundaries encourage you to do the same? _____

You need to set boundaries for others and yourself. Setting these boundaries will make your temple more pleasing to God. What are some of these boundaries?

- When you say no, mean it.

- When asked to do something that goes against your lifestyle change, you need to stay the course you have set for yourself.

- When you know someone is capable of dealing with his or her problem or situation, you need to step back and let him or her.

- You may need to remove yourself from a situation. If a person tears you down or does not respect your decisions, you need to take a break from that relationship.

- Let others assume responsibility for their own actions. It's not your burden to take on.

- Do not let anyone or anything interfere with your relationship with your loving Father or fulfilling your calling.

Food for thought:

1. Has reviewing this material taken any pressure off of you so that you can focus on your needs? How has this helped you?

2. Why are establishing boundaries important?

3. What are some boundaries you need to establish in your life?

Journal your thoughts

Day 5

THE CEILING
(YOUR ATTITUDE)

The ceiling in our temple has to be well planned. The ceiling can change the atmosphere of the sanctuary. Many temples have vaulted ceilings, which make the room look larger and feel airy. The ceilings can be inspirational and uplifting with painted murals or beautiful architectural designs.

Nugget of the day: Give thanks to him who killed the firstborn of Egypt. His faithful love endures forever. He brought Israel out of Egypt. His faithful love endures forever. He acted with a strong hand and powerful arm. His faithful love endures forever. *(Psalm 136:10-12 NLT)*

We always have something for which we can be thankful. At times, we may have to make an effort to see our blessings because we are in the midst of a storm but even in the storm we receive blessings. How sad that the Israelites overlooked so many of their blessings because all they could focus on was what they did not have. The Israelite's negativity cost them the Promised Land. Their offspring received the gift that they forfeited since they were so focused on grumbling. They had so many signs and witnessed so many miracles, and yet all they could do was complain? The Red Sea was parted, their shoes did not wear out, rocks provided water, they were delivered from slavery, and they were supplied with food daily. And they chose to remain focused on the negative.

My prayer is that you realize you receive blessings every day from our God. You too need to focus on these blessings instead of your problems. Most of the time we will realize our storms are actually light showers when we change our attitude and look at the positive rather than the negative. Even in our darkest days, we miss many blessings when we do not open our eyes and hearts to see them. When we do, we will see all God is doing for us. You do not want to miss your promise lands because you grumble too much. You have a lot at stake so you must choose: do you complain or do you count your blessings?
****

For God is working in you, giving you the desire and the power to do what pleases him. Do everything without complaining and arguing, so that no one can criticize you. Live clean, innocent lives as children of God, shining like bright lights in a world full of crooked and perverse people. Hold firmly to the word of life; then, on the day of Christ's return, I will be proud that I did not run the race in vain and that my work was not useless. But I will rejoice even if I lose my life, pouring it out like a liquid offering to God, just like your faithful service is an offering to God. And I want all of you to share that joy. Yes, you should rejoice, and I will share your joy. (Philippians 2:13-18 NIV) No one wants their temple to feel closed in and confining. Our attitude is like the ceiling. People love to walk into a beautiful church and stand in awe of the ceiling and how uplifting it can be. They love to look up toward Heaven and see the splendor. The ceiling can change the entire atmosphere of the sanctuary. Looking up in our temples will point us to God. When we keep our eyes fixed on God, He can change our attitude and help us see things more positively. When we have a positive attitude, we can see the good in our lives, work through struggles and be intent on winning the battle. When we can see how God uses various challenges and struggles to draw us closer to Him, then our relationship will grow stronger. On the other hand, when we allow negativity to guide our lives, not only will our relationships with others suffer, but also our relationship with God. When a temple has negative energy, a person will find it hard to find comfort in this place. We need to have a ceiling in our temple that helps to restore the positive energy one needs to be able to draw closer to God. It is imperative that we gaze at the ceiling of our temple often and reassess how we are living our lives. *A cheerful heart is good medicine, but a crushed spirit dries up the bones.* (Proverbs 17:22 NIV)

The brain is a powerful organ. It is the control center of the body. Our thinking, whether it is positive or negative, has the ability to assist or hinder our lives, improve our health and alter the way we look at life. Too often we do not allow the brain to work to its full capacity. We put limits on what it can do. There are many ways we can enhance how our brain functions. We can use prayer, positive thinking, and visualization. When we attempt to make changes in our lives, we need to enlist all the resources at our disposal.

Keeping a positive attitude does not mean we deny the challenges or difficult times in our lives. Maintaining a positive attitude is what will get us through these times with as few battle scars as possible. Positive thinkers admit they have battles, but they plan to win them. They do not let others fill their heads with defeating thoughts. At times, doubts may creep in, but the difference between positive and negative people is that positive thinkers may allow themselves a moment of self-pity and then they will use prayer, self-talk or visualization to change their attitude. And then they move forward. They will once again be ready to fight and persevere. Negative people let negative thoughts define their lives. They may have good intentions, but always seem to find the downside of every life event.

Making changes in your lifestyle is no different. You have to decide how you are going to look at these changes. When you see that these changes are right for you, you will see the value of exercising and eating right. You will want to establish boundaries and find peace. You will want to find the time to address these changes. When you look at the work needed to make changes as a burden, you will find it hard to incorporate them in your life. You may even make excuses as to why you cannot exercise or try to justify your poor eating habits. Being positive, looking for and celebrating the small changes that occur gives you the incentive to keep working on these changes rather than giving up.

Positive thinking is nothing new. The Bible has given you many verses to help you keep a positive attitude in your everyday living, or when life throws you a curveball. God knows you will face challenges at some point in time so He has given you guidance on how to handle these situations. God looks at things differently than you do. He sees these challenging times as teachable moments. These moments will help define where you are in your Christian walk. *Consider it pure joy, my brothers and sisters, whenever you face trials of many kinds, because you know that the testing of your faith produces perseverance. Let perseverance finish its work so that you may be mature and complete, not lacking anything.* (James 1:2-4 NIV)

When you face a trial, you have a choice. You can accept the challenge and use it to bring you closer to God, learn how to deal with adversity and let God's glory shine through you or you can allow the challenge to hinder or destroy you. *And we know that in all things God works for the good of those who love him, who have been called according to his purpose.* (Romans 8:28 NIV) For many, the very thing we thought would break us makes us stronger. We develop better-coping skills, grow in faith and become stronger people.

If you accept Christ as your Savior and believe the Bible is the ultimate Word of God, then you must trust that God has a plan for your life. God is using this period of your life as you work to improve your lifestyle to bring you closer to Him. This is a mark of an excellent father. God knows what is best for you and He will stand by you as you go through this challenge and will show His glory throughout, always remaining faithful.

Remaining positive and staying the course will bring you many blessings: having more energy, being in better physical shape, having a stronger faith and experiencing a happier life.

What negative thoughts inhibit your ability to make lifestyle changes? _____

How can you retrain your brain to think positively about these issues? _____

The Bible cautions us to "lean not on our own understanding." We only have a small glimpse of God's plan. We only see the present. We do not know what tomorrow will bring so we need to trust God, who sees the whole picture, to guide us through to the end. *Trust in the LORD with all your heart and lean not on your own understanding; in all your ways submit to him, and he will make your paths straight. (Proverbs 3:5-6 NIV)*

Look up the following Bible verses about trials and record what they mean to you personally.

Psalm 91:1-2: _____

Romans 8:38-39: _____

1 Peter 1:6-9: _____

If you are going to accept God's truths, then you also need to remember that there will be blessings as you go through these trials. You will see God's glory if you allow Him to work in your life. You must keep your eyes, ears, and heart open to these blessings or you may miss them. Some blessings are subtle, such as a beautiful sunrise greeting you after a difficult night. It may be a friend calling at just the right moment to offer words of encouragement. You may stumble upon the perfect Bible verse when you feel you are not strong enough to make changes or face trials. In 2 Corinthians 6:3-10 Paul tells us how he saw the good in his struggles and was able to share his faith and help bring others to Christ. *We put no stumbling block in anyone's path, so that our ministry will not be discredited. Rather, as servants of God we commend ourselves in every way: in great endurance; in troubles, hardships and distresses; in beatings, imprisonments and riots; in hard work, sleepless nights and hunger; in purity, understanding, patience and kindness; in the Holy Spirit and in sincere love; in truthful speech and in the power of God; with weapons of righteousness in the right hand and in the left; through glory and dishonor, bad report and good report; genuine, yet regarded as impostors; known, yet regarded as unknown; dying, and yet we live on; beaten, and yet not killed; sorrowful, yet always rejoicing; poor, yet making many rich; having nothing, and yet possessing everything. (NIV)*

When you keep a positive outlook, you will find good no matter what stage of your life you are currently experiencing. In the Bible, Paul freely admits he faced struggles. He recognized these struggles were bringing him closer to his God. Paul found joy in his salvation and in knowing He would spend eternity in God's presence.

What blessings has God given you this past week? If none come to mind, take some time to reflect on your week. _____

We live in a cynical world. All one has to do is read a newspaper, watch the news, look at Facebook or spend time listening to the conversation of others. People love to outdo one another when sharing their troubles and woes. People seem to enjoy sharing negative gossip about others. Seldom do we hear praise reports, rejoice in other's accomplishments or hear the good works others are doing. We need to put an end to all our negative talk and start looking for the good in others and ourselves. We need to take hold of our own thoughts. Let's allow our lights to shine in the midst of challenges and find the courage to rejoice as we endure trials. *In the same way, let your good deeds shine out for all to see, so that everyone will praise your heavenly Father. (Matthew 5:16 NLT)* We all have the ability to experience life to its fullest. It is time for us to be grateful for the opportunities life presents and to look for the blessings hidden within life's challenges. *You are all children of the light and children of the day. We do not belong to the night or to the darkness. So then, let us not be like others, who are asleep, but let us be awake and sober.* (1 Thessalonians 5:5-6 NIV)

Food for thought:

1. How does it make you feel when you realize God is in charge?

2. What holds you back from submitting your life to God?

3. When you allow God to be in control of your life, do you find peace?

4. What are some of the positive outcomes you will witness in your life when you improve your lifestyle and live healthier?

5. Take some time to contemplate these verses and then write a prayer to God asking for strength to endure, eyes to see good in others and to maintain a positive attitude each day. *The LORD is my strength and my defense; he has become my salvation. Shouts of joy and victory resound in the tents of the righteous: "The LORD's right hand has done mighty things! The LORD's right hand is lifted high; the LORD's right hand has done mighty things!"* (Psalm 118:14-16 NIV)

Journal your thoughts

Week 2

Day 1: Review Bible verses
Day 2: The Sanctuary
Day 3: Laying The Floor
Day 4: The Vestibule
Day 5: The Chapel

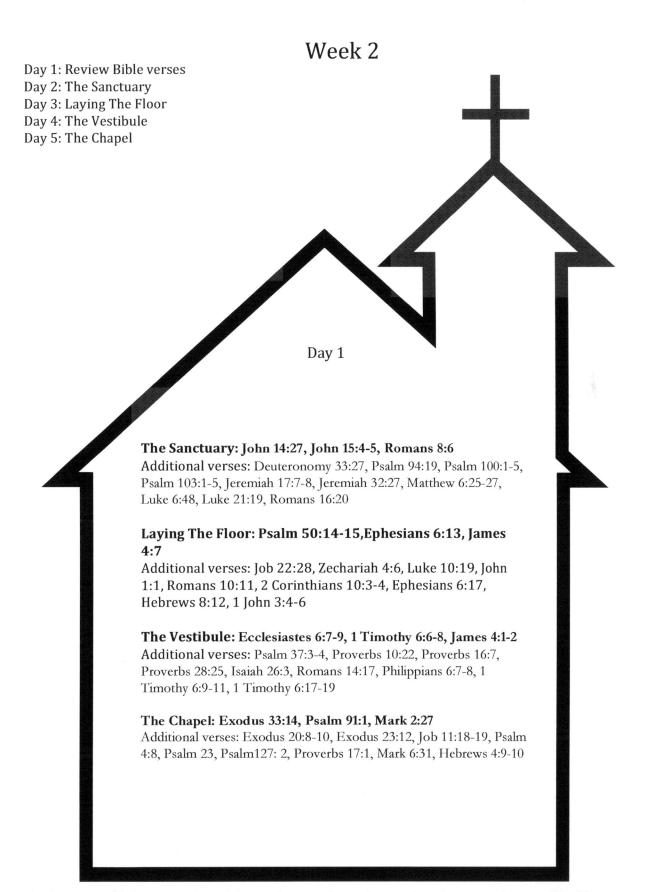

Day 1

The Sanctuary: John 14:27, John 15:4-5, Romans 8:6
Additional verses: Deuteronomy 33:27, Psalm 94:19, Psalm 100:1-5, Psalm 103:1-5, Jeremiah 17:7-8, Jeremiah 32:27, Matthew 6:25-27, Luke 6:48, Luke 21:19, Romans 16:20

Laying The Floor: Psalm 50:14-15,Ephesians 6:13, James 4:7
Additional verses: Job 22:28, Zechariah 4:6, Luke 10:19, John 1:1, Romans 10:11, 2 Corinthians 10:3-4, Ephesians 6:17, Hebrews 8:12, 1 John 3:4-6

The Vestibule: Ecclesiastes 6:7-9, 1 Timothy 6:6-8, James 4:1-2
Additional verses: Psalm 37:3-4, Proverbs 10:22, Proverbs 16:7, Proverbs 28:25, Isaiah 26:3, Romans 14:17, Philippians 6:7-8, 1 Timothy 6:9-11, 1 Timothy 6:17-19

The Chapel: Exodus 33:14, Psalm 91:1, Mark 2:27
Additional verses: Exodus 20:8-10, Exodus 23:12, Job 11:18-19, Psalm 4:8, Psalm 23, Psalm127: 2, Proverbs 17:1, Mark 6:31, Hebrews 4:9-10

Assignment: Take some time this week to work on decreasing the stress in your life. Try to incorporate one of the techniques into your daily schedule for the next week. Write how you felt about the activity afterward.

THE SANCTUARY
(RESTORING PEACE)

Every temple needs a sanctuary. It is the holiest place in the temple. A sanctuary is also a refuge or a place that offers protection.

Nugget of the day: The one thing I ask of the Lord—the thing I seek most—is to live in the house of the Lord all the days of my life, delighting in the Lord's perfections and meditating in his Temple. *(Psalm 27:4 NLT)*

Can you imagine living in God's house all your days? Life would be beautiful. Right now, we may not be in the physical presence of the Lord, but spiritually we can be. We can create heaven on earth. Sure, it won't be the same, but we can experience life as God intended for us to live. We all have a choice as to how we live our lives. Too often we choose to live a fast-paced, hectic life and lose sight of God. We can choose to slow our days down and experience God. When we decide to live according to God's Word, our lives become less stressful. We can calm our lives by sitting in God's presence and meditate on His Word. We can hear Him speak to us and allow Him to guide us. We can focus on the good and count our blessings instead of focusing on the things we cannot control. We can speak words of encouragement instead of being critical. We can reach out and help others instead of focusing on ourselves. We can ask God to accompany us throughout our day and have Him in our house.

My prayer is that you make spending time in God's presence your priority. There are so many things you can do throughout your day to stay connected to God and live a life that is less stressful. You have a choice. You can choose to live a life of kindness and giving, or you can let your world be self-centered. Each time you model your life after Jesus' life, you move a little closer to the house of the Lord.

****

Our sanctuary is the place where the Holy Spirit resides. It needs to be a peaceful and comforting place so that we can hear the Holy Spirit speak to us. We need a place where we can stop, take deep breaths and relax while spending time in the Word of God. ***Don't you know that you yourselves are God's temple and that God's Spirit dwells in your midst?*** *(1 Corinthians 3:16 NIV)* When we allow stress to control our lives, it disrupts our peace, and our lives can be in turmoil. Stress can make it hard to hear the Holy Spirit speak to us as well as prevent us from spending time in God's Word.

Everyone has some stress in his or her life. No one is exempt from it, and it affects each person differently. How people deal with stress can have a significant effect on their overall health and quality of life. Stress in life can be from external sources such as the environment, our lifestyles or from relationships with other people. Stress can be from internal sources due to illness, worry, anger, unforgiveness, poor behaviors and negative attitude. People handle stress in a variety of ways. Some studies show stress can cause problems for both the mind and body. The body responds to stress by releasing hormones that increase blood pressure, heart rate and can raise blood sugar levels.

There are two main types of stress: acute and chronic stress. Acute stress is temporary and can be beneficial. It has the potential of being exhilarating when in small amounts or exhausting when too much. We experience this type of stress when we are in danger or when we challenge ourselves. It allows us to activate the fight or flight response so that we can meet deadlines, get a competitive edge such as in sports or workplace and get thrills out of life such as riding a roller coaster or downhill skiing. This type of stress is also called an adrenaline rush.

The second type is chronic stress. This kind of stress is the most detrimental to the body. It is ongoing and may cause a person to think they have little hope of things changing. It takes a toll mentally and emotionally as well as physically. Too often people who experience chronic stress get so used to it that they never deal with it. They let this type of stress follow them throughout life and do not understand why they are always tired, cranky or have trouble focusing. Chronic stress can also cause problems with: fertility, increased muscle tightness, pain, digestive and urinary systems, weight gain, our sleep, heart problems, cause depression and weaken the immune system.

Acute stress can boost our immune system, but chronic stress can weaken it. When our immune system is weak, the body cannot defend itself from germs or illnesses. A study by Meridian Stress Management Consultancy in the UK reports almost 180,000 people die a year from stress-related illnesses. In the United States, emotional stress is a major contributing factor in deaths from six areas: cancer, heart disease, respiratory disorders, cirrhosis of the liver, suicide and accidental deaths. [1]

It is understandable that stress builds up in a person as they go through life with its many responsibilities, challenges, and struggles. For some of us, stress is just part of everyday life. Every decision, every obstacle, and even happy events have the potential to cause us stress. When we make educated choices with God's guidance, we need to trust in those decisions. Stress comes when we begin to second-guess ourselves. Attempting to make changes in our lifestyle and alter our habits can also add pressure to our lives. If we do not recognize this and address it, stress can limit our ability to make the necessary changes.

Often stress can cause us to resort to "comfort foods" or to eat more frequently as we attempt to take our minds off of what is worrying us. Eating this way adds to our stress level. While trying to make changes, it is imperative that the body remains strong. As we embark on our journey, our bodies and minds need to be prepared to fight the battles we will encounter as we attempt to make changes. We do not want to make these changes harder by adding undue stress. We want the body to run like a well-oiled machine, and it cannot do this if we allow stress to control our lives. Letting stress have control, causes us to be run down physically, spiritually, emotionally and mentally. It also strains our relationship with God.

In what areas of your life does stress play a role? _____

If you are affected by stress, what are some of the symptoms you experience? _____

How do you deal with this stress? _____

How does stress alter your relationship with God? _____

Everyone deals with stress differently. You need to recognize how stress affects your body. From my own experiences, I know how it affected my body. My muscles in my shoulders and back were in constant spasm, which caused chronic pain. I held my breath. It wasn't until after I had gone through the cancer treatment that I realized I had forgotten how to take a refreshing breath. I woke up after a night's sleep groggy and not well rested. The "what ifs" kept me awake. Stress took the peace and joy out of my life. I was too focused on all that I had to do and all that was causing me problems that I forgot to keep my eyes on the One who could restore that peace and joy. Rather than spend time in God's Word and believing His truths, I believed what the world was telling me. I would let people's opinions and actions change how I felt about things. I spent many sleepless nights worrying about things I had no control of and often would never come true.

"Be careful, or your hearts will be weighed down with carousing, drunkenness and the anxieties of life, and that day will close on you suddenly like a trap. (Luke 21:34NIV) We need to take stress more seriously and recognize how it manifests in our own bodies. Too often it controls much of our lives. By having tactics in place to deal with stress, you can keep it from wreaking havoc in your life. To relieve stress, I have found the following strategies to be beneficial:

- Remind yourself to breathe deep cleansing breaths.
- Focus on relaxing your tense muscles. (This is addressed in a later chapter)
- Use positive self-talk to remove negative thoughts.
- Rehearse beforehand how you can handle a stressful situation you are going to face.
- When dealing with others, stay calm, speak in a quiet tone, keep your composure if there is disagreement and maintain a relaxed posture.
- Stay in God's Word, seek His guidance and arm yourself with His Word.

As you can see, we not only need ways to deal with stress but more importantly, we need to trust God. We have to be able to use His Word to ward off the stress and find comfort. When we realize God is in control and we relinquish our worries and cares to Him, we will restore peace. When our world appears to be spinning out of control, we have lost our ability to trust that God will get us through. Trusting God takes practice. If we learn to trust God with the small things, it will be easier to give Him control over the more significant challenges. *Many are the plans in a person's heart, but it is the Lord's purpose that prevails.* (Proverbs 19:21 NIV) We need to remember we cannot control everything in life but we can control how we react.

If you are going through a difficult time in your life or just emerged from a struggle, you may have some side effects from stress. Take some time to recognize how stress is affecting your life. Answer these questions honestly.

1. Do you find yourself holding your breath or taking quick short breaths rather than taking full breaths?
2. Do you have constant muscle tightness or keep your shoulders in shrugged like position?
3. Do you have persistent or frequent headaches?
4. Do you clench or grind your teeth or have jaw tightness?
5. Do you hold your hand in a clenched fist, or exhibit nervous habits?
6. Do you get aggravated by insignificant things and let them bother you all day?
7. Do you get angry quickly?
8. Do you hold grudges?
9. Do you frequently experience sleep disturbances or spend much of the night worried about things?
10. Do you feel overwhelmed, an inability to concentrate, or out of control?
11. Do you find yourself withdrawing and are not interested in the activities you once were?
12. Do you have panic attacks or increased heart palpitations?

Although it is understandable that stress will be present in our lives, we must address it if we are going to be successful in changing our lifestyles. Here are some ways that might be helpful to lessen stress.

Identify what is causing the stress in your life. It might include: the changes you are attempting to make, relationships, finances, your job, loss of free time, decreased energy or illness. List these factors now.

Prioritize the things you need to accomplish. Focus on the things that matter the most, for example, family, health, and career. Having lofty goals can be overwhelming. When you establish small, obtainable goals you will be more successful achieving them. What are some of the priorities you need to focus on at this time?

Avoid scheduling conflicts. Plan and prioritize what needs to be done each day accordingly. Make sure to take time for fellowship.

Know your limits. It is okay to say no to the demands that prevent you from making necessary changes in your life. You need to make time to spend with God, exercise and prepare healthy meals. If you are fatigued, stop to rest. Not only are you helping yourself, but you are also setting a good example for your family. Are there any limits you need to set?

Ask for help. Most of the time people are willing to help you if you would just ask. When you allow the right people to be part of your life, you improve your relationships, lessen your stress, and it makes the journey more enjoyable.

Prioritize your finances. Finances are often a significant contributor to stress. Set up a budget and live by it. When you live within your means, you reduce the stress in your life. Spending money you do not have may be fun at that moment, but it leads to many sleepless nights of worry. You need to make sure you are spending money on things you need. Instead of eating out, prepare food at home. Not only will you save money, but you will also enjoy healthier meals. Rather than go to the movies, enjoy visiting the free activities your city offers and explore parks and museums or utilize the library and all its free resources. Also, you will have some exciting adventures and get much-needed exercise.

1. What needs do you spend your money on (tithing, home, utilities, transportation)?

2. In what areas can you decrease your spending?

3. What can you do for fun and entertainment that will not hurt your budget?

Let go of the things you cannot control. You need to learn how to cope with things that cause stress in your life, such as traffic situations and changes in schedules that you cannot control. You need to turn these things over to God and let Him deal with them. Worrying about things only brings more stress and could make the situation worse. Worry and stress can interfere with your healthy lifestyle.

Food for thought:

1. What are you worried about that you cannot control?

2. How can you handle things that disrupt your schedule or upset you?

3. Are there people in your life who cause you stress? What are you doing to handle this situation?

4. Give these things over to God. Write a prayer relinquishing the control of these things and ask God to guide you.

5. What changes can you make to decrease stress?

Journal your thoughts

Day 3

LAYING THE FLOOR
(LETTING GO OF STRONGHOLDS)

Laying the proper floor takes skill. The floor needs to be stable so that a person can walk safely.

Nugget of the day: All of them ate the same spiritual food, and all of them drank the same spiritual water. For they drank from the spiritual rock that traveled with them, and that rock was Christ. Yet God was not pleased with most of them, and their bodies were scattered in the wilderness. *(1 Corinthians 10:3-5 NLT)*

Have you ever taken the time to think that most of us miss our promised land because we spend a significant portion of our time complaining and finding fault with our lives rather than seeing the good? God has given each of us a unique calling with special blessings. Instead of appreciating these, we often want what another person has, or we are jealous of their talents. It is up to us to accept our gifts and talents and use them for God's glory. In this day and age, with social media, it is easy to get caught up in all the negativity. All one has to do is spend some time on the Internet to see people who are unhappy with their lives and who are willing to find fault with everything and everyone. We need to rise above this. We need to take time to appreciate our lives, spend time in thanksgiving, accept our gifts and talents and utilize them for the good of all.

My prayer is that we all live a good life here on earth and make it to our promised land. I pray you learn to see the good in life, in yourself and in those around you. Make a conscious effort to see the blessings God has bestowed on you and take the time to enjoy them. God wants you to have good things in this life. Spend some time in thanksgiving and let God know you accept and appreciate the gifts He has given you. Your whole outlook changes when you look at your life positively. As you change your attitude, you will see doors open and will enjoy your promised land.

****

We all need a solid ground on which to stand. *Now I stand on solid ground, and I will publicly praise the LORD (Psalm 26:12 NLT)* Our temple is no different. We need a strong, level floor on which to stand. Strongholds can be either positive or negative. These strongholds can let us stand securely or stumble through life. When God is in control, and we look to Him for our stability, this is a good stronghold. Our floor is solid, and we can maneuver through our world accomplishing the plans God has set before us. When a floor is uneven or is sagging, a person will find they lose their balance or fall. When a stronghold is negative such as when we hold onto anger, guilt, shame, and stress, it can disrupt our relationship with both God and people. This makes our floor unstable. Our floor will cause us to stumble and to lose our focus. This instability will make it hard for us to find peace in our lives and fulfill our callings. Trying to stabilize ourselves, we tend to grasp for anything that we can use to try to stabilize us. When we grasp something positive such as prayer, Christian fellowship or healthy habits we can stabilize our lives. When we grasp onto negative strongholds such as food, alcohol, or immoral behavior we cause chaos in our lives.

What do you try and use to stabilize yourself when you fell insecure? _____

People who dwell on their past failures or struggles allow these things to become negative strongholds. By doing this, they allow these past problems to define who they are as a person. Satan knows each one of our weaknesses, and he will use our struggles to keep us beaten down and unable to let go of our past. When we are feeling good or have successfully moved forward in our lives, Satan will remind us of past failures and try to get us to dwell on them rather than our successes. We are no threat to the devil when we are struggling. He knows that when we are fighting internal battles, it makes it hard for us to advance the Kingdom of God. Satan knows that when we feel unclean on the inside, we will be less likely to clean up our physical body. Satan loves to tell us we are not capable of being successful, we are not loveable or that we have no self-worth. All of these are LIES. We know that Satan is the master of lies and deceit.

If we are going to release these strongholds it is essential to make sure your external temple is structurally sound. It is only when you look to God for who you are that you will be able to shed your negative self-image and see yourself as God sees you. When we dwell in God's presence and stay in His Word, He can shed light on who we truly are and how valuable we are to Him. We are not fighting worldly battles, we are fighting spiritual battles, and thus we must arm ourselves with the right weapons if we are going to be victorious. (2 Corinthians 10:3-5) God has provided this weaponry for us in the form of His Word. His Word is more powerful than Satan's lies. We must learn to correctly use this weaponry if we are going to be victorious.

Your brain is a complex computer, and it is programmable. Every time someone criticizes you, your brain retains this data. Each time you think an unkind thought about yourself, the mind processes this information. The key to letting go of the negative strongholds is to fill your mind with God's Word. Continue to combat and replace the negative data with the positive. *You must have the same attitude that Christ Jesus had. (Philippians 2:5 NLT)* You cannot stop all the information from getting into your brain, but you can quickly replace it with the word of God.

Not all strongholds are from Satan. At times we can be our own worst enemy. We hold onto hurts, guilt, shame, and we let anger control us. This stress and anger can become negative strongholds. These emotions can also limit our ability to change unhealthy habits and see the good in life. Learning to change your attitude in response to stress, anger, shame, guilt, and unforgiveness is a lifelong project. We all have to deal with these issues at some point in our lives. When you allow these emotions to control you, your body is in a constant state of alertness and is working overtime. The body is in a continuous guarded position causing the muscles to tighten up. Your temple will be in disarray if you do not address these issues. Here are some techniques to help calm the body and fight the strongholds. Along with prayer and using God's Word, there are ways to relax your body and rid it of stress so that you can focus more easily on the Word.

Pray: Pray without ceasing. Prayer has a calming effect on your mind and body. You need to use prayer in every situation. When you let God be part of your solution, you will have a more positive attitude. When you can trust God, and know that He is in control and has a plan, you will see His glory. When you can include God in your everyday life and spend time in His Word, He speaks to you and draws you closer to Him. God alone can give you the peace and joy you desire in life. When you remain in contact with your Creator, He will nourish you and give you the strength to get through difficult times. *"I am the vine; you are the branches. If you remain in me and I in you, you will bear much fruit; apart from me you can do nothing. (John 15:5 NIV)*

Do you see Jesus as your vine and how do you allow Him to nourish you? _____

_____

Meditation: This is a way to focus the mind on one thing. Meditation has to be practices to be effective. It is best when done for short periods of time at first, then expanded upon as you become more comfortable with the technique. You need to prepare a quiet place removed from all distractions. Sit or lie down in a comfortable position and be able to maintain this position throughout the session. It is easy to find meditation programs on the Internet as well as CD's to use in your home. While meditating, it is an excellent time to practice listening to God: *Be still, and know that I am God. (Psalm 46:10 NIV)*

Meditate on God's Word: Use the Bible cards provided for you or make up your own. Spend time reading and rereading them until you know them by heart. Think about each verse and memorize them so that when stress starts to creep into your life, you can call them to mind.

Appreciate changes: Look for the changes that are occurring. They do not have to be large ones. Appreciate the small changes that will lead to the big ones. Look at the positive things you have accomplished: you passed on an unhealthy food even though you wanted to eat it, exercised when you wanted to watch television, or you felt more energized on a particular day. Take some extra time to meditate on how your life has changed since you began this journey. Sometimes you need to make time to think about the changes you've made. What are some of the bright moments on your journey so far? _____

Laugh: Hang out with friends who make you laugh, or watch a funny movie. We have all heard the phrase "laughter is the best medicine." This is true in so many ways. Research has shown that laughter has many effects on our bodies. [1] Some of the benefits include: stimulating many of our organs, increasing the intake of oxygen to the heart, lungs, and brain, relieves stress, improves circulation, and allows muscles to relax. Laughter may help in enhancing the immune system, helping to cope with stressful situations, and assisting people forget about their pain.

Look up the following Bible verses and write what they mean to you.

Proverbs 17:22 _____

Job 8:21 _____

Proverbs 15:13 _____

Nehemiah 8:10 _____

God knows the importance of laughter and how it can be a source of healing. This is why He included it in the Bible.

What are some ways you can include laughter in your day? _____

    God showed His sense of humor in the Bible. *They have left the straight way and wandered off to follow the way of Balaam son of Bezer, who loved the wages of wickedness. But he was rebuked for his wrongdoing by a donkey--an animal without speech--who spoke with a human voice and restrained the prophet's madness.* *(2 Peter 2:15-16 NIV)* Balaam may have been shocked initially, but after he obeyed God, he had to appreciate God's way of getting his attention.

    Being able to find humor in our struggles and mistakes can make the trials of life more manageable. God has a sense of humor, and He uses it frequently. I often see God using humor in my life to teach me a lesson or to help me get through a rough patch. There are times when I ask Him a question or pray to Him requesting something, and He gives me my answer in a humorous way. If God can use humor to get us through life, we too should find humor in what life is throwing at us. It may not ease all the pain, but it can dull it or can give us temporary relief, allowing us to think more clearly.

Watch how you speak to yourself: Let your mouth speak only kind words. You can be your own worst enemy. That small, inner voice can destroy you if you let it. You need to make sure you talk to yourself the way you expect others to speak to you. If you tell yourself you will never lose weight or make changes, then that is precisely what will happen. If you hear these words, either from others or your lips, you will eventually start to believe them. They become a self-fulfilling prophecy. God in His infinite wisdom knows that our thoughts can defeat us and He gave us verses to guard against this. *Above all else, guard your heart, for everything you do flows from it.* *(Proverbs 4:23 NIV)* He also gave us a solution to combat our negative thoughts. *Finally, brothers and sisters, whatever is true, whatever is noble, whatever is right, whatever is pure, whatever is lovely, whatever is admirable—if anything is excellent or praiseworthy—think about such things.* *(Philippians 4:8 NIV)*

Look up the following Bible verses. Record how they might change your mindset regarding how you speak to yourself.

Romans 12:2 _____

Colossians 3:2 _____

2 Corinthians 10:5 _____

1 Peter 5:8 _____

John 6:68 _____

What are some of the negative thoughts you need to remove from your life? _____

Below are some Bible verses you can use to retrain your inner voice.
When your inner voice says: I have messed up so bad that God cannot forgive me this time.
Respond: But God died for me while I was still a sinner. (Romans 5:8)

When your inner voice says: I am not loveable.
Respond: My God is in my midst; He will save me and rejoice over me with gladness. He quiets me by His love and will exalt over me by loud singing. (Zephaniah 3:17)

When your inner voice says: I am not worthy of God's love.

Respond: God so loved me that He gave His only Son so I will have eternal life. (John 3:16)

When your inner voice says: I cannot do this.
Respond: For God has not given me a spirit of timidity, but of power, love and discipline. (2 Timothy 1:7)

When your inner voice has negative thoughts.
Respond with: I will submit my thoughts to God and the devil will flee from me. (James 4:7)

When your inner voice says: I cannot break my strongholds.
Respond with: I will seek the Lord and His strength; I will seek His face continually. (1 Chronicles 16:11)

Your turn; write out the negative thoughts that consume you and replace them with the authoritative Word of God. Keep them near you so that you can use them every time you have to correct the negative thoughts that are trying to hold you captive. Perhaps you can place these verses in your phone so they are readily available.

Exercise: You need to exercise at least three times a week. There is so much research showing that exercise affects your attitude. When you are physically active, it releases neurochemicals into your brain. The primary neurochemicals are dopamine, norepinephrine, and endorphins. These three neurochemicals have been shown to improve mood, increase alertness and improve cognitive function. It also helps remove adrenaline and cortisol, which are stress hormones. Exercise requires you to focus and therefore can distract you from the struggles you are facing. (2)

Eat well: Diet is critical. Foods can alter your mood and increase the stress in your body. Some of the foods that are good for combating stress are green leafy vegetables, salmon, oatmeal, blueberries, pistachios, cashews, seeds, dark chocolate, avocados, raw carrots, and celery. Stay away from sugar, gluten, and processed food. (3)

Remove yourself from negative conversations: People can drag you down, and they can fill your head with negativity. You must guard against negativity at all times, which may entail changing your daily habits. For example, if at work you eat lunch with a group of people who are continually belittling others, spreading gossip or just speaking negatively, you may have to find an alternative group or spend this time with God. Set boundaries for your family and friends who bring negativity into your world. When someone wants to tell you a negative story, stop him or her immediately. Do not let people fill your head with negative comments. You have the power to control what you allow your mind to hear.

Music: Listen to your favorite upbeat music. Christian music is not only uplifting, but it also fills a spiritual need.

Get adequate sleep: Sleep is essential for your brain to function at optimal capacity. When you lack sleep, your mind has a difficult time functioning. When you receive adequate rest, your body wakes up refreshed. You can look at a situation from a different perspective. Lack of sleep alters some parts of the brain's activity, which in turn can have an impact on attitude.

Aromatherapy: There are many essential oils that can be used for relaxation, and there are many ways to dispense them. The easiest way is to use a diffuser, which can be purchased online or in stores. You can use cotton balls with several drops of essential oil placed in the vents of your car. I recommend only pure essential oils. (Aromatherapy is addressed to a greater extent in a future chapter)

Make an "I am thankful list": Many things happen every day that are good. When you struggle, it is so easy to miss these things. Spend time each day and list at least five good things that happened to you. It can be as simple as seeing a beautiful sunrise, or the fact that you woke to see another day. Life is good; you need to take the time to recognize this.

Become aware of how you are holding your body and the muscles: Learn to recognize when you are guarding yourself by tightening your muscles. When you are tight, utilize some relaxation techniques.

Stop clenching teeth: You need to become aware of when you are doing this and make a conscious effort to stop. Often people clench their teeth when sleeping. An easy way to prevent this is by using a mouth guard. Custom ones made by a dentist are best as they are often more comfortable to wear. However, they are much more expensive than an over the counter mouth guard, which can be molded to fit a person's teeth. Many sporting goods stores have them.

Rehearse how you will handle situations: Do this frequently. If you know you are about to enter a situation that is going to cause you stress, address it beforehand. Talk to yourself about how to stay calm and how best to react to the situation.

Deep Breathing: When people are stressed, they tend to take short quick breaths rather than deep relaxed breaths, which decreases blood oxygenation. You can do deep breathing throughout the day. Breathe in through your nose and feel your stomach rise and then slowly exhale. Do this 10-20 minutes a day. Make sure that when doing the breathing you are getting the deep breaths that cause the abdomen to rise and fall. When your body is stressed, breathing is shallow and occurs more in the upper lungs, which are located in the top of the rib cage. This shallow breathing decreases the oxygen intake. It hinders your ability to expel carbon dioxide, which causes a build up toxins within your body. Shallow breathing also affects a person's posture because of the recruitment of the neck muscles to allow this type of breathing. The neck muscles become tight putting pressure on the upper ribs and causing a head forward posture. Relearning the proper way to breathe may take some time to master. Doing this while driving or sitting at your desk is an excellent time to practice. Deep breathing is also very effective when done in conjunction with yoga and meditation.

Here is a deep breathing technique. Get into a comfortable position either sitting or lying down. If lying down, it may be best to place a pillow under the knees. Place one hand on the abdomen. It is often easier if the eyes are closed to avoid distractions. Breathe in through the nose letting the belly rise so that it is pushing the hand up. Breathe out through the mouth, allowing the abdomen to come back down. Start out slowly, doing it for 2-5 minutes and increase the time as the technique becomes more comfortable. If this method is going to be effective in handling stress, it must be practiced first when one is relaxed. Try using the 4-7-8 breathing technique. (Breathe in for a count of 4, hold for a count of 7 and exhale for a count of 8.) This technique will help stop the negative thought process because the counting pattern will act as a distraction.

Yoga: This practice incorporates deep breathing, meditation, and light exercise into one session. Studies have shown that yoga helps to combat stress. It also reduces fatigue, improves flexibility, increases muscle tone, gives mental clarity and awareness and improves circulation and cardiovascular health. Many yoga programs are available on the Internet that you can do in your home, or many gyms offer classes. You must attend more than one class to receive the benefits. As with every program, there can be both good and bad instructors. If you do not like one instructor, try another until you find one with whom you are comfortable. Make sure that this is a Christian based program.

Visualize: This is a great technique to decrease stress. Picture yourself in a peaceful setting such as walking on a beach or sitting on a mountain with Jesus by your side. Before beginning visualization, get into a comfortable position either sitting cross-legged or reclined in a chair. Be cautious about lying down because it can lead to falling asleep. Use deep breathing with the eyes closed. Once relaxed, imagine a place or spot that elicits peace or serenity and try using all the senses to imagine the scene. One of my favorite images is sitting on a mountain reading the Bible while watching the sunrise with a cool breeze blowing and birds chirping. There are Christian websites to find visualization techniques that also provide sounds to enhance the experience.

Acupuncture: This can offer a deep relaxation. The needles used are very thin. It is not painful, and most of the time you do not even feel the needle being inserted. The needles are often left in for 20-30 minutes. Acupuncture is an ancient form of Chinese medicine and operates on the principle that Qi is the energy force that controls the body's health. These forces move through pathways called meridians. When the body is stressed, these meridians can become disrupted. While getting acupuncture, the heart and breathing rate may slow, muscle tension decreases and the person may go into a very relaxed state. I recommend this both for stress release and pain relief. I find acupuncture very relaxing. Often, while receiving acupuncture, I use the quiet time to pray. Because I am relaxed, I can focus on my prayer and have quality time with our loving Father.

Get a massage or do a self-massage working on muscles that are tight: Massage helps to reduce the tension in the muscles, relieves pain caused by muscle tightness and can reduce your stress. It is not always economically feasible to get a professional massage. However, you can do a self-massage on tight muscles. Use coconut oil combined with a relaxing essential oil to help reduce tension even more. Working on the neck, low back and face can be very beneficial, as we tend to tense these muscles when we are stressed.

Progressive muscle relaxation: By tensing and relaxing muscle groups, you can relieve tension in your body. With this technique, you tense and relax muscles one at a time as you use a deep breathing technique. There are many scripts for this on the Internet.

Practice relaxing and destressing techniques frequently: By practicing these techniques when you are in a relaxed state, you learn to do them correctly. They will become a habit and you will more readily use them when you need to calm yourself.

Punching bag: Set up a punching bag in the basement or use a punching ball. Use this to help to get rid of anger and frustration.

Schedule social activities: When there is something to look forward to, the anticipation can occupy your thoughts. Socializing is very important to help ward off depression.

Take a walk, enjoy nature: Getting in the sunlight along with the walking can do wonders for your body. Sunlight increases serotonin and facilitates vitamin D production. This helps to improve your mood.

Seek the help of a Christian therapist: If you find you are unable to break the negative patterns in your life or feel you are dealing with depression, get professional help.

Food for thought:

1. Do you see yourself as a positive person or a negative person?

2. What can you do to change your attitude so that it is more positive?

3. Write a prayer or letter to God telling Him exactly how you feel. Don't hold anything back. Talk to Him as you would a parent or close friend. In the prayer, ask for help in dealing with these feelings. Invite the Holy Spirit to enlighten you and help you deal with the issues that are holding you back from being positive.

4. Did you find in any of the above suggestions something that you think would be useful in helping manage your stress? Which ones?

5. How are you going to incorporate them into your life?

6. Start your thankful list. When you count your blessings, you can see how active God is in your life.

Journal your thoughts

Day 4

THE VESTIBULE
(CONTENTMENT)

The vestibule is a small chamber that opens into the sanctuary, serving as the entrance hall. How a person is greeted in the entrance hall can affect their attitude and how they enter the sanctuary.

Nugget of the day: Trust in the Lord with all your heart; do not depend on your own understanding. Seek his will in all you do, and he will show you which path to take. (Proverbs 3:5 NLT)

Contentment can be summed up in eight words: trust in the Lord with all your heart. We do not have superpowers or the ability to foretell the future. Therefore, we need to rely on God to lead us in this world. Most children do not fret over the problems they will face during their day. They live for the moment and trust that their parents will take care of any problem that may arise. We need to follow this example. We need to place our faith in God. When issues arise, turn them over to our Father. When we put expectations on our lives and do not expect to find contentment until these factors are a reality, we will never be at peace. Our world is unpredictable. There are too many variables that can change everything in a matter of minutes. Trusting God is the only way we will find contentment in an uncertain world. Satan loves to rock our world and shake our faith in God. God is the only One that can foresee the future. He is the only One that knows what His plans are for our lives. We experience contentment when we accept that God is in control and trust that He will provide for our needs. Contentment is not something we can buy or achieve on our own. When we change our attitude from self-centered to God-centered we will find peace.

My prayer is that you realize God is the key to living a content life. By trusting God, you can appreciate what you have, and live within your means. When we look to God and live our lives accordingly, we know that we are on course to serve our purpose on earth and glorify God. I pray we adopt a childlike attitude and look for God's blessings in all situations. Contentment is only attained when you trust in the Lord with all your heart.
****

The vestibule can be one of the hardest areas to design so that it is welcoming and a place where people want to enter. When a person is not content with life, the vestibule can be cold and uninviting. It makes it hard for a person to want to enter the sanctuary because they are not comfortable with where they are in life. There are many external and internal pressures on every one of us. At times, the world can make us feel guilty that our lives are not like everyone else's. Often, people put so much value on materialism and doing things in a specific manner that when we veer away from the so-called norm of society, it can be hard to accept the Christian lifestyles we have chosen. When we are greeted warmly in the vestibule, we will understand it is not about what we have, rather whom we are as Christians that allows us to live the lives God specifically designed for us. *I know what it is to be in need, and I know what it is to have plenty. I have learned the secret of being content in any and every situation, whether well fed or hungry, whether living in plenty or in want.* (*Philippians 4:12 NIV*) This truly is the secret to life. We live in a world that values material things and is becoming more "I" centered every day. Too often we are made to feel as if we are not living a complete life unless we drive a new car, take a lavish vacation, have the latest television, live in a large house or have a prestigious career.

What keeps you from being content? _____

Why do you feel this way? _____

Then he said to them, "Watch out! Be on your guard against all kinds of greed; life does not consist in an abundance of possessions." (*Luke 12:15 NIV*) The Bible contains over 2,000 verses in regards to finances, which is fifteen percent of the Bible. (1) God knew that money would be something that could control our lives. He has given us ample teachings as to how it can either destroy us or further His kingdom. God does not tell us that money itself is evil. *For the love of money is a root of all kinds of evil. Some people, eager for money, have wandered from the faith and pierced themselves with many griefs.* (*1 Timothy 6:10 NIV*) The problem comes when we love money and put it above all else in our lives. It is how we go about attaining possessions that can destroy our lives. When we are dependent on money for our happiness or security, it stands in the way of our relationship with God. This dependency on money weakens our foundation. Rather than trusting God, we trust the almighty dollar.

Lack of contentment is not limited to material things. We often put conditions on our lives such as I will be happy when I get to be a manager at my job, I will enjoy life more when I go on vacation or retire, I will be content when I have children or grandchildren.

What conditions do you think need to exist for you to be content? _____

We spend so much time wishing our lives away that we never really get to experience all life has to offer. The journey to reach our goals is actually where we learn the skills to develop our trust in God. This experience is essential to building our temples. We worry so much about getting to our destination that we do not see all the blessings God is bestowing on us along the way. We do not appreciate the work, the people we are meeting, and miracles that are taking place. God uses these opportunities to draw closer to us. He knows that once we have all we want, we tend to forget Him. *I consider that our present sufferings are not worth comparing with the glory that will be revealed in us.* (*Romans 8:18 NIV*) We need to take time to appreciate all the blessings we receive as we work towards our goals. Rather than celebrating only the end victory, take time to celebrate each milestone. Are you happy when you lose one or two pounds? Are you happy when you can walk further than the last time? Are you happy when you eat less junk food? When will you be happy?

As you are working toward changing your lifestyle, are you putting conditions on the outcome?

_____

What are these conditions? _____

One of the reasons we may fall short of attaining our goals is we cannot live up to the expectations we put on ourselves. We may lose five or ten pounds, plateau, then get discouraged and give up. We don't take the time to appreciate the changes we made and the effort it took to attain a specific goal. Another issue is that if we lose the weight or improve our fitness, but we are not satisfied with whom we are, we will still not be content. We can improve the outer appearance, but we also need to fix the inside if we are really going to live a healthy lifestyle. Where do we find this contentment? It comes from knowing who we are in Christ and knowing our Creator loves us. It hinges on trusting God wholeheartedly and giving Him control of our lives.

What do the following Bible verses tell you about contentment and how you should live your life?

Matthew 6:25-26 _____

Matthew 6:32-33 _____

1 Timothy 6:6-7 _____

There is nothing wrong with having goals and dreams for your life. In truth, God wants you to grow and to become a better person. God has placed dreams and goals in your heart. He has given you specific gifts and talents so that you can be successful in answering God's call for your life. God wants you to use your abilities for His glory, not for yours. Living a healthy lifestyle needs to be one of your goals. God wants this for you because He knows when you are healthy you will be able to achieve the plans He has for you.

Contentment is so much more than having everything you desire in life. When you are content, it will be easier to continue to make changes necessary to improve your health. You will enjoy the journey when you enthusiastically celebrate the accomplishments. This recognition of small victories will help you not to be discouraged when change is slower than anticipated or you take a step backward.

Contentment in earthly things will never last. Things break or become outdated, goals change, careers come to an end, and people let you down. Your satisfaction must come from your faith, trusting God will provide for you and will guide you on your journey. *For where your treasure is, there your heart will be also.* *(Matthew 6:21 NIV)* When you finally surrender your life to God, you find the peace and contentment for which you have been searching. It is then you will see how rich and fulfilling your life can be. *For the kingdom of God is not a matter of eating and drinking, but of righteousness, peace and joy in the Holy Spirit, because anyone who serves Christ in this way is pleasing to God and receives human approval.* *(Romans 14:17-18 NIV)*

Contentment is:
- Finding the good in every situation and seeing God's blessings, even in your trials.
- Being thankful for what you have.
- Appreciating each and every gift you receive from God.
- Relishing the moment and taking time to celebrate it before looking ahead to the next milestone you want to achieve.
- Having a calling and knowing you are serving a divine purpose.
- Trusting God will guide you, give you strength and abilities to help fulfill your calling.
- Living within your means and being satisfied.
- Living a life that is pleasing to God and when you fail seeking and accepting God's forgiveness.
- Forgiving those who have hurt you.
- Sharing your talents and wealth.

Contentment is not:
- Worrying about your problems.
- Comparing your gifts to others and feeling as if you have been cheated or you are not living up to your potential.
- Putting conditions on what you think will give you peace.
- Letting material things dictate who you are and your self-worth.
- Holding onto anger or hatred.

That each of them may eat and drink, and find satisfaction in all their toil—this is the gift of God. *(Ecclesiastes 3:13 NIV)*
How can you apply the above verse to your life? _____

Food for thought:

1. How has your idea of contentment changed as you work through this study?

2. In what areas of your life do you lack contentment?
How can this be addressed?

3. Do you compare your gifts and talents to other people? If so, how is this stealing your contentment?

Journal your thoughts

Day 5

THE CHAPEL
(REST)

Many churches have a smaller room called a chapel where members can retreat to in order to find peace and spend some quiet time with God. Here they can worship privately or in a small group.

Nugget of the day: Those who live at the ends of the earth stand in awe of your wonders. From where the sun rises to where it sets, you inspire shouts of joy. *(Psalm 65:8 NLT)*

Have you ever wondered why God gives us night and day? At times, I think I would be so much happier if I didn't have to sleep. There is so much to do in this world, and I could accomplish so much more if I did not have to stop what I am doing to rest. Then I witness a beautiful sunrise and realize our God, in His infinite wisdom, knows we need the newness of each day. Each morning He gives us a display of His wonder. He greets us with a cheerful good morning telling us; I Am thinking of you. Each sunrise is a reminder that we have a brand new start. We can put our mistakes and troubles behind us and look forward to a new day and a clean slate. It is God's way of telling us He is not giving up on us. The sunrise is a reflection of our Dad's love for us. It lets us witness another wonder only God could create. It tells us life is good. Each sunset is God's way of telling His children good night. He gives us a way to end the day and put our worries to rest. It is at night that we can quiet our minds, spend some alone time with God and relax. We can lay our bodies down and recharge.

My prayer is that each morning you accept the gift of a new day and leave your past behind. Each evening, take the time to enjoy the sunset, breathe, relax and let the stress of the day melt away. God has blessed you with these beautiful displays of His awe and wonder. It is a gift given to you every morning and every night. There are no requirements for you to accept them and every day they are different. They welcome you to the start of a new day, and then they wish you a good night.
****

Everyone needs a place of rest. In this hectic day and age, we often find it hard to have a place where we can relax. Too often, we run ourselves ragged and do not get adequate rest. This can lead to having a difficult time getting through the day, having a short temper and being restless. Rest is essential for people to be able to perform their duties, which God has assigned. We all need a room that allows us to sit in God's presence and recharge. We also need to be able to go there to get the best possible sleep so we can be the best we can be. When we do not get adequate sleep, we cannot function properly. If we do not have a room that is conducive to getting a good night's sleep, we will awaken groggy and lethargic. God knows we need sleep and so our temples must have a chapel.

By the seventh day God had finished the work he had been doing; so on the seventh day he rested from all his work. Then God blessed the seventh day and made it holy, because on it he rested from all the work of creating that he had done. (Genesis 2:2-3 NIV) God knew the importance of rest. He also took the time to rest and appreciate what He had accomplished. If the Creator of the universe recognized the importance of rest, shouldn't we?

Read Exodus 20:8-10. Why do you think God established the Sabbath? _____

Do you take time to rest and enjoy your day? ____ What do you do during this time?

_____

We live in a society that values busyness. People often place their self-worth on how much they accomplish in a day, week or year. They love to outdo one another and show everyone how productive they are throughout the day. I too once fell into this group of people. I felt my children, and I always had to be busy. I thought I was not a good mom unless we were involved in all the activities in school, scouts, and sports. After my children got older, I was busy from the moment I jumped out of bed, until late in the night when I collapsed into bed. I seldom took time to eat a nice meal or relax. I did not understand why I became sad when the evening came, and the darkness was present. Then I had that "aha" moment when I realized the dark was a reminder that in a few hours I would fall into bed exhausted. Rarely did I have the energy to even change out of my clothes. I had to get a few precious hours of sleep before I would have to get up and do it all over again. At the time, I enjoyed our active life, but it took a toll on me physically, emotionally, mentally and spiritually. I was always tired, and if I sat down for a few moments in a meeting or to visit, I would fall asleep. How many of you make this same mistake? Maybe it is not with your children, but with your job or your social life.

What activities in your life interfere with your ability to relax and cause you undue stress?

_____

How do the following verses speak to you personally?

Matthew 11:28-29 _____

Mark 6:31 _____

Psalm 37:7 _____

I have since learned that the key to living a fulfilling life is also taking the time to sit and appreciate all that is around me. I live in the moment rather than wondering what precious time I am wasting sitting still. I enjoy quiet moments with God, sitting in His presence or reading His Word. *He says, "Be still, and know that I am God; I will be exalted among the nations, I will be exalted in the earth."* (Psalm 46:10 NIV) This command was not only given so God could spend time with His beloved children but also so we can recharge our minds and bodies. I have learned the importance of sitting with family and friends and enjoying their company. I love to sit and watch the sunrise and sunset. I enjoy taking walks while listening to praise music or sharing a good conversation with a friend. I have also learned that taking time to relax has helped me become more productive. I am now more creative, and although my projects may take longer to accomplish, I enjoy the activity rather than pushing myself because it is something I must do. Most mornings before taking on the day, I sit in God's presence and read His Word before going off to work. In the evenings, I look forward to the darkness because I know most of the time I will have a peaceful evening and get a good night's sleep.

How do you make time to sit in God's presence and connect with Him? _____

Do you find it important to make the time even when your schedule may be hectic? _____

If so, how does this help to prepare you for the day ahead? _____

Sleep is also a key component to living a healthy lifestyle. We all need sleep and when we are sleep deprived our body, mind, and spirit suffer. Sleep research has shown that the lack of sleep or poor quality of sleep affects every tissue and system in our body. Our brains, hearts, lungs, immune system and metabolism all suffer when we lack sleep. It also causes us to have an increased risk of some diseases and disorders. These include cardiovascular disease, diabetes, high blood pressure, depression, and obesity. [1] When we are sleep deprived, we can become moody and irritable. We tend to eat more, activating the hunger hormone ghrelin, causing us to crave sugary and fatty foods. [2] This, in turn, causes weight gain. People also exhibit a lack of focus, poor coordination, poor decision-making and increased impulsivity when sleep deprived. Impulsivity causes a person to react differently than they would have, had they not been fatigued. Other physical signs of sleep deprivation are a poor skin condition, impaired eyesight due to tired eye muscles, slurred speech and susceptibility to sickness. A person may also experience micro-sleep, which causes a person to nod off for several seconds, allowing for a lapse in their attention to a task. [3] According to the NHSA, falling asleep while driving is responsible for at least 100,000 crashes, 71,000 injuries and 1,550 deaths each year in the United States. [4]

It varies as to the amount of sleep an individual needs. Most adults require 7-9 hours of sleep each night. However, after the age of 60, the amount of sleep needed tends to decrease. If we are striving to live healthy lives, we must also recognize the importance of a good night's rest.

Sleep can be interrupted for a variety of reasons. One of these reasons is due to the blue light emitted from electronics and LED lights. The blue light can suppress the secretion of melatonin. [5] Another contributing factor can be the type of mattress we sleep on or the bedding we use. Many toxic chemicals have been added to mattresses to make them flame resistant. Some chemicals that may be used are boric acid, formaldehyde, and flame-retardants. [6] For some people, these chemicals can cause skin irritation, restless sleeping or breathing problems. Alcohol can cause sleep problems. [7] Foods can also cause us to lose sleep. Spicy foods can cause indigestion and possibly change our body temperature due to capsaicin. High-fat diets can cause fragmented sleep and more daytime sleepiness. [8]

Ways to enhance sleep:

- Reduce stress in your life. Perform meditation or deep breathing techniques before bed.
- Keep the room temperature cool.
- Make sure the room is dark. You may need to use light blocking curtains or blackout shades.
- Keep your bedtime consistent so the body is familiar with a sleep pattern.
- Don't drink fluids within 2 hours of going to bed, and make sure to use the bathroom before getting into bed.
- Maintain a healthy body weight. Excess weight can cause or worsen sleep apnea. [9]
- Avoid drinking alcohol before bed.
- Take a hot bath or shower before bedtime.
- Reduce your caffeine intake.
- Use your bed only for sleeping. When you do work or watch television in bed, it is harder to fall asleep.
- Avoid looking at bright screens 2-3 hours before bedtime. Some electronics have controls to turn off the blue light in the evening.
- Keep electronic devices away from the bed. Charge your phone on the other side of the room.
- Exercise daily. Research has shown 150 minutes of moderate to vigorous exercise weekly improves sleep quality up to 65 percent. [10]
- Use essential oils.

- Foods that help promote sleep: [11]

Tart cherry juice is rich in melatonin.
Foods rich in calcium such as kale and collards, help promote sleep.
Foods with potassium and B6, such as bananas, help produce melatonin.
Lean proteins such as salmon, as well as healthy fats such as nuts, are high in the amino acid tryptophan, which increases serotonin. [12]

- Replace worn mattresses.

Food for thought:

1. What are some habits that may be hindering your sleep?

2. What are some things you can do to improve your sleep?

Journal your thoughts

Week 3

Day 1: Review Bible verses
Day 2: Wiring Our Temples
Day 3: Designing The Electrical Circuits
Day 4: Testing The Circuits For Overload
Day 5: Rewiring The Temple

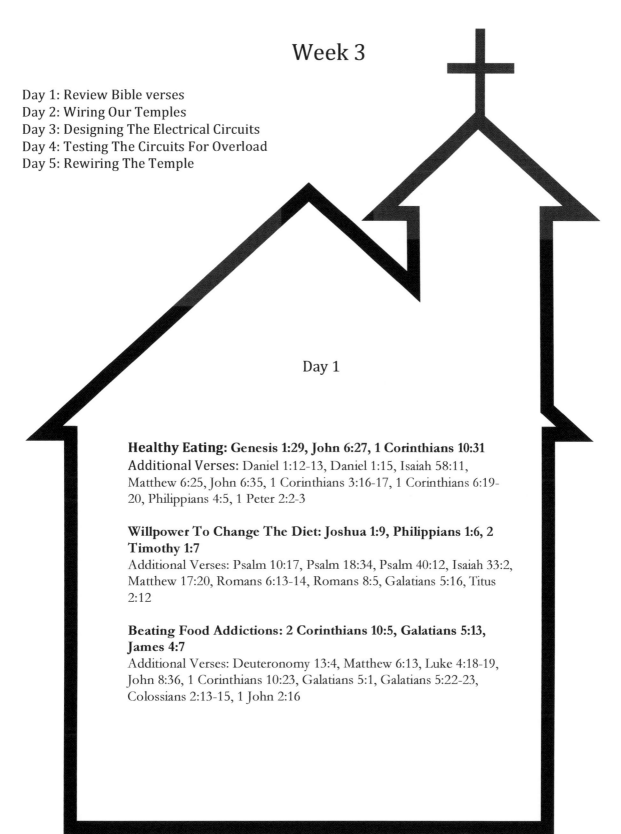

Day 1

Healthy Eating: Genesis 1:29, John 6:27, 1 Corinthians 10:31
Additional Verses: Daniel 1:12-13, Daniel 1:15, Isaiah 58:11,
Matthew 6:25, John 6:35, 1 Corinthians 3:16-17, 1 Corinthians 6:19-
20, Philippians 4:5, 1 Peter 2:2-3

**Willpower To Change The Diet: Joshua 1:9, Philippians 1:6, 2
Timothy 1:7**
Additional Verses: Psalm 10:17, Psalm 18:34, Psalm 40:12, Isaiah 33:2,
Matthew 17:20, Romans 6:13-14, Romans 8:5, Galatians 5:16, Titus
2:12

**Beating Food Addictions: 2 Corinthians 10:5, Galatians 5:13,
James 4:7**
Additional Verses: Deuteronomy 13:4, Matthew 6:13, Luke 4:18-19,
John 8:36, 1 Corinthians 10:23, Galatians 5:1, Galatians 5:22-23,
Colossians 2:13-15, 1 John 2:16

Assignment: The assignment this week is twofold. Spend this week reading the scriptures and learning to use them to fight off temptations.
Take time to compare the food God has provided for you to the processed food you like to eat. Look at the food: examine the colors, the shapes, feel the texture, smell the aroma and taste the two types of food. Take the time to savor the taste of each. Do this with a variety of foods and report to your group what you experienced.

WIRING THE TEMPLE
(FUELING YOUR BODY)

Electricity provides the temple with power to give it warmth, energy, and lighting.

Nugget of the day: Why spend your money on food that does not give you strength? Why pay for food that does you no good? Listen to me, and you will eat what is good. You will enjoy the finest food. (Isaiah 55:2 NLT)

We spend so much money and energy on things that hinder our well-being rather than on what nourishes us. God knew what He was doing when He created the earth. He provided us with all the essentials to live healthy and fulfilling lives. Man, through science, has been trying to improve on what God provided for us. Mankind also created a belief system that did not include God and called it faith. Man changed the rules to make them fit his own wants and needs. In the world today, there is so much sickness and diseases such as diabetes, heart disease, obesity, and cancer. We need to get back to the basics and realize God will feed us, not only physically but also spiritually. God, our Creator, knows what we need to live healthy lives. God gave us everything we need.

My prayer is that you listen to God. The Bible has all the information you need to live a healthy life. Unlike people, who have ulterior motives, God has your best interest at heart. You honor God when you eat His vegetables and fruits. You give Him glory and honor when you follow His teachings. You are the one that truly benefits from being fed by God. Your life becomes more fulfilled and meaningful. You have a sense of peace in your soul, are healthier, and you enjoy life much more. So, get back to the basics and let God feed you in every aspect of your life. You will be fulfilled when you accept God's plan for your nourishment.
****

Wiring is essential in a temple. Without electricity, the temple will be cold, dark and lifeless. The same applies to our bodily temples. When we provide our bodies with the correct power source, we can function much more efficiently. The fuel we receive from our food can either provide or deplete our bodies of energy. It is our choice as to how we power our temples. During the next three weeks, we are going to study the best ways to provide energy for our temples.

If God did not see the diet as important, He would not have included information about nutrition in the Bible. God, in His infinite wisdom, would not address any issues unless they help us grow in faith, improve our lives and bring us closer to Him. The Bible is the greatest self-help book ever written. It is packed with ways for us to live healthier and more fulfilling lives. It provides essential instructions on how to live each day. So, when are we going to start listening and stop trying to make it on our own?
Take some time to review the Daniel 1:6-16.

What were the benefits Daniel and his men received from eating vegetables and water?

_____

Daniel knew the benefits of a healthy diet. He chose to adhere to his beliefs even when others pressured him. It took a lot of strength to do what Daniel did. He had to stand up to people who could not only destroy him but also destroy his friends who followed his lead. Daniel was able to convince others to eat healthily and improve their lives because he stood up for what he knew was right. We often face this same dilemma when we choose to maintain healthy lifestyles. Well-meaning friends and family try to convince us that we need to go off our diets whether it is at home, in a restaurant or at a party. We are often pressured to "just try this." We may give in so as not to hurt their feelings. It takes willpower to eat the right way. When we set an example, others will see the real benefits of a clean diet and may want to change theirs, but if we give in just to please others, we cannot lead by example.

Is it hard for you to eat healthy around your friends and family? _____

What are some of the ways family and friends pressure you into eating the way they do? _____

_____

How can you prepare yourself so that the next time you are pressured you can remain strong and eat the way you know you should? _____

_____

Are you willing to take Daniel's ten-day challenge? _____

What are some obstacles that prevent you from doing this for 10 days? _____

_____

Daniel lived his life to honor God, and God rewarded him for remaining faithful. Daniel knew that God was the only One who could guide him in this world. He knew God was his strength and so he spent much time in prayer. *Now when Daniel learned that the decree had been published, he went home to his upstairs room where the windows opened toward Jerusalem. Three times a day he got down on his knees and prayed, giving thanks to his God, just as he had done before.* (Daniel 6:10 NIV)

How often do you pray for God to give you strength to live a healthy lifestyle? _____

How can you include God more frequently in your daily life so that He can give you strength when you are weak or you are feeling pressure from others to go off your diet?

_____

The following Bible verses speak of God's ability to give us willpower when we are weak. How do these verses speak to you?

Romans 13:14 _____

Jeremiah 32:27 _____

1 Corinthians 9:24-25 _____

Colossians 3:17 _____

God can give you strength and willpower to overcome any obstacle in your life. You must be willing to go before Him and ask for this strength and then lean into Him for support. When you veer from God and His Word, you will feel weak. One way you can choose God over food is to ask yourself these questions: is this candy bar, french fries, cinnamon roll, etc. more important than God's plan for my health and wellness? Will eating this food restore my temple or tear it down? You must memorize and use Bible verses to ward off temptation and to give you strength.

How important is your diet in God's eyes? You don't have to look any further than the first book of Genesis. It is here God gives you your first lesson. *Then God said, "I give you every seed-bearing plant on the face of the whole earth and every tree that has fruit with seed in it. They will be yours for food.* (Genesis 1:29 NIV) Travel a little further to *Deuteronomy 32:13-14* and you will receive more dietary tips. *He made him ride on the heights of the land and fed him with the fruit of the fields. He nourished him with honey from the rock, and with oil from the flinty crag, with curds and milk from herd and flock and with fattened lambs and goats, with choice rams of Bashan and the finest kernels of wheat. You drank the foaming blood of the grape. (NIV)* God made perfect food that would nourish our bodies and man thought he could improve upon it. The arrogance of man has led us to believe that we could improve on God's great works and His perfectly orchestrated world. In doing so, we have created a mess which has caused us to compromise our health and well-being. Man has also created shortcuts in food production, compromising the nutritional value of our food. By taking matters into our own hands, we now have GMO's (genetically modified organisms) that, in my opinion, threaten our health. GMO's are the result of transplanting the genes from the DNA of one species into the genes of an unrelated plant. These genes can be extracted from bacteria, viruses, insects, animals or humans.

We need to get back to the basics and allow God to once again be in control of our food. We need to understand that only God can produce the food that can truly nourish us. He has provided us with the proper vitamins and minerals to fuel our bodies. God knows not only the importance of eating this way on earth but also in Heaven. In the book of Revelation, God has shown us that He will provide the perfect diet in Heaven. *Then the angel showed me the river of the water of life, as clear as crystal, flowing from the throne of God and of the Lamb down the middle of the great street of the city. On each side of the river stood the tree of life, bearing twelve crops of fruit, yielding its fruit every month. And the leaves of the tree are for the healing of the nations. (Revelation 22:1-2 NIV)* Not only does the first chapter of the Bible provide us with God telling us that He has provided us with healthy food to eat, but the last chapter of the Bible also refers to God providing us with water and fruit to nourish us.

Since God will provide us with healthy food in Heaven, wouldn't He want the same for us here?

I often hear people speak of Heaven and how they are going to be able to enjoy all the foods that they are not supposed to eat on earth. I cannot imagine that God would allow man-made foods or chemicals in Heaven when He knows they are harmful to His children. God's food will not only satisfy us but will also be pleasing to our palate. In truth, when we are in the presence of our loving Father, we will realize that He did know what was best for His children. We will no longer desire food that is unhealthy or impure. Instead, we will enjoy food that genuinely satisfies us. In Luke's Gospel, Jesus talks about us eating at His table. *So that you may eat and drink at my table in my kingdom and sit on thrones, judging the twelve tribes of Israel. (Luke 22:30 NIV)* Can you even imagine what this will be like in Heaven? I can assure you, that when we walk away from the Lord's Table, we will be well fed both nutritionally and spiritually. There will be no heartburn or indigestion.

At the end of the ten days they looked healthier and better nourished than any of the young men who ate the royal food. (Daniel 1:15 NIV) Sometimes I have to stop and marvel at all the thought that God put into His creation. Everything He has placed on this earth has a specific purpose. Every type of food has a particular role in nourishing our bodies. Each fruit or vegetable has a particular combination of vitamins and minerals that will not only give us energy but also keep our bodies healthy and provide healing. He gave us such a variety of produce that we can enjoy many combinations of food. Along with nourishment, we can use food to bring families together to share a meal and make eating a joyful experience. When I take the time to study His creation of food, not only does it amaze me as to how it provides me with nourishment, but also how beautiful and appealing it is to the eye. The colors are vibrant, and the shapes are unique. The smells of these foods have a variety of effects on us. They are calming, stimulating, mood enhancing and help with improving our focus as well as add to the taste of our food. The tastes vary from sweet to sour, bland to bursting with flavor. Too often our palates have become accustomed to the taste of processed food and have lost their desire for the healthy foods God has given us. We may need to retrain our palates and change how we think about healthy food. There really is no excuse for people to say they do not like fruits and vegetables. There are so many from which to choose. If you have not found vegetables or fruit you like, you may need to explore the many varieties and options God has provided us with on this great earth.

Have you ever taken the time to think about and appreciate how much effort God put into creating such amazing foods for us to enjoy and receive nourishment? _____

What are some thoughts you have as you contemplate this? _____

_____

Compare your favorite processed food with one of God's creation. Look at how much more appealing it is to your sense of sight and smell. What are the differences? _____

_____

After comparing the two, can you see how God's foods are more beneficial to your diet? _____

_____

　　If you are going to lead a healthy life, you need to start with the basics. Living by the I AM F.E.D. (faith, exercise, diet) model is an excellent example to follow. You need to trust God and know that He is the Great I AM and our loving Father who is providing for His children. God will not steer you wrong. His food will fuel your temple and provide you with the energy you need to answer your callings.

Food for thought:

1. How does it make you feel that God has provided for all your needs and wants you to live a healthy life?

2. What are some concerns you have at this time as to whether or not you can live this healthy lifestyle?

3. Are there people in your life that are hindering you from making changes?

4. Come up with a game plan so that the next time people tempt you, you will have the strength to stand firm.

Below are some Bible verses that can help you on your journey.

When your mind says, "I can eat what I want."
God says, *"You say, "I am allowed to do anything"—but not everything is good for you. And even though "I am allowed to do anything," I must not become a slave to anything."* (1 Corinthians 6:12 NLT)

When your mind says, "this is too hard!"
God says, *"For I can do everything through Christ, who gives me strength."* (Philippians 4:13 NLT)

When your mind says, "Why does it matter what I eat?"
God says, *"Don't you realize that your body is the temple of the Holy Spirit, who lives in you and was given to you by God? You do not belong to yourself, for God bought you with a high price. So you must honor God with your body."* (1 Corinthians 6:19-20 NLT)

When your mind says, "This is not working."
God says, *"The Lord is my strength and shield. I trust him with all my heart. He helps me, and my heart*

is filled with joy. I burst out in songs of thanksgiving. (Psalm 28:7 NLT)

When your mind says, "what is wrong with going off my diet for a day."
God says, *"Instead, clothe yourself with the presence of the Lord Jesus Christ. And don't let yourself think about ways to indulge your evil desires. (Romans 13:14 NLT)*

When your mind says, "I have no willpower."
God says, *"He gives power to the weak and strength to the powerless. (Isaiah 40:29 NLT)*

When your mind says, "go ahead, everyone else is eating what they want."
God says, *"Don't copy the behavior and customs of this world, but let God transform you into a new person by changing the way you think. Then you will learn to know God's will for you, which is good and pleasing and perfect." (Romans 12:2 NLT)*

When your mind says, "no one else cares what I do with my life. "
God says, *"And so, dear brothers and sisters, I plead with you to give your bodies to God because of all he has done for you. Let them be a living and holy sacrifice—the kind he will find acceptable. This is truly the way to worship him. (Romans 12:1 NLT)*

Add your own self-defeating thoughts and let God answer them.

When your mind says, _____

God says: _____

When your mind says: _____

God says: _____

God always has an answer for all of your questions, doesn't He?

Journal your thoughts

Day 3

DESIGNING THE ELECTRIC CIRCUITS
(IDENTIFYING FACTORS THAT PROMOTE HEALTHY EATING)

Many things in our temple require power. Therefore, they must design a plan that uses the energy efficiently. Developing this plan takes time and patience.

Nugget of the day: If you need wisdom, ask our generous God, and he will give it to you. He will not rebuke you for asking. (James 1:5 NLT)

God does not expect us to be perfect. When we accept that we do not have to be perfect in this world, it takes a lot of pressure off of us. We do not have to put undue expectations on ourselves. Relieving this stress frees us up to enjoy a better life. It gives us the ability to try new things without fear of failure. As we begin to make changes in our diet, we will make mistakes and will have to make corrections. When we pray to God, He can give us the insight to make these changes. We also have to be willing to be patient with ourselves. Changing our lifestyle is a learning process. When we trust God, He will lead us and help us to make changes so we can live the lives He has planned for us. The Bible is packed with information as to the changes we need to make and how to do it. When we utilize this information, we will be successful.

My prayer is that you realize you do not have to be perfect in this world to make a difference. God uses you right where you are. I pray that you learn to trust God and know that He is faithful. He has given you the desire to make changes in your life. When you trust God, He will guide you and provide you with the knowledge, wisdom, and resources to accomplish this goal. You are capable of doing many things that you may not even be aware of at this time. When you turn your life over to God and trust Him, He works in mighty and mysterious ways. Spend some time offering God your life and asking Him to lead you on this journey. Thank Him in advance for the good works He will perform in your life and the journey He will share with you.

✳✳✳

There is a lot to learn before we can establish a new diet. There may be obstacles that can cause a person not to be able to maintain the new diet. Unless addressed, these obstacles can hinder our success. We want our bodies to be as efficient as possible so we need to try and identify these things that may hinder us. We need to come up with a plan to help us be successful with changing our lifestyles.

Trying to change to a healthier lifestyle is not always easy, especially when just starting out. There are so many pressures, false advertisements and misleading information that influence our perception as to what is healthy living. People will try to pressure you into eating their way, give you bad advice or make you feel guilty for choosing to eat healthy. We have to relieve ourselves from these pressures and live our lives the Biblical way. When we use the Bible as our guide, we find that living a healthy lifestyle pleases God. Honoring God should be our number one priority. We will accomplish much more than when we try and improve our lifestyles on our own. I truly believe failure to enlist God's help and trusting Him is why so many people fail when trying to change. We cannot do anything without God supporting us and providing us with the strength to make permanent changes. We may be able to change temporarily, but God is the One who gives us the willpower to stay strong. There are many instances where people attempt to do this on their own and fail. People are continually joining weight loss programs and are successful for a short period only to gain all the weight back at a later time.

Taking care of our bodies requires us to understand that our bodies are worth the effort. We have to accept the truth that God loves us and that He created us to be the person we are right now. This is why we must have sturdy external walls. We have to realize that God did not make a mistake when He created us. To be able to treat our bodies with respect, we need to remember that our bodies are His temple and treat them as such. We need to release unrealistic social norms that predetermine what weight and body types are considered to be "beautiful." Too often these ideals cloud our minds. Then we feel as if we have let ourselves, and possibly others down when we do not reach or maintain these goals. With this being said, we must strive to try and maintain healthy body weight and keep our bodies in good physical shape. This way we can participate more fully in life and fulfill our callings. We are often harder on ourselves than others are on us. When we set goals that are unrealistic, not attainable or unsustainable, we become discouraged and give up. It is best to set small, short-term goals and adjust them to our own needs as we go along. Each person is different. Just as our food choices will be different, so will our results. Know that you will make mistakes, you will have temptation and struggles and that's okay. Rather than be upset, forgive yourself and move on!

Do you see your body as a temple for God? _____ Why or why not? _____

_____

If your body is a temple for God, don't you owe Him the respect of taking care of it? _____

In what ways does food control your life? _____

51

"No one can serve two masters. Either you will hate the one and love the other, or you will be devoted to the one and despise the other. You cannot serve both God and money. "Therefore I tell you, do not worry about your life, what you will eat or drink; or about your body, what you will wear. Is not life more than food, and the body more than clothes? Look at the birds of the air; they do not sow or reap or store away in barns, and yet your heavenly Father feeds them. Are you not much more valuable than they? Can any one of you by worrying add a single hour to your life? (Matthew 6:24-27 NIV) False idols are more than money and material goods. They are anything that comes between our Heavenly Father and us. These gods become a distraction. We can only see as far as the next meal, gadget or activity. Rather than being secure in who we are in Christ, we become secure in who we are in our earthly pleasures. Take some time to read this verse. Let it sink deep into your heart and let it become ingrained in your life. You must choose: Do you worship God or the food you eat?

Which do you choose to worship? _____

Let's be realistic for a moment. We all know what types of food we need to eat to maintain healthy lifestyles. Everyone knows that fruits and vegetables must be an essential staple in our diet. We all know that maintaining a diet consisting of mostly junk food, makes us unhealthy and often overweight. Healthy eating is not rocket science. There are many things we can learn as we embark on this new journey. If we live our lives based on the fundamentals of healthy eating, we will all be in much better shape. What holds us back from eating healthy is not that we don't know what we should eat. It is all the distractions of this world and our internal struggles. Until we completely surrender our lives to God, we will continue to battle.

What do you need to surrender to God? _____

The line in the following Bible verse is for your name. God speaks through the Bible to each one of us. The Bible will become more personal and alive in our lives if we insert our name into some of the verses.
But he said to_____, "My grace is sufficient for you, for my power is made perfect in weakness." Therefore I will boast all the more gladly about my weaknesses, so that Christ's power may rest on me. That is why, for Christ's sake, I delight in weaknesses, in insults, in hardships, in persecutions, in difficulties. For when I am weak, then I am strong. (2 Corinthians 12:9-10 NIV)

What is God saying to you with these verses? _____

If you honestly and wholeheartedly want to make a lifestyle change, you have to trust God with your life. You need to know that when you seek Him in your moments of weakness, He will give you strength and empower you to overcome your food addictions.
Before starting a new diet take some time to pray and ask God to guide you on this journey.

Dear God,
Please give me strength as I embark on this new journey. I want to restore my body so that it is a temple that honors You. You know my weaknesses; please help me when I am tempted by the foods that are harming my body. Help me find nourishing foods as a replacement so that I may enjoy and find pleasure when I eat. Help me to find my strength in You oh Lord, because I know that with You all things are possible. You have provided me with many delicious foods that give me energy. Please change my taste buds so that these are the foods I crave. I can do all things through You, and I relinquish control to You. Guide me and lead me to a healthy lifestyle. Show me your glory throughout this journey. In Jesus name, I pray. Amen

You need to remember that as you embark on this new journey, you will receive pressure from many sources to continue living an unhealthy lifestyle. One of your biggest distractions comes from the enemy. He is ruthless in his attack because he knows that a healthier person is a threat to his world. When you improve your lifestyle, you will have more energy and motivation to answer the calling God has placed in your heart. The devil knows that you will be able to share your love for God and the Good News of Jesus Christ with more people when you are healthy. He knows that if your lifestyle improves because of your faith and you become more secure in Christ, others will witness God's glory. The enemy will try to do whatever it takes to destroy you and keep you from becoming a good and faithful servant. He loves to tell you that you are not worthy, no one cares about you, or you are a failure (only a few of his many lies). Remember these are his words, not God's Words. God does not see any of His children as worthless or unworthy of love.

What lies does the devil tell you that keep you from changing your lifestyle? _____

_____

What are some of God's Words that can replace these lies? _____

_____

Most likely you will get pressure from well-meaning family members, friends, and coworkers who will try to discourage you from making these changes. At times, family members will tease you or make negative comments about your diet. You need to remember this often occurs because they need to justify their eating habits. I regularly have people telling me it is not worth all the trouble. They do not want to give up their lifestyles, and they enjoy eating whatever they like too much to give it up. These same people have health issues of their own, and some are limited in participating in physical activity. It will take an effort to stand up to people you care about and respect.

What pressures do you face from family members or friends that cause you to struggle on your diet?

_____

Many people we will encounter are uneducated on the importance of diet. The only information they hear is from advertisements and magazine articles. This information is biased toward the product being sold or reviewed. Try to counterbalance these negative influences by talking with people you know who have opted for a healthy lifestyle. Ask them questions and get tips from them as to how they were able to change their lives. Go to dinner with them or go to their home for a meal to see that you can enjoy yourself while eating well. At times, the medical field downplays the importance of diet both for prevention of illnesses and as a way to naturally heal our bodies. When I consulted with the hospital dietician after my surgery, she told me it was okay to eat anything and not to change my diet while undergoing treatment for cancer. I absolutely believe diet played an essential role in my recovery and allowed me to maintain my lifestyle while receiving chemotherapy and radiation. My body needed to have the proper nutrients to keep my healthy cells from being destroyed by the chemotherapy. Because chemotherapy tends to tire out a body, it was imperative that I provided it with the proper fuel to restore energy. Junk food drains the body, making it sluggish and slow. People in the medical field have their strengths and weaknesses. Just because they are in these professions, does not mean they understand all the ramifications of healthy eating. They know what they know based on their education and advanced medical training. Many have not received training in nutrition. It is not that we should distrust our doctors, but we do need to be an educated advocate for ourselves. You need to take responsibility for your health. You need to ask questions and do your own research. No matter whose advice you seek, you should always do your own research. You alone have your best interest at heart.

Do you put so much confidence in a medical person, that you do not do your own research when it comes to caring for your body? _____

Drug companies are always promoting their products. They want the consumer to buy their drugs so they run commercials that can be misleading. They downplay all the side effects. These ads quickly report the negative side effects while showing healthy people happily enjoying life. The fine print is often hard to read and goes unnoticed. At times medication is necessary. However, quite often nutrition can enhance or provide a better alternative. You need to make sure you do your research or talk with doctors who can help you make the changes necessary to decrease or eliminate medications that may be causing adverse effects on your body.

Are there any changes that you can make in your life that would help eliminating the need for medication?

_____

Beware of advertisement. Just as drug companies can make everything sound so wonderful, you must also be aware of food advertisements. They can be very misleading. Commercials are written to convince people their product is worthwhile. You need to be a well-educated consumer and not take an advertisers word for the truth. Many ads use keywords that make their product sound healthy even though there is no real nutritional value in their food. You need to evaluate each product for yourself to make sure the food is worth eating.

What food advertisements have you found to be misleading? _____

Take some time to ponder these questions.

Do you eat to live or live to eat?
What foods do you include most in your diet?
Are you addicted to food?
Do you reward yourself by eating?
Do you eat fast food?
Do you eat junk food?
Do you eat processed foods?
Do you know what you are really eating?
Do you read the packages or do you just take the manufacturers word?
Do you eat large portions?
Do you drink a lot of water or do you drink soda and sugary beverages?
Do you feel you can eat anything you want because some medicines and surgeries can heal you?

One of the first questions you need to address is: **Do you eat to live or live to eat?** There is a difference. This is an important question because the answer can determine how you value food, how you live your life and how well you maintain your body. The answer to this question determines whether or not you are invested in a healthy lifestyle.

How would you answer this question right now? _____

Eating to live: Food is essential to life. A well-balanced diet maintains your body, provides it with fuel and allows you to lead a productive life. It helps you maintain a strong immune system, which enables you to resist germs and fight infections. It can enable the body to heal when it is sick. The proper nutrient can help the body to develop, replace and repair cells and tissues. For the body to function at its maximum capacity, it must receive the proper nutrition. A person must consciously eat the right foods and make sure they have a balanced diet.

Living to eat: When a person lives their life to eat, much of their daily activity and routines are driven by their next meal, what they can snack on or where to get a sugar fix. Too often a person consumes all the wrong foods.

Watching people at parties is fascinating. People will gather around the snack table, pull up a chair, and sit there all night consuming an enormous amount of food. Much of this food has little or no nutritional value.

They wait for the next food item to be put on the table. People spend more time eating rather than enjoying each other's company. I used to do this as well. Then I would leave feeling sluggish, bloated and have a food hangover the next day. Now that I am on a strict diet, I go to parties, and I sit away from the food table. I eat before I go so that my body gets the nourishment it needs. Parties are now more enjoyable because instead of focusing on the food, I get to enjoy good conversations with people. I have noticed the same occurs in restaurants. People are so focused on the food on the menu or what others have ordered that they lose the purpose of eating together: sharing good conversation while nourishing their bodies. There is nothing wrong with enjoying the food you consume. However, you need to consume the right food. Over time you will come to appreciate a healthy diet.

Food for Thought:

1. Become more aware of how advertisements and other people influence your way of eating.

2. When you change your thinking so that you realize you are eating to live and not living to eat, does it change the way you see food?

Journal your thoughts

Day 4

TESTING THE CIRCUITS FOR OVERLOAD
(CHANGING YOUR DIET)

There are many circuits necessary to provide the power for the temple. These circuits have to be designed so to distribute the power evenly, or the wires will become overheated causing a fire.

Nugget of the day: Suddenly, they saw the fingers of a human handwriting on the plaster wall of the king's palace, near the lampstand. The king himself saw the hand as it wrote, and his face turned pale with fright. His knees knocked together in fear and his legs gave way beneath him. (Daniel 5:5-6 NLT)

Have you ever thought about the phrase "the handwriting is on the wall" and wonder where it evolved? It is a phrase often used in conversations. How often does God put the handwriting on the wall for us and we miss it? It may not be literally on the wall, but He definitely gives us signs. It may be in the form of a Bible verse, a comment from a complete stranger, or that small voice inside us. God uses many sources to get His point across. We need to keep our eyes and ears open and trust our Dad to guide us through life. God has put the handwriting in the Bible. It tells us the importance of eating healthy diets and living healthy lifestyles. We need to take the time to read the writing.

My prayer is that you heed the "writing on the wall." Take our Father's advice and make good decisions. We all know our Father gives us this handwriting not to torment us, but to make our lives better and more fulfilling. When you follow God's advice, you will find your life becoming more productive. You will be able to live your life with less stress and find peace and joy that only God can give you. So spend some time reading the Word God has given us because it was written to help you, not hinder you.
****

Even when you have a plan, there can be things that can affect your new diet. You need to take time and review what might hinder your ability to get into the practice of eating a healthy diet. You are responsible for your eating habits and making sure you do not overload your body with excessive food or poor food choices.

Food is a comfort for many of us. It may not be the taste of the food that is addicting as much as what it represents. Think about your comfort foods. Cookies may symbolize the joy of Christmas. Fried chicken may be a reminder of Sunday meals as a child. Hot chocolate warms us on a cold evening. Popcorn made in oil and coated with butter is what we ate at the theatre. One of the keys to eating and enjoying the new diet is finding new comfort foods. You need to retrain your taste buds.

What foods give you comfort and why? _____

_____

What are some healthy foods you enjoy and might become new comfort foods for you? _____

_____

Become aware as to how you address your food. You need to be mindful of how you talk to yourself subconsciously. When you talk about needing a sugar fix, chocolate or a diet soda you convince yourself you need this food in your life to please you or to help you survive. You need to change your way of thinking. You need to see these foods as a detriment to your health. I often refer to junk food as "crap." One day while speaking to a group about my diet I realized that when I call junk food crap, it gives it a negative connotation. It turns me off to eating something that I once enjoyed. After all, who wants to eat crap? My mouth no longer waters when I hear someone talk about cookies or candy. It is a different story if you talk to me about a good salad or a healthy snack.

What are some of the terms you use to address your unhealthy food and give it a place of honor in your life?

_____

How do you address healthy food? _____

What are some terms you can use for healthy food to give you the same satisfaction?

_____

Nutritious food is worth the cost. Many people complain that it costs too much to eat nutritiously. However, it is more expensive to treat cancer or other diseases than it is to eat healthily. Americans spend a lot of money on cars and homes. Every four to five years many of us will sell our cars and get new ones. People will continually make home improvements and at some point will likely sell their house and buy a new one. We have to live in our bodies our entire lives, so we should choose to live in a body that is at its optimum. These bodies need the proper exercise and nutrition. Now you have a decision to make. Do you choose to live in a body that can be pain-free and disease free? Or will you live in a body that limits your activity with below average performance?

There is research that has shown that people who consume mainly vegetables and fruits are not as likely to develop cancer or some other diseases. Many scientists believe that at least thirty percent of all cancers are directly related to diet. Some of these scientists believe the percentage is closer to 70 percent. [4] Cardiovascular disease, diabetes, and arthritis are just a few other diseases that are caused or worsened by eating a poor diet. People often spend a lot of money on food that does not nourish the body. Because much of the money may be spent at fast food restaurants or getting drinks and snacks at a convenience store, people do not realize how much money they waste on junk food.

List some of your unhealthy expenses this past week: _____

_____

Educate yourself as to what you are eating. Our bodies were not designed to eat chemicals. When God created us, He created us to be hunters and gatherers. We were meant to survive on diets rich with fruits, vegetables, whole grains, nuts, seeds and lean meats. These foods give our bodies nourishment while they satiate our appetite. God provides us with all the nourishment we need. We were not meant to eat genetically altered food or food processed in a factory with chemicals. We need to look no further than the Bible and the book of Genesis to see that God had a plan for us. *Then God said, "I give you every seed-bearing plant on the face of the whole earth and every tree that has fruit with seed in it. They will be yours for food.* (Genesis 1:29 NIV) Need more proof; review the book of Daniel. Daniel knew His God provided for him. He chose to listen and ate only vegetables and fruit. The results proved Daniel made the right diet choice.

Have you ever thought about the strength it took for Daniel to stand up to the chief official and refuse to eat unhealthy food? _____

The result was that all the men benefitted from eating Daniel's way. If it were not for his courage, others would have suffered the effects of poor eating. How can you be the strength for your family and friends?
_____

Have you thought about how important it is for others to see you eating a healthy diet? _____
Your example may be just the one to help them change their eating habits.

Who do you care about that needs help in changing their lifestyle? _____

Spend some time in prayer asking God to help you accept Daniel's challenge. Ask God to release the strongholds that are preventing you from accepting this challenge.

There is no perfect diet. Research has shown there is an alarming number of people in the United States who are overweight (68.5%) with 34.9% of those being obese. (5) This weight issue not only because of the amount of food people consume, but the type of food they consume. There are many diets out on the market. No one diet is the perfect diet. Every person you talk to will have a variation of the perfect diet. Each person believes his or her way is right. Each person responds to various foods differently to be at our best. Some people do best with little or no meat; others need some meat to be the most productive. Do your own research. Understand foods and what they offer to your diet. Then make an educated decision as to how you are going to eat. Know that you will have to make adjustments as your knowledge grows. I still tweak my diet and remove things I find I should not eat and add new foods I find that will enhance my diet. Again, pray in this area. Our loving Father gave us food to nourish our bodies. He knows what we need to live healthy lifestyles. Beware of fad diets or diets and foods that promise miraculous weight loss while still eating junk or processed food. Even if you lose weight on these diets, you are still getting empty calories, and you may be thinner, but not necessarily healthier.

Be a well-informed consumer: Diet plays a significant role in how healthy you are and how you feel. Consumers must educate themselves as to what types of foods their bodies need and how to read labels to avoid ingredients that negatively affect them. Just because a label says it is healthy or natural does not mean it is good for you. The government has very loose requirements as to what a company can or cannot put labels. Many of the foods labeled "natural" contain genetically modified organisms (GMO's). Processed food labeled organic can still have unhealthy ingredients added. The best foods to consume are non-processed foods, which include fruits, vegetables, grains, and lean meat. It is also important to buy organic and local whenever possible. Which foods should be organic will be addressed in a later chapter.

Eat plant-based foods whenever possible. Plant-based foods are vital in your diet. These foods are vegetables, fruit, nuts, grains, and beans. They are usually best prepared raw or minimally cooked. Plants provide us with the essential vitamins and minerals that our bodies need to be healthy and fight disease. They contain fiber. Fiber is necessary in your diet because it aids in the elimination of waste products. As fiber passes through the digestive system, it removes waste, which can be disease-causing when not eliminated regularly. Fiber is often referred to as roughage or bulk. (6) Some good examples are brown rice (not instant), whole grains, oatmeal, popcorn, fresh fruit such as pears, bananas or apples, potatoes with skin, carrots, celery, bell peppers, and beans.

Keep cancer-fighting foods in your diet. Diets need to include antioxidants because they are crucial to your health. The antioxidants are potent vitamins, which help protect the cells in your body. The best sources of antioxidants are from foods that contain beta-carotene, lycopene, vitamins C, E, and selenium. (7) It is best to include an array of colorful vegetables in your diet since the different colored produce contains different phytochemicals, which will improve your immune system. (8) Use spices when cooking. Spices can help boost the immune system. Some of these spices are turmeric, rosemary, basil, and coriander.

Drink plenty of water: Our bodies consist of 60-75% of water. Water helps regulate body temperature, remove waste and toxins and aids in the transporting of nutrients throughout the body. Water works as a shock absorber and helps improve nerve cell function. (9) These are just some of the reasons water is essential to our bodies.

Proper preparation of food: When buying healthy food, it is imperative to prepare and store it correctly. Wash all the fruits and vegetables to get rid of the pesticides. Steam vegetables until tender since overcooking removes the nutrients. When using oil to cook, use only healthy oils. Burning or charring food creates carcinogens in the food. Microwaving food decreases the nutrients in the food. If you choose to use a microwave, never use plastic containers as it releases chemicals into your food.

Food for thought:

1. What steps can you take to become a well-informed consumer?

2. What have you learned in today's session that you can use to improve your lifestyle?

3. How has your frame of mind affected how you eat?

4. How can you change your thinking?

Journal your thoughts

REWIRING THE TEMPLE
(BREAKING FOOD ADDICTIONS)

There are times after the electrician checks the circuits; he may need to adjust his work. When the temple owner uses the lights or outlets, he does not want to trip the circuit breaker.

Nugget of the day: Keep watch and pray, so that you will not give in to temptation. For the spirit is willing, but the body is weak." (Mark 14:38 NLT)

Take some time to study this verse. This verse is in the Bible to teach us a valuable lesson that takes years to grasp. What did Jesus do when His disciples were unable to keep watch for Him and fell asleep? Did He rant and rave at them, or give up on them? No, Jesus used the moment to teach them. Jesus knows we are not perfect, and He knows that no matter how hard we try, there will be times we will fail. He knows that there will be temptations in this world and we will, at times, succumb to them. Jesus wants us to know there is help. God will give us strength, and He will pick us up when we fail. He can break addictions and help us overcome temptations. We need to accept that we will have battles in this world, and we need to seek the guidance of our loving Father to overcome them.

My prayer is that you realize you are human and with this humanness comes imperfections and struggles. Be patient with yourself and know it will take time to improve your diet and change habits. I pray that you learn to lean on God. His strength will sustain you when you feel as if the pressures of this world are too much to handle. If Jesus, the perfect One, can be patient with His disciples when they fail, you need to be patient with yourself. Rather than get down when you struggle, use the opportunity to grow in faith and learn to put your trust in the One who can help. He will break your addictions and the chains that bind you in this world. I also pray that you learn by Jesus' example and that you too are patient with others. Rather than getting upset with them when they fail, you need to gently point them to the One who can change their life.

****

Food has always been part of our lives. As young children, our parents were responsible for providing us with a healthy diet so that we grew big and strong. It is now our responsibility to provide the proper nourishment for our bodies. We may have to rewire our brains as to how we view the food we eat or to break food addictions. Junk food can be very addicting and can consume most of a person's thoughts. Therefore, we need to address this issue before attempting to change our diet. For many, a food addiction can be harder to break than a cigarette or alcohol addiction. Some research shows that sugar can be as addictive as cocaine. [1] The brain gets used to the sensation it receives from the junk food we take in, and it will continue to need more junk food to sustain that feeling. [2] People need to understand that eating a small portion of unhealthy food can lead them right back to their food addiction. You need to watch what foods you eat and understand what foods are addictive to you. For many people, the foods that are most addictive contain sugar, wheat or dairy. [3]

Answer the following questions honestly to determine if you have a food addiction. Becoming aware of the problem is the first step to breaking the habit of poor eating.

1. Do you continue to eat even when you have just finished a nutritious meal and are full?
2. Once you start eating junk food, can you stop?
3. Are there specific foods or drinks you feel you cannot give up?
4. Will you keep eating even when you feel sick?
5. Do you have physical withdrawals when removing certain foods from your diet?
6. Do you feel tired or sluggish after eating?
7. Does consuming the same amount or type of food not produce the same amount of pleasure as it once did?

8. Do you use food to change your emotions (combat a lousy day, relieve your stress)?
9. Do you feel guilty after you binge?
10. Do you always think of food or drink, wondering when you can eat or drink it again?
11. Does food take precedent over other areas of your life?
12. Is food more important to you than having a healthy body or being physically active?

Food addictions are hard to break. However, if you are going to take charge of your diet and health, you are going to have to cut these emotional and physical attachments to certain foods and drinks.
When dealing with an addiction, you have to realize that no matter what the habit is, it distracts you and it prevents you from honoring God in the way you should. Satan loves to feed into your addictions because it keeps you from doing God's work to your fullest potential. When you are overweight, not properly fed or both, you have decreased energy and ambition. It limits your ability to do God's work. You need to realize that Satan is trying his best to pull you down and you need to go to the One who lifts you up. *No temptation has overtaken you except what is common to mankind. And God is faithful; he will not let you be tempted beyond what you can bear. But when you are tempted, he will also provide a way out so that you can endure it.* (1 Corinthians 10:13-14 NIV)

What does God want to provide for you? _____

How have you seen God hold true to His promises? _____

Let us draw near to God with a sincere heart and with the full assurance that faith brings, having our hearts sprinkled to cleanse us from a guilty conscience and having our bodies washed with pure water. Let us hold unswervingly to the hope we profess, for he who promised is faithful. (Hebrews 10:22-23 NIV) Too often the reason we do not see God's faithfulness is that we give up on Him. We pray and when He does not answer our prayers on our timeline or exactly how we expect, we give up hope or we stop praying and seeking God's guidance.

What lies does the enemy tell you that hold you back from trusting in God that He can break your addictions?
_____

How can you hold onto the promises of God? _____

Here are some suggestions as to how to curb your addiction to food.

Pray: Ask God to help you overcome your food addiction. Every time you have an urge to eat or drink something you know you shouldn't, immediately turn to the One who can give you strength when you are weak. *Keep watch and pray, so that you will not give in to temptation. For the spirit is willing, but the body is weak."* (Mark 14:38 NLT)

What did Jesus do when He realized His disciples could not stay awake? _____

He did not scold or belittle them. He encouraged the disciples and taught them how to overcome their weaknesses.

Restock your pantry and refrigerator: Remove foods that are unhealthy and addicting, that may cause you to binge and replace with food that has good nutritional value. Stock your pantry with herbs and spices that can be used to enhance the flavor of your food.

Change your shopping habits: Plan your menus and only buy the ingredients needed to make healthy meals and snacks. Shop after you have eaten so as not to buy on impulse.

Put snack foods in small containers: This way you will only eat a little at a time, and help you not binge on everything at once.

Avoid temptations: When going out to eat, make sure to look at the menu ahead of time. Choose your entrée even before entering the restaurant so you can make a healthy choice. Stay away from all-you-can-eat buffets or restaurants that offer you no healthy options.

Educate yourself about nutrition: It is much easier to stay on a healthy diet when you know why you are eating this way and how it affects your body.

Replace your old comfort foods with new comfort foods. Find a way to associate healthy foods with pleasure.

Only eat when hungry and control your portion size. It is okay to enjoy your food; just watch how much food you consume at a sitting. Learning how much food to eat and how to portion your food sets you up for success. After each bite put the fork down, chew thoroughly and savor every mouthful.

Exercise regularly: Exercise not only helps you control your weight and improve your fitness, but it also raises the dopamine levels in your brain. Exercise helps control your brain's reward center.

Address your emotional needs: If you are struggling emotionally, it is much harder to watch the food you eat. You need to address the issues that are prohibiting you from being successful. If you need professional help, seek a Christian counselor.

Food for thought:

1. What foods are the most addicting for you?

2. What type of changes can you make in your diet?

3. What is holding you back from improving your diet?

4. Who can you look to for advice and support as you make changes in your diet?

5. Write a prayer asking God to help you improve your diet and to give you the motivation necessary to accomplish this.

6. Keep a log of your daily food intake, including all snacks. This diary will help you get a grasp on which foods you are eating and how much you are consuming.

Journal your thoughts

Week 4

Day 1: Review Bible verses
Day 2: Conserving Our Energy Supply
       Cleaning, Storing and Preparing
       Food
Day 3: Using the Right Gauge Wire
       GMO's and Cooking With Oil
Day 4: Quality Control
Day 5: Juicing And Smoothies
       The Dangers Of Sugar

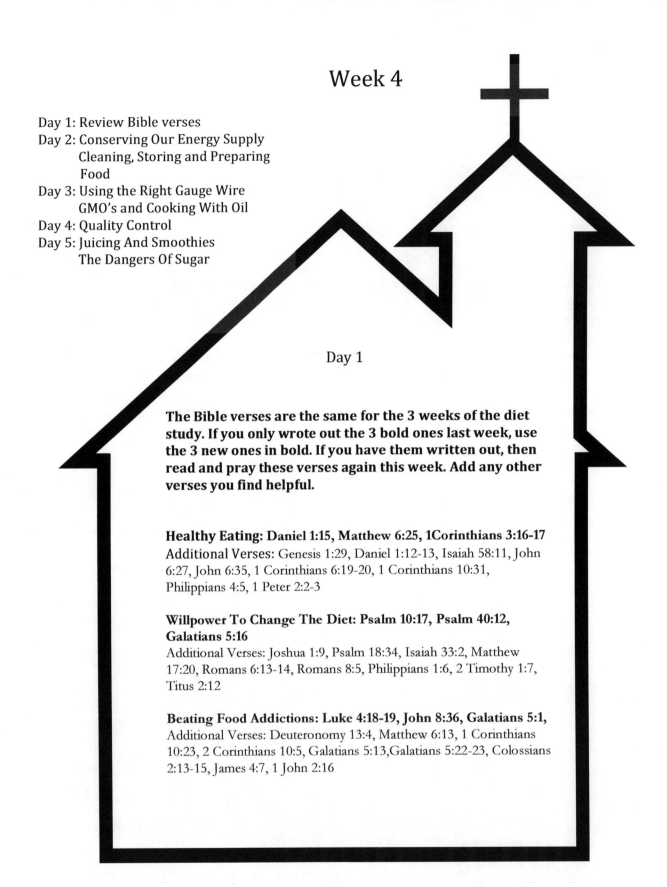

Day 1

The Bible verses are the same for the 3 weeks of the diet study. If you only wrote out the 3 bold ones last week, use the 3 new ones in bold. If you have them written out, then read and pray these verses again this week. Add any other verses you find helpful.

Healthy Eating: Daniel 1:15, Matthew 6:25, 1Corinthians 3:16-17
Additional Verses: Genesis 1:29, Daniel 1:12-13, Isaiah 58:11, John 6:27, John 6:35, 1 Corinthians 6:19-20, 1 Corinthians 10:31, Philippians 4:5, 1 Peter 2:2-3

Willpower To Change The Diet: Psalm 10:17, Psalm 40:12, Galatians 5:16
Additional Verses: Joshua 1:9, Psalm 18:34, Isaiah 33:2, Matthew 17:20, Romans 6:13-14, Romans 8:5, Philippians 1:6, 2 Timothy 1:7, Titus 2:12

Beating Food Addictions: Luke 4:18-19, John 8:36, Galatians 5:1,
Additional Verses: Deuteronomy 13:4, Matthew 6:13, 1 Corinthians 10:23, 2 Corinthians 10:5, Galatians 5:13,Galatians 5:22-23, Colossians 2:13-15, James 4:7, 1 John 2:16

Assignment: Try one of the food substitutes suggested on day 4 and report to the group what you tried.

CONSERVING YOUR ENERGY SUPPLY
(BUYING FOOD)

The energy in our temples needs to be conserved. We need to make sure we have enough energy to power our temples to make them warm and inviting.

Nugget of the Day: You can make many plans, but the Lord's purpose will prevail. *(Proverbs 19:21 NLT)*

Don't we all love to be in control? We like to be in charge and make our own decisions. The world teaches us that independence is a good thing and that we should not rely on anyone. God teaches just the opposite. He wants us to give up control and trust in Him. God wants to guide us through life, knows our true heart, and what is best for us. God knows what we were created to do in this world and how we can make a difference. When we try to make it on our own, we meet so much resistance and life often becomes a struggle. We encounter many closed doors and have to take many detours. God can open these doors we need to pass through. There is only one requirement: we must relinquish control, letting God be in charge.

My prayer is that you realize God is a much better commander of your life than you. When you give Him complete control, you will be amazed at just how much easier life can be. You will find peace and joy that only God can give. It will replace the fear of going into unknown territory. We will stand in awe as we see what we are truly capable of accomplishing. We will find we can do things we never thought possible. Go ahead; turn over the wheel to God. At first, it is difficult, but soon it is nice to sit in the passenger seat. Enjoy the ride.

****

Eating healthy food is an investment in our lives, and we need to take care of our resources. There are many things we can do to help ensure we purchase healthy nutritious food that is fresh and make it last. Conserving our energy supply (food) is essential to being able to nourish our bodies the right way.

In their hearts humans plan their course, but the Lord establishes their steps. *(Proverbs 16:9 NIV)* We need to learn to rely on God in every aspect of our lives, and this includes buying and preparing our food, especially as we begin this new journey. When we first start out, going to the store can be a challenge because we will have to walk past the foods that once gave us comfort and our taste buds still long for. Before we even step foot in the grocery store, we need to pray. Pray that God gives us the strength to walk past the foods we are addicted to and that He helps us find pleasure in the new foods. We will be much more successful on this journey if we invite God to shop and prepare our food with us.

When you change your diet and eat food that is nourishing for your body, your food bill will most likely go up initially because you will have to restock your pantry and refrigerator with food that is healthy and clean. After you have made the initial investment, the food bill should not be that much different if you are cautious with what you buy. One of the biggest mistakes people make is buying too much food at one time. When the food is not laden with chemicals and preservatives, it will go bad much more quickly. There are things you can do to lower your food bills and make sure you are getting the quality food your body needs.

Tips for buying food:

Prepare before you go to the store: Plan out meals and compile a shopping list. Do not add extra items to the cart. It is easy to want to buy extra fruit and vegetables, but if you are not going to use these in a timely manner, they will spoil.

Buy locally: Whenever possible buy food locally. Because the food is not transported long distances, it will be fresher, and it will last longer. Freshness accompanies an increase in nutritional value. Many cities have farmer's markets where people can go to buy a variety of fruits and vegetables. These local markets will carry the foods that are in season for your region.

Buy what is in season: The body responds best to eating the fruits and vegetables that are in season. When in season, the produce is usually more flavorful. During the different seasons, the body has different nutritional needs. [1,2] Some foods are good for more than one season.

Spring: This is a season of new growth. Therefore, the foods you eat should represent this time. Leafy greens are ideal in the spring. Some of these vegetables include Swiss chard, romaine lettuce, spinach, basil, asparagus, broccoli, cauliflower strawberries, and honeydew.

Summer: The body needs food that acts as a coolant and will help replace fluids lost from sweating. Summer foods include strawberries, watermelon, apples, pears, plums, arugula, eggplant, summer squash, tomatoes, zucchini, broccoli, cilantro, and peppermint.

Fall: This is a time to prepare the body for winter. The body does best with warming autumn food. Foods to consume during this time are carrots, squash, brussel sprouts, hot peppers, pumpkin, grapes, pears, sweet potatoes, garlic, onion, ginger, and peppercorn.

Winter: The body wants warming foods. Root vegetables are a good choice. Winter foods include carrots, potatoes, onions, winter squash, nuts, dates, kale, butternut squash, and brussel sprouts. Meats to eat during this season are beef and chicken.

Natural does not mean the same thing as organic: Labels that say natural do not necessarily mean the food is healthy. There are minimal regulations as to what is required to put natural on the label. Therefore, the buyer must **BEWARE**. The USDA states natural meat, eggs, and poultry must be minimally processed and contain no artificial ingredients. Since natural is not well defined, they can produce the food with GMO's, pesticides, antibiotics, or preservatives. Often there are chemicals and sugars added to these products. [3]

Read the ingredients on all labels: Products you think may only have one or two ingredients can be deceiving. They may contain artificial colorings and flavorings. Many products contain high fructose corn syrup. Some manufacturers and stores that advertise they are health conscious can fool you. Many of these products offered might have ingredients you do not want to put into your body. You still need to read all product labels so that when you get the item home you have not wasted your money on a product you will not use.

Buy Non-GMO and organic products whenever possible: GMO stands for a genetically modified organism. The produce that can be GMO's are corn, Hawaiian papaya, edamame (soybeans), zucchini, and yellow summer squash. Stores that sell the non-GMO product will have them marked as USDA certified organic or have a seal on them that they are verified by a third party not to be a GMO product. Unfortunately, many processed foods use GMO produce. Because of this, you should check the ingredients before purchasing processed foods. Dairy and meat products can also be affected when the animals have been fed GMO feed. Again, you should check the meat and dairy labels to verify GMO products have not been used. [3]
Organic refers to how the product is farmed and processed. Organic farming does not allow the farmers to use synthetic fertilizers, most pesticides, antibiotics or growth hormones for livestock and no GMO products. Overall organic produce is better for you to consume. Some produce does not have to be organic due to fruit or vegetables having a thick exterior skin or shell preventing the edible part from being exposed to all the pesticides and chemicals. It is important to know which products should be organic and which do not have to be. (This is addressed later.)

Buy your fresh organic foods in small quantities: These products tend to spoil quicker. It is better to go to the market several times a week, rather than buy all the groceries at one time.

Frozen organic foods last longer and may be cheaper. These products are often frozen at the peak of their ripeness, so if you are on a tight budget, this may be a way to save money. Frozen vegetables and fruits can be bought in larger quantities because they last longer. It is best not to buy frozen foods that have been chopped, peeled or crushed because this may deplete some of the nutrition. (5)

Grass-fed beef: Be cautious when buying grass-fed beef. Some farmers use grain at the end of the animal's life so they can fatten them up. Some farmers give the cattle the option of grain. The cattle will choose the grain, and this ruins the nutritional value of the meat. The label needs to read 100% grass fed. Grass-fed beef provides omega 3 fatty acids, which are important for brain and heart health. It also provides a higher level of vitamins and helps to decrease our cancer risks. (6)

Avoid canned food when possible: The linings of most canned foods contain BPA, which can interfere with the estrogen in your body.

Buy healthy seafood: Wild-caught Alaskan salmon and Sockeye salmon are the healthiest. Farm raised fish can present with many of the same problems of land raised animals. They have a decreased nutritional value, may be fed GMO products and have diseases. (7) When eating fish, we want the omega-3's, but Dr. Mercola reports that farmed fish being fed grain can have up to 50% less omega 3's. (8)

Avoid buying products in plastic whenever possible: Plastic is not healthy to store our food in so try and buy products in glass jars or transfer the food to glass containers when you get the product home.

Using these guidelines can help us to eat healthier and save money at the same time. Happy shopping.

Food for thought:

1. Can you see that reading the product labels can be beneficial and can help you eat healthier?

2. How can you alter your shopping habits to improve your diet and still eat within your budget?

3. Which of these tips can you implement in your life now to improve your eating habits?

Journal your thoughts

CLEANING, STORING AND PREPARING FOOD

Choosing to eat healthily is an investment in your body. Therefore, you want to conserve the food you buy rather than waste it. Here are some suggestions to help with preserving the food.

Cleaning the produce: When you bring your produce home from the store, before putting it away soak them in water and vinegar to remove the pesticide and chemicals. Then place them in glass bowls with a lid. Not only will this make it easier to grab healthy snacks on the run, but also help preserve the produce for an extended period.

Storage: Storing fruits and vegetables correctly helps to keep them fresh longer. Below are a few helpful tips.

Tomatoes are best stored on the counter to prevent them from losing their flavor. If you do put them in the refrigerator, leave them out on the counter for 24 hours before eating to restore some of the flavor.

Store potatoes in a cool dark place. Keep them away from onions to give them a longer life. Storing potatoes with apples will keep them from sprouting as quickly.

Greens are affected by heat. When I get them home from the store, pour cold water over them and then dry in a salad spinner. Keeping the greens moist will cause them to spoil quicker. Salad greens can also be kept in a salad bowl with a paper towel on top to absorb the moisture and then covered with a lid. Keeping the lettuce leaves dry is also important when serving in a salad. Since salad dressings are made with oils, the oil will repel the wet leaves, making them less flavorful.

Avoid plastic and Styrofoam™ storage containers: Plastic and Styrofoam are common materials used to store and serve our food. Plastic water bottles are a convenience. Some studies show that these items can be detrimental to our health. When plastic is heated or made cold, it can be even more toxic. There are more chemicals than BPA in the plastic that can wreak havoc on our bodies. Phthalates have been found to be toxic to the reproductive system. [1] Subjecting plastic to high heats such as a dishwasher or boiling water can cause the plastic to leach toxic chemicals into our foods. [2] Plastic is much harder to clean and can have grooves and lips that can allow for bacteria to grow and contaminate our food. It is best to use glass, ceramic or stainless steel to store and serve your food.

Glass containers: When possible store food in glass containers. Glass containers will not leach chemicals into your food, and they are much more sanitary. They are easy to clean. Stock your cabinets with a variety of sizes of glass dishes with lids, making it is easy to store leftovers and to make healthy lunches to take to work. Glass is also suitable for keeping some of the fruits and vegetables in after they are cut up. Mason jars also make great containers. I store all my seeds, beans, nuts and dry goods in glass canisters in the panty. By storing leftovers in glass dishes, it makes it more convenient to heat up the food in the oven.

Cookware: pots and pans: We are working hard to keep chemicals out of our bodies, and yet many people cook with Teflon™ coated cookware to save time and make cleanup easier. Teflon is made with the chemical perfluorooctanoic acid (PFOA) and is a carcinogen. The pans, when heated to temperatures over 400 degrees, can expose you to fumes that cause flu-like symptoms in humans. It is called polymer fume fever. These vapors are also toxic to birds and kill hundreds of them a year. [3] When these pots and pans get scratched or start to flake, even more toxins are released into the food. [4] The best types of cookware to use to ensure our safety are glass, stainless steel, cast iron, ceramic or clay cookware.

Aluminum has been associated with Alzheimer's disease. It is best to be safe with your health and avoid using aluminum pots and pans as well as aluminum foil. The stainless-steel cookware will have aluminum encapsulated in the stainless steel so that it does not touch the food. When baking foods, use glass dishes. Many safe baking dishes have lids that can be heated up to avoid using aluminum foil. Your health is worth the extra effort it may take to clean up after preparing your food.

Freezing food: Freezing fresh fruit and vegetables can help preserve them. Buying the fruit and vegetables while at their peak of freshness makes for better freezing. The best way to seal in the freshness is to freeze them as soon as they are brought home from the store. The key to keeping the food fresh is making sure the food is wrapped as tightly as possible to keep the air out of the produce. Maintain the freezer temperature at 0 degrees and do not overfill it. Overfilling the freezer prevents the air from circulating, and damage to the food will occur.

Buy fresh vegetables and place them in small containers so when you want some for dinner, you have a variety from which to choose. Then you have vegetables that are ready to prepare by steaming or in a stir-fry. I often put beans, onions, cauliflower, carrots, and broccoli together for a good vegetable medley.

Fresh strawberries: These berries are easy to freeze. After rinsing them, pat dry and place them on a cookie sheet. Freeze for several hours to prevent them from sticking together and then transfer the berries into a container and return them to the freezer. Use them in smoothies, pancakes or other baked treats. They can be stored for up to 6 months.

Food preparation: Often during the week it is hard to find time to cook or prepare healthy foods for lunches and dinners. I have come up with an easy way to make meals for the whole week in a short period. Preparing ahead of time, allows me to have a variety of foods available during the week. I steam most of my vegetables on Sunday. I prepare enough salad for several days, keeping ingredients that will make the salad soggy in separate containers so that I can add them quickly when packing my lunch. At this time, I also make any recipes that I want to use with my meals during the week. I put the food in small glass bowls, which makes it easy to grab them during the week for lunch. Mixing and matching the food allows me to have a variety of options for lunch and dinner. I am guaranteed to have a healthy meal even when I have to eat and run. Cutting up fresh fruit and vegetables and storing them in glass bowls in the refrigerator makes for grabbing a quick, healthy snack.

Emergency packs of food: We all know that when we are hungry, it is easy to be tempted to go off our diets. You need to prepare for hunger emergencies. When at work, there is often tempting food in vending machines and laid out in lunchrooms. When driving, fast food is easily accessible and cheap to purchase. One of the keys to eating healthy is to have good, nutritious food available for just this purpose. You can make emergency kits to store in desk drawers, purses and glove compartments of your car. Make packets of nuts, seeds and dried fruits (that do not have sugars added) to keep on hand. Some prepackaged items provide nutrition also that you can make available when you cannot get the fresh items. Preparing ahead of time can prevent you from breaking down and eating foods, not nourishing to your body.

Food for thought:

1. How can some of these ideas help you to make more conscious healthy choices?

2. How can you incorporate some of these ideas in your daily life?

3. Are you willing to forgo some of the conveniences to maintain or improve your health?

4. Are you more aware of some healthy food prepping or storing habits that you have adopted that alters your foods nutritional value or causes health risks?

Journal your thoughts

USING THE RIGHT GAUGE WIRE
(GMO'S)

When the electrician wires the temple, he must make sure he uses the right gauge wire for the circuit.

Nugget of the day: Jesus told him, "I am the way, the truth, and the life. No one can come to the Father except through me. *(John 14:6 NLT)*

There should be flashing lights and warning signs in this section of the Bible. People not only need to read it, but they also need to understand it and take it to heart. The Bible is the truth. It is our owner's manual for life. How often do people say if only life came with instructions it would be much easier? Well, it does; the Bible is a comprehensive and exact manual. The problem is, we humans do not like to be told what to do. God created this owner's manual for our benefit. Who better to create this manual than the Creator Himself? He knows exactly what we need. He knows how important every aspect of our life is and how we must care for our bodies, minds, and souls. People need to read it and understand it. How many of us buy a product and try to assemble it without reading the instructions? When completed, it is missing parts, is unstable or needs to be redone? All because we think we can do it on our own. God knew we could not, and so He sent His beloved Son.

Jesus taught us how God wants us to live. However, we have preachers, teachers, and parents teaching us that we can live life however we want. We have health professionals telling us diet does not matter and yet people have ailments they cannot heal. People tell us God is whomever we make Him. I have had people tell me eternity is what we make it; it will not be the same for everyone. God and Jesus are not ever changing to fit our needs and desires. They are the one constant in our ever-changing world. They do not change, so we always know what to expect from Them.

My prayer is that you read your owner's manual thoroughly and live by its principles and laws. Not only trust what it teaches about faith but also how to live healthy lives and how to take care of yourself. I pray that you accept God and Jesus for who they are and do not make them who you want them to be. I pray all my nugget buddies accept Jesus as their personal Savior and do not veer from His teachings. God has not changed the rules of healthy eating. Our bodies have not evolved to thrive on processed or chemically laden foods. I also pray we raise our children to believe the truth and know how to live complete and satisfying lives in Christ. After all, we want them to spend eternity with us.

****

Then God said, "I give you every seed-bearing plant on the face of the whole earth and every tree that has fruit with seed in it. They will be yours for food. (Genesis 1:29 NIV) Notice who gave us our produce? God did, and He does not make mistakes, nor do His creations need improvement. God knew how to create each type of crop so that it would nourish our bodies. Humans often think they can do better than God and therefore they have tried to alter what God perfected. The results: making a product that is far less than perfect. Let's face it; we cannot do better than God. Once we realize God really does know what He is doing, our world will be a much better and healthier place to live. We need to use the right foods to nourish our bodies.

GMO's are genetically modified organisms, which means that the genetic makeup of the plant is altered with DNA from another source such as bacteria, viruses or other living organisms. These modified crops have an increased tolerance to pesticides. Thus, farmers use even more pesticides on these plants. The American Academy of Environmental Medicine has issued a warning to doctors. It reads as follows: "*With the precautionary principle in mind, because GM foods have not been properly tested for human consumption, and because there is ample evidence of probable harm, the AAEM asks: Physicians to educate their patients, the medical community, and the public to avoid GM foods when possible and provide educational materials concerning GM foods and health risks.*" [1] Studies have shown that the GMO products can have an impact on our health. After the introduction of GMO's in 1996, Americans have experienced more health problems. More Americans are presenting with three or more chronic illnesses. They also have more food allergies, reproductive, and digestive problems. Autism, as well, is on the rise. *Although there is not sufficient research to confirm that GMOs are a contributing factor, doctors groups such as the AAEM tell us not to wait before we start protecting ourselves, and especially our children who are most at risk.* [2]

The crops that can be genetically modified are as follows:
Corn
Soybeans
Cotton
Canola
Sugar Beets
Alfalfa
Papaya
Zucchini and yellow squash
Not only do we consume these products, but many farm animals also consume grains that are GMO products. This is why we must be cautious as to what type of meat we consume.

Organic produce can be expensive but worth the added cost when buying certain fruits and vegetables. The produce cannot be a GMO product since farmers cannot plant GMO seeds. Pesticides harm our health and have been shown to have some adverse effects on fetal and childhood development. One study has shown that eating organic produce not only reduces our exposure to pesticides but also improves the food's nutritional value. Organic foods help with healthy growth and development during early childhood. It has also been shown to reduce our risks to certain diseases including cancer. [3] Another benefit to eating organic fruits and vegetables is that the antioxidants in the produce are significantly higher. [4] We know that antioxidants are crucial to ridding our bodies of free radicals, which can harm our bodies. (This is addressed later in the book.) Some fruits and vegetables are more affected by pesticides, and so if you are on a limited budget these 15 foods should be purchased organically or homegrown:

Apples (this includes applesauce and juice): Apple peels retain the pesticides. The skin is the healthiest part, containing phytochemicals to reduce cancer risks and heart disease.
Strawberries (research has shown the antioxidant levels in organic strawberries is 19% higher)
Grapes
Celery (most highly contaminated)
Peaches (some of highest concentrations of pesticides)
Spinach
Sweet bell peppers
Nectarines
Potatoes: Potatoes are a must to buy organic as they contain the highest pesticide count among fruits and vegetables.
Tomatoes
Hot peppers
Kale
Summer Squash
Collard Greens

The produce that does not have to be organic is as follows:
Onions
Sweet corn (Make sure it is not a GMO)
Pineapples
Avocados
Cabbage
Sweet peas
Asparagus

Mangoes
Eggplant
Kiwi
Cantaloupe (domestic)
Sweet potatoes
Grapefruit
Papayas (make sure it is not a GMO)
Mushrooms

COOKING WITH OIL

For the Lord your God is bringing you into a good land—a land with brooks, streams, and deep springs gushing out into the valleys and hills; a land with wheat and barley, vines and fig trees, pomegranates, olive oil and honey; a land where bread will not be scarce and you will lack nothing; a land where the rocks are iron and you can dig copper out of the hills. (Deuteronomy 8:7-10 NIV) God gave man pure oil from plants that He knew would nourish our bodies. Once again, humans have decided that they could make oils that were better to use. They found they could manufacture cooking oils cheaper allowing them to make a more substantial profit. We need to be an informed consumer and use only the oils that will nourish us and not harm our bodies.

Some of the oils that we use to cook with have adverse effects on our bodies. There are health benefits when using certain oils on uncooked dishes, but when heated they are damaged, thus making them harmful to consume. If we are going to make a conscious effort to eat healthy food, we must also make a conscious effort to prepare our foods so as not to damage the nutrients or poison the body.

The most important thing to consider when cooking with oil is whether or not it is stable when heated up. Many of the oils will oxidize when heated. One of the indicators for how well the oil responds to heat is by paying attention to its smoke point. A smoke point occurs when the oil is heated to a certain temperature; causing the oil to break down and release free radicals. This break down lets off small lines of smoke. Few oils can withstand heat without losing their stability. When cooking with oil, it is essential to know it's smoke point temperature. When the nutrition world started to research cooking oils, they learned that canola, vegetable and seed oils were linked to many health conditions. People then turned to olive oil. Although olive oil has many health benefits, these are better obtained when the oil is not heated.

The best oil of choice for cooking, in my opinion, is coconut oil. It offers many health benefits both when heated and when used in foods that are not cooked.

Coconut oil: Over 90% of the fatty acids in this oil are saturated which makes coconut oil stable enough to be resistant to heat-induced damage. [1] Its smoke point is 350 degrees for unrefined oil, and 400 degrees Fahrenheit for refined coconut oil. Therefore it should not be heated to higher temperatures. Use coconut oil for cooking, consuming as is and as a substitute for other oils in recipes. Studies have shown that coconut oil has many benefits. It strengthens our immune system, improves brain and heart function, increases energy and is good for the hair. [3] Dr. Axe reports that coconut oil may also help prevent and treat cancer, reduce inflammation, reduce arthritis, cure urinary tract and kidney infections, improve digestion, prevent gum disease, prevent tooth decay and improve skin issues. [4]

Coconut oil is a healthy saturated fat, and we need saturated fats for cell function and growth. This oil has rich antioxidant properties. These antioxidant properties inhibit the oxidation of other molecules. Oxidation can produce free radicals that cause damage to our cells. Coconut oil is high in medium and short chain fatty acids so that the body can easily digest it and it is sent immediately to the liver to help with energy production. [5] It can also help improve blood cholesterol levels. [6] Studies have shown that coconut oil improves the HDL (good cholesterol) and it lowers the LDL (bad cholesterol) and triglycerides. [7]

70

Over 40% of this oil is composed of lauric acid making it the richest natural source available. Only breast milk has higher levels of lauric acid. Research has found that lauric acid helps in fighting viruses and disease and improving the immune system. [8] Lauric acid has also been shown to work as a preventative against some cancers. [5] It has also been found to help boost the metabolism, which may help with weight loss. Other possible benefits of this oil are that it can improve thyroid health, help promote bone strength by allowing better absorption of calcium, vitamin D, and minerals, and helps improve the way the body handles blood sugars since it can improve insulin use within the body. It also improves the immune system and brain function. Some research shows it helps reduce the symptoms of patients with Alzheimer's. Add coconut oil to smoothies, tea, salads, oatmeal or other foods.

Oil pulling is another effective way to use coconut oil. This is an excellent way to remove bacteria in your mouth. It is also believed to help eliminate toxins in your body. The benefits are that it kills bad breath, heals bleeding gums, and decreases inflammation. It also soothes a sore throat, prevents cavities and whitens teeth. [9] When I went through chemotherapy, it helped prevent the metal taste most people get as a side effect. Technique: Do oil pulling the first thing in the morning, possibly while in the shower. Use 1-2 tablespoons of coconut oil and swish it around in your mouth 10-15 minutes. When finished, spit it out in the toilet and rinse your mouth with warm water, spit out the water and then brush your teeth.

The two types we need to be familiar with are:
1. Unrefined may also be referred to as virgin or pure. This form has more of a coconut flavor and retains more of its nutritional value when being processed. Virgin and extra virgin coconut oil are the same, unlike olive oil, which has different amounts of fatty acids.

2. Refined coconut oil is more processed than the unrefined. When it is refined, most people notice less of the coconut taste. This form also has a higher smoke point when used for cooking. If the oil is refined, make sure that is done by a chemical-free method (expressed pressed). The refined works well for cooking at higher temperatures.

Extra virgin olive oil: Olive oil is a healthy oil when not heated. [10] When heated, the oil is prone to oxidative damage. It is best used when added to cold foods such as salads or drizzled on vegetables. It is also beneficial for applying to the skin. There are two types: virgin and extra virgin olive oil. The extra virgin oil has many more health benefits.

Olive oil is primarily composed of monounsaturated fat, called oleic acid, which is an antioxidant. It also contains omega 3 and 6 fatty acids. [11] Fatty acids are essential to improving our brain health, sharpening our focus and memory. Due to its antioxidant properties, olive oil is helpful in slowing the aging process. [10] This oil has also been shown to help in the prevention of cardiovascular disease, arteriosclerosis and certain types of cancers. [12] Olive oil contains polyphenols that strengthen the cell walls and improve the elasticity of the arterial wall. [13] Other studies have shown olive oil to be effective in weight loss, and help with depression and mood disorders. The healthy fats in olive oil help to balance hormones when dealing with PMS and menopause. Olive oil will hold its nutritional value longer when stored in a cool dark place. As soon as you use the oil replace the lid. It is best to buy smaller containers so that it does not expire before it is all used.
Be cautious when purchasing olive oil since many of the brands have GMO canola oil in them or other additives. Research the brand to know where it is from and who is bottling the olive oil to ascertain its purity. It does not take much time and will be beneficial for your health.

Do not use vegetable oils for cooking. These oils include corn, soy, sunflower, safflower or canola oils. These oils are composed of polyunsaturated fats referred to as omega 6's, which in large amounts are harmful to the body. The body needs to keep a ratio of 4:1 between the Omega 3's and 6's in our system. When these are unbalanced, and the omega 6's outnumber the omega 3's in our cells, complications arise. [14] This imbalance has been linked to heart disease, type 2 diabetes, irritable bowel syndrome, inflammatory bowel syndrome, asthma, and cancer. [15] Over 90 percent of canola oil is refined oil that is genetically modified. To improve the stability of the oil, it is partially hydrogenated. This partial hydrogenation can have adverse effects on our health. (16,17)

Hydrogenated oils: These are called trans fats and are made when hydrogen is added to vegetable oil causing it to solidify when it is at room temperature. This oil has been shown to raise bad cholesterol, lower good cholesterol and increase our risk of heart disease. Manufacturers use it in their food products because it has a longer shelf life. Some restaurants choose to use this because they do not have to change their oils as frequently. Products that often contain trans fats are baked goods, potato, corn and tortilla chips, fried foods, margarine, and creamers. In the United States if there are less than 5 grams of trans fat per serving the label does not have to include this information. People often eat more than one serving at a time, thus increasing their total intake of trans fats. In turn, this will affect their health. Get in the habit of reading food labels before purchasing a product.

Journal your thoughts

Day 4

QUALITY CONTROL
(FOOD SUBSTITUTES)

When building our temples, we only want to use the best quality materials so that the building does not collapse or need constant repairs.

Nugget of the day: He cuts off every branch of mine that doesn't produce fruit, and he prunes the branches that do bear fruit so they will produce even more. (John 15:2 NLT)

God most definitely knows His children. He knows us better than we know ourselves. God will watch over us. He will remove the obstacles that are detrimental to our living Christian lives if we allow Him. There may be things we do in this world that bring us pleasure while doing them but cause us much strife later because of the guilt and shame they inflict. There are also good things in our lives that bog us down and make us too weary to focus on our calling. God will help us to find our priorities and focus on what we need to do. Too often we never get to complete our callings because distractions rob us of this joy. The world makes us think that to be successful we need to be continuously busy. The devil also wants us to be distracted, so we do not achieve what God has planned for us. God knows we need to focus only on a few things and we need quiet time to rest our bodies and minds as well as to find time to sit in our loving Father's presence.

My prayer is that we ask God to prune our lives. When we ask this of God, we must also listen to Him. Although we often want to do everything in this life, in reality, we cannot. Instead, when we remove the distractions in our lives, we will bear much fruit in this world. We will find that when we focus on what God is calling us to do, we will be successful. So, let God expose any distractions in your life that needs to be removed. Then get down to the business you are supposed to be doing. When you accept that God is in charge and allow Him to prune your life, you will not only find you have time to do His will, but to also stay in the Word and recharge. It is then you will live the life God has planned for you, and you will produce much fruit.

****

Why spend money on what is not bread, and your labor on what does not satisfy? Listen, listen to me, and eat what is good, and you will delight in the richest of fare. (Isaiah 55:2 NIV)

I feel very strongly that God is telling me to print this Bible verse in large print so that we do not miss what He is asking of us. God took the time to provide us with nourishing food so that we could live productive lives. He does not want us to waste our energy, time, or money on things that are detrimental to our health. Just as buildings need to be constructed with high-quality materials, we need to nourish our bodies with the right foods. Too often I witness friends, and family members who miss out on all life has to offer by choosing to eat poorly. Their energy level is low, and they have so many aches and pains that they are limited in how much physical activity they can do in a day. They are missing out on not only fulfilling their calling God has for them, but also experiencing all the beauty and wonder God has given us in this great world.

What about you? Are you able to live life to its fullest or do you allow food to be a priority in your life, thus limiting what you are able to do? _____

Think about all the food you have consumed today, how much of it was healthy nourishing food?

_____

Were there things you missed out on today because you lacked energy or were physically limited?

_____

Why should we consume food that is unhealthy for us when we have healthy alternatives? We have to be an informed consumer if we want to benefit from the food we eat. The guidelines for labeling food are very lax, and manufacturers use this to their advantage to get consumers to buy their products. We cannot let their sales tactics lure us into buying food that can harm our bodies or provide no nutritional value. When we do, we are wasting our hard earned money. Let's make sure we put our money into quality food so that we use the right food to fuel our bodies and keep us healthy.

We need to be a healthy food advocate for our families and ourselves. The only way to do that is to be well educated as to what type of foods we should eat and what we need to avoid. The healthiest foods are the fresh fruits and vegetables. When we do choose to buy packaged food, we need to inspect each label as to what ingredients are in the product. Do not assume that a product is healthy for you. Even simple products can have chemical additives. The other day I bought balsamic vinegar from a health-conscious store, expecting it would be free of chemicals. Much to my surprise, later that day when I was preparing to make a salad, I checked the ingredients, and it had caramel coloring in it. Don't get caught buying products you will not use once you get home. Check each label before purchasing the product.

You can still use many of your favorite recipes when substituting for the ingredients that should not be in your diet. Here is a list of products and ingredients to avoid and what to use as a replacement:

Breadcrumbs: Instead, use almond meal, rolled oats or ground flax seed seasoned with herbs. My kids love almond meal baked chicken. I roll the chicken in organic eggs and then almond meal seasoned with many herbs. I place this in a glass-baking dish with a small amount of coconut oil on the bottom and bake it at 350 degrees.

Canned tomatoes: Most canned tomatoes have BPA on the can's lining. Due to the high acidity of the tomatoes, the BPA leaches into the food. BPA is associated with an increased risk of breast and prostate cancer, reproductive abnormalities, heart disease and neurological problems. [1] I often substitute organic tomato sauce or marinara to make homemade pizza, chili or another recipe calling for canned tomatoes. Many

73

companies now sell tomato sauce in jars, or you can make homemade tomato sauce.

Cereal or instant oatmeal: Steel cut oats or quinoa with berries and seeds make a good breakfast. I usually make enough oats to last for the week and put them in small glass bowls so that it is easily accessible in the morning.

Chips or salty snacks: Replace chips with air-popped popcorn. Use organic butter and then sprinkle with Himalayan salt and cayenne pepper or cinnamon. You can also make zucchini or kale chips.

Chocolate: Use cacao nibs or powder in your recipes. Cold pressing unroasted cacao beans makes cacao a healthy form of chocolate. Cocoa is not healthy because the cacao bean is roasted at a high temperature. This process destroys the antioxidants that are in the cacao bean. [2] If you must have chocolate, buy only organic dark chocolate bars with cacao count over 72%. Add cacao nibs to berries or other fruits. The sweetness of the fruit brings out more of the chocolate taste we are used to without getting the sugar and additives. One of my favorite treats is strawberries, blueberries, goji berries, and cherries topped with sunflower seeds, pumpkin seeds, ground flax seed and cacao nibs.

Croutons: Substitute almonds, nuts, and seeds on a salad. I love to use pumpkin seeds, chia seeds, sunflower seeds and goji berries to top my salad.

Dressing: It is easy to make your dressing with healthy ingredients. Use ingredients such as lemon juice, olive oil, various kinds of vinegar, and herbs. I use balsamic vinegar and olive oil on my salads. Unhealthy salad dressing can take away some of the nutritional value of your salad and add unwanted calories. Many salad dressings that say they use live oil also use other oils. So make sure to read the full list of ingredients.

Eggs: Some people want to keep eggs out of their diet. If this is the case, substitute chia seeds for eggs. Mix 1 tablespoon of seeds to 1 cup of water and let them sit on the counter for 15 minutes before adding to a recipe.

Energy bars: Most energy bars are loaded with sugar and other ingredients that are not of any nutritional value. If you do buy energy bars, make sure they use natural sweeteners such as dates, honey or maple syrup. I make my energy balls by placing 2 cups of pitted dates, 1/2 cup of almonds, 2 cups raw cashews, 1 cup figs, ½ teaspoon of cinnamon, ½ cup raw coconut, 1 tablespoon of vanilla extract in a blender and then add 4 tablespoons of water. When well blended add any other ingredient to enhance the flavor. I also like to add ½ cup cacao nibs and ½ cup oats. The mixture should be moist but not sticky. I then roll them into balls and place them in a glass container to store in my refrigerator. These make a great snack.

Fast food: Many fast foods have little nutritional value. Many of the restaurants serve more food than anyone should consume at any one meal. The average fast food meal contains 1,205 calories. This is over half of the recommended daily allowance of 2,000 calories, and most of these are empty calories. [3] There are often so many additives that we are not getting the nutrition we need in these meals. Research has shown that people who frequently eat fast food have more depression, heart problems, and weight issues. [4] When traveling, look up what restaurants are in the area beforehand so that you are prepared and do not make bad food choices. When I travel, I prepare food ahead of time and take it with me. I make salads and meals that do not need to be heated up. I make hard boiled eggs that I can eat for breakfast and bring my smoothie maker. I also have a variety of nuts, seeds, fruits, and cut up vegetables. It takes a little extra planning, but it is worth the effort. By eating a healthy diet when I travel, I have good energy and no digestive problems. Initially, this may seem like a lot of extra work, but when we get into the practice of eating healthy all the time, we will prefer to be prepared because we know how much better our bodies feel when they are well nourished.

Flour: Instead of using white or wheat flour use coconut flour or almond flour.

Fruit juice: Fruit juice contains high levels of fructose, a form of sugar, which is released rapidly into the bloodstream. When eating fruit, we get the benefit of fiber, phytonutrients, and antioxidants. The fiber helps to slow the absorption of sugar into the blood. Fruit juice, especially if processed, does not offer the same benefits as the fruit. [5] Making a homemade fruit smoothie can be an alternative to fruit juice as would drinking filtered water with lemon, lime or orange slices added. I have learned that many smoothies sold at restaurants and juice bars have extra sugar and additives, so you need to beware of this too. Always ask what ingredients are going into your smoothie or other food.

Hot chocolate: Every once in a while, on a cold night we need something extra to comfort us. I find my hot cacao mixture to be a good substitute. I use 8 ounces of organic milk or coconut milk, ½ teaspoon vanilla, 2 tablespoons cacao powder, ½ teaspoon cinnamon and ½ teaspoon of honey. It is a different taste than we usually associate with hot chocolate, but I find it comforting and a special treat.

Ice cream: Ice cream is loaded with sugar, and the dairy can be difficult for the body to digest. I have purchased a machine that allows me to make fruit ice cream. I place my frozen fruit in the machine, and it makes it into a frozen swirl. I then can add toppings such as cacao nibs, raw coconut or nuts for a delicious treat.

Instant rice: Use wild rice, brown rice or quinoa. Quinoa is a whole grain that is a complete protein and can be used as an alternative to rice or pasta in most recipes.

Margarine: Replace this with organic butter or avocado puree.

Mayonnaise: A great substitute is mashed avocado or Greek yogurt.

Meat: If you do not want to use grass-fed beef or organic chicken, then you can substitute one ounce of meat with 1/4 cup cooked beans or lentils. Grill large portabella mushroom caps in place of burgers. Instead of meat on a salad, you can use nuts or seeds. To boost the flavor of the nuts or seeds you can toast them in a skillet.

Microwave popcorn: The bag itself is lined with perfluorooctanoic acid, which is the same toxic chemical used in Teflon cookware. Many of the companies that produce this product use trans fats. Microwave popcorn contains diacetyl, a chemical used as a butter substitute. This chemical has been known to cause "popcorn workers lung" because the workers repeatedly inhale this chemical. [6] You can use air-popped popcorn and flavor it as you like. I like to add cayenne pepper and organic butter to season my popcorn. If you use salt, use Himalayan salt.

Non-organic potatoes: Use organic potatoes. Conventional potatoes are high in pesticides. The USDA Pesticide Data Program has identified thirty-five different pesticides on these potatoes. Six of these pesticides are known or probable carcinogens, six can be toxic to reproduction or development, seven are neurotoxins, and twelve are suspected of disrupting hormones [7,8] A substitute with more nutritional value is sweet potatoes, which can be used in any potato recipe. These potatoes nourish the body with many vitamins including vitamin A (beta-carotene), vitamin C, manganese, copper, pantothenic acid, and vitamin B6, potassium, dietary fiber, niacin, vitamin B1, vitamin B2, and phosphorus. Another alternative for mashed potatoes is mashed cauliflower.

Oil substitutes: Replace your vegetable oils with coconut oil. Another alternative when making a stir-fry or vegetable dish is to use organic vegetable broth. You can use olive oil for recipes that are prepared at room temperature or on cold items.

Pasta: Use zucchini, cucumbers or spaghetti squash in place of pasta: Cucumbers and zucchini can be shredded or use a spiral kitchen appliance to make these veggies into noodle form. To use spaghetti squash, cook them just like any other winter squash. Scoop out the seeds and rub the inside with salt and olive oil, then roast in a 400° oven for 45 minutes until the flesh is completely tender. Use a fork to gently lift out the tender flesh in long delicious strands. Quinoa can also be used as pasta.

Pizza crust: There are many recipes on the Internet on how to make a pizza crust out of cauliflower.

Soda, diet soda, and sports drinks: Most diet soda contains aspartame, which increases sugar cravings and can cause weight gain. Soda can contribute to kidney problems, heart disease, raise cancer risks, type 2 diabetes, increased belly fat, fatty liver disease and erode our teeth. [9] The phosphoric acid has been shown to decrease bone density, increase acidity and decrease the nutrients in the body. [10] Sports drinks often have large amounts of sugar. Instead of these drinks, use coconut water or filtered water with a splash of lemon, lime, or orange. Another alternative is unsweetened tea. When drinking tea, make sure the tea bags do not contain epichlorohydrin or are plastic.

Sour cream: Replace in recipes with Greek yogurt.

Sugar and sweeteners: Researchers at the University of California, San Francisco have shown that sugar is a contributing factor in approximately 35 million deaths around the world each year. [11] Sugar increases the risk of breast and ovarian cancers, feeds cancer cells, suppresses the immune system, decreases calcium and magnesium absorption, contributes to obesity, causes copper and chromium deficiencies, contributes to heart disease, causes hyperactivity, crankiness, impairs focus, and arthritis. Sugar is an inflammation-causing ingredient. [12]
   It is best to limit any sweetener but when a recipe calls for sweetener you can substitute maple syrup or honey. Replace 1-cup sugar with 3/4-cup pure maple syrup or raw honey and reduce recipe liquid by 3-5 tablespoons. Unsweetened applesauce also works well in most recipes.

Aspartame and artificial sweeteners: These sweeteners have been linked to headaches, change in vision, sleep problems, memory loss, dizziness, hives, joint pain, diarrhea, change in moods, seizures, abdominal cramps and pain, fatigue, weakness, as well as brain cancer. [13] The body cannot completely break down these sweeteners so they are often stored in the body and can lead to weight gain. These sweeteners change the gut microbiome, which has been associated with diabetes. [14] The use of artificial sweeteners tricks the brain into thinking it is going to get something sweet. Since there are no accompanying calories, the body craves carbs, increasing your dietary intake. These sweeteners may possibly be addicting. Some other names for artificial sweeteners include Splenda™, saccharin, acesulfame potassium and sucralose.

Table salt: Table salt has been shown to increase hypertension. All of the natural minerals are stripped from this product and then replaced with potassium iodine in potentially toxic amounts. It is stabilized with dextrose, which turns it purple, and is then bleached white. [15] Himalayan salt is a healthy choice to use as a replacement. Himalayan salt has many benefits for our bodies. This salt contains all 84 elements found in the body, and it promotes bone strength, healthy ph balances, sinus health, blood sugar health, vascular health, regulates water content in the body and prevents muscle cramps. [16] Another healthy alternative is Celtic sea salt.

Tortilla wraps: Use lettuce leaves as a substitute.

Veggie dips: Hummus, avocado dip or homemade salsa makes nice vegetable dips.

White bread and food made out of white flour and refined flour: White bread provides empty calories and may contain bromide. Potassium bromate is a dough conditioner that many commercial bakers use. Bromide can disrupt the function of our thyroid gland. Bromide causes the body to have lower levels of iodine. Iodine is needed in our body to fight cancer and tumor formation. [17] If you need to eat bread, choose whole grain bread with this listed as the first ingredient on the package. Some bread, labeled as wheat bread, hearty grain or 9 grains, may not be whole grain bread. [18] There are recipes on the Internet on how to make healthy bread.

Avoid products that have the following ingredients in them.

Artificial colors: Many of these are linked to allergic reactions, organ damage, birth defects, fatigue, asthma, hyperactivity, skin rashes, headaches, and cancer. The most common ones used are Red 40, Yellow 5 and Yellow 6. All of these have known carcinogens in them. [19,20]

High fructose corn syrup: This ingredient is in many processed food items. Statistics show that the average person consumes over 60 pounds of this a year. [21] This sweetener has been linked to weight gain, diabetes, cancer, high blood pressure, heart disease, an increase in cholesterol levels, leaky gut and fatty liver and liver stress. [22]

Monosodium glutamate (MSG) - MSG is an excitotoxin, which has been found to cause damage to nerve cells, destroy brain cells and cause neurological disorders. MSG has also been found to increase a person's appetite, causing weight gain. It is often found in canned vegetables, processed meat, Chinese food, potato chips and soup stock. People who are sensitive to MSG may have reactions to it. Some of the symptoms include headaches and heart palpitations. MSG has many other names, so when looking at labels, we need to be an educated consumer. Some of these names are: hydrolyzed vegetable protein, calcium or sodium caseinate, hydrolyzed plant or animal protein, yeast extract, glutamate, textured protein, soy protein isolates, barley malt, glutamic acid, vegetable protein extract, natural flavor and malt extract. [23,24]

Partially hydrogenated soybean oil: Not only does this contain trans-fat, but it also contains soy. Often the soy is a GMO product, adding another negative component.

Soy products: Most soy products are genetically modified. They contain anti-nutrients and toxins. These interfere with the absorption of vitamins and minerals. Soy products may also affect Alzheimer's. [20] One report shows that soy can elevate the blood level of estrogen up to 22,000 times the normal level. Soy contains phytoestrogens, which can mimic estrogen and wreak havoc on both women who have too little or too much estrogen production in their bodies. [25,26] It can also block stomach enzymes and zinc absorption. Many believe the only safe soy products are organic fermented soy products, which rids the soy of the anti-nutrients it contains. [27]

Day 5

JUICING AND SMOOTHIES

Nugget of the day: I realized that no one can discover everything God is doing under the sun. Not even the wisest people discover everything, no matter what they claim. (Ecclesiastes 8:17 NLT)

Wouldn't it be nice to understand everything God has planned for our lives? What if every time we opened the Bible we had a clear understanding as to what God had to say? Would we stay in the Word? Sometimes we just have to sit back and marvel at the greatness of our God. He is capable of doing anything at any time. Our God is the only Being that could write a book, which continues to baffle and challenge even the most knowledgeable scholars, yet simple enough for the ordinary person to read it, and find comfort. Who else could pen a verse that can address the needs of many people and also provide insight into many situations? The Bible is written with such supreme wisdom that it is the only book that is as alive and fulfilling today as it was when it was first penned. It never ages. Not only is the Bible still alive, but so is our God. He still performs miracles in our lives, and He continues to have an active role in the world. Rather than trying to figure God out, we need to appreciate His superiority and allow Him full access to our lives. Rather than question Him, we need to trust Him and let Him guide us. Any good soldier obeys his captain and knows the captain is privy to information that is not always shared with those beneath him. We need to know that we are not privy to all the information that God possesses. As the captain, God knows that too much information could be detrimental or cause us to make irrational decisions.

My prayer is that you realize that God is in control and He has far more knowledge than you can ever imagine. Take some time to appreciate just how great our God is and thank Him for being in control and leading you through life. Accept that God always has your best interest at heart. He will protect you and watch over you when you step out of the way and follow Him. It takes good soldiers to place trust in their leader and to allow the captain to give the orders. Imagine how much easier your life would be if you would just surrender to our all-knowing and all-powerful God and let Him be in charge.
****

Then God said, "I give you every seed-bearing plant on the face of the whole earth and every tree that has fruit with seed in it. They will be yours for food. (Genesis 1:29 NIV) Do you ever take the time to marvel at how much thought and love God put into giving us food for life? God has given us a beautiful array of colors, shapes, and tastes to choose from when nourishing our bodies. Nutrients abound in these foods, and each one has a unique purpose. These fruits and vegetables not only serve to nourish us, but to maintain a healthy body and help heal our bodies from many sicknesses and diseases. There are so many varieties of fruits and vegetables to choose from that our pallets will never get bored. We have dulled our taste buds by giving them so many man-made foods that we have lost our taste for real food. We need to return to eating real, God-given foods, and our taste buds will rejoice once again. There are so many fruits and vegetables that offer us so many nutrients, but we cannot take them all in in a day. By juicing or making smoothies, we can compact these fruits and vegetables to get more nutritional value out of our foods.

<u>Juicing</u> involves extracting the juice from the pulp of the fruits and vegetables and removing much of the fiber. <u>Smoothies:</u> The fruits and vegetables are finely chopped and pureed so that all of the fiber and juice is used to make this thick drink.

Juicing and smoothies are similar in that they can combine a variety of vegetables and fruits in one drink so that we get many of the nutrients our bodies need daily. They also present with their unique advantages. Eating these vegetables and fruits instead of juicing or blending them will fill us up too quickly, limiting our nutritional intake during the day. For many people, juicing and smoothies are the only way to get the recommended daily intake of vegetables and fruits.

Too often we allow much of our diets to be taken up with too much meat or food that offers little or no nutritional value. The recommended daily serving of vegetables and fruits is 6-8 servings. Drinking juice or smoothies can help you reach this goal. Another advantage to blending our vegetables and fruits is that our bodies utilize the nutrients much better when the blending process breaks them down.

People who are actively receiving cancer treatment may find blending their produce a much easier way to get the nutrients they need to keep their bodies strong and enable them to fight cancer. Juicing and smoothies are especially helpful for those who have trouble swallowing.

Benefits of juicing or drinking smoothies:

Provides the body with phytonutrients: These are essential to help fight cancer and boost our immune system.

It is easier for the body to digest vegetables and fruits: We don't often chew the fruits and vegetables enough to break them down so that our bodies can utilize the nutrients. When they are in liquid form, it is easier for our bodies to digest.

Detoxifies the body: When using the right combination of vegetables, juicing and smoothies are an efficient way to detoxify the liver and intestines.

Provides the body with a broader array of vegetables and fruits in our diet: Allows us to ingest vegetables and fruits we usually would not eat due to taste or texture.

Hydrates the body. Watery fruits and vegetables can hydrate our bodies.

Retains the nutrients: Cooking and baking vegetables and fruits often reduce the number of nutrients in the food. Using produce in the raw form preserves the nutrients.

Juicing and smoothies have specific advantages and disadvantages.

JUICING:

Advantages: Drinking 12 ounces of juice allows us to take in 2-3 pounds of vegetables and fruit.[1] It is best to juice mostly vegetables with minimal fruit since fruit is higher in sugars and calories. A person can use a juicer, and it will extract the juice from the fiber. The nutrients will be digested quicker when the fiber is not present in a drink. By removing the pulp, a person can get more vegetables and fruits at one sitting. Juicing places less stress on the digestive system. Juicing allows us to extract 70% of the nutrients from the produce and because there is no insoluble fiber, our bodies absorb 100% of these nutrients. [2] Juicing is better if you are having intestinal problems or difficulty breaking down your food.

Disadvantages: When juicing, the fiber is eliminated, therefore allowing the juice to get into the bloodstream very quickly, which can cause a spike in blood sugar. Juicing cannot be used as a meal replacement due to not having protein. It is more expensive at first due to the cost of a good juicer, and it requires more fruits and vegetables to juice. Juicing takes more time, has more waste and it can be difficult and time-consuming to clean the machine.

SMOOTHIES:

Advantages: They can be made using a blender, retains the fiber, which aids the digestion system and improves elimination. Since there is fiber in the smoothie, it allows for the slower release of the nutrients and helps to remove the toxins in the digestive system. The slow release of nutrients helps us to feel fuller for an extended period and does not cause a spike in the blood sugar. Chia and flax seeds can be added to provide the body with healthy omega-3 nutrients and protein. By adding protein to a smoothie, it becomes a meal. Using a blender to make the smoothies makes it more cost-effective.

Disadvantages: Some of the nutrients attach to the fiber and therefore are eliminated rather than utilized, so it loses some of its nutritional value. It is harder on the intestines due to them having to digest and absorb the fiber. Some people do not like the consistency.

How to make juice/smoothies:

Use organic vegetables and fruits when possible, especially the produce that is more prone to be contaminated by pesticides. If we are eating healthy, we want our bodies to consume the healthy foods.

Start slowly: Juice vegetables that are easier to digest and that you enjoy. As you get used to juicing, you can gradually add new vegetables.

Drink a smoothie on an empty stomach: It is best to drink 2 hours after a meal or wait 20 minutes to eat a meal. Other food prevents the body from absorbing the nutrients quickly.

Make only enough juice to use in one sitting. The nutritional value starts to decrease after 15 minutes of air exposure, so it is best to drink immediately. (3) If you make excess, it will store for up to 24 hours in an airtight glass jar. If there is air in the jar, it will cause oxidation.

Be cautious with the fruits and some vegetables: It is best to use mostly vegetables with only one serving of fruit so that there is not a lot of sugar released into the bloodstream. Also be cautious with using excessive amounts vegetables that have high sugar content.

Don't always use the same produce: By alternating the vegetable and fruits, we allow the body to get different vitamins and minerals it needs to maintain its health.

Use lemon or limes: These counterbalance the bitterness of some of the vegetables. They are also good to help improve the alkalinity of the body.

Keep produce as cold as possible: Use cold produce when possible since the blades of the blender produce heat, and if the ingredients get heated, it may decrease their nutritional value. Chop up the produce into small chunks and do not overload the blender since this makes the blades work harder, thereby increasing heat.

Blend the chia seeds and flax seeds first: The body digests flax seed and chia seeds more efficiently when they are ground. Grind them first because when they are put in with fruits and vegetables, they often don't get ground entirely.

The best vegetables and fruits to use for juicing and smoothies are: aloe, apples, avocado, beets, berries, bok choy, broccoli, cabbage, carrots, celery, citrus fruits, cherries, cranberries, cucumber, dandelion greens, ginger, kale, mustard greens, papaya, parsley, pineapple, spinach, tomatoes, and wheatgrass.

THE DANGERS OF SUGAR

How can something that tastes so sweet be so wrong for us? So many people associate sugar with being a special treat and use it as a reward for doing something good. Sugar is misused in our diets. As I have become more aware of the dangers of sugar, I am concerned about how we allow it to control our lives and destroy the people we love. I too have been guilty of using sweets as a reward for my children and myself. I have allowed it to interfere with my health, leading to excessive weight. It took hard work and determination to get sugar out of my diet. Rather than see it as a treat, I now see it as a vice that can damage my body. Take a look around you and see how sugar has caused harm to your family and friends. How many of your loved ones have illnesses that are caused by or worsened by sugar?

How has sugar disrupted your family or friends lives? _____

As I look at my surroundings, I struggle with how sugar disrupts the lives of those around me. I watch with frustration as students who receive meals from school are fed chocolate muffins and chocolate milk for breakfast and are told this is a well-balanced diet. I watch these same children eat entrees with little nutritional value, consume fruit cups with heavy syrup and get juice laden with sugar for lunch. They are told this is healthy diet and it will give them energy. I watch parents send their beloved children to school with lunchboxes packed with chips and cookies because they are giving them a special treat only to see these children struggle throughout the day. At first, these children cannot sit still and then later as the sugar high wears off, they cannot stay awake. I see teachers continually reprimand students all day for being unable to sit still and having poor behavior and then when they finally do sit quietly, give them candy as a reward. I watch as people who struggle to perform their daily activities due to obesity continue to consume large amounts of sugar.

When I was at the cancer center, the clinic only offered sweet treats to their patients and had large candy bowls filled with chocolate on their counters. I cringe when I hear doctors tell cancer patients sugar does not have a role in causing cancer, affecting its progression or altering their prognosis. Then there are those who work out regularly in the gym just to go home and eat some sweet treat as a reward and cannot understand why they can't lose weight. Holidays are a time of overindulging in cookies and candies and people laugh about putting on weight during these seasons. For many, rather than find this appalling, they see it as a holiday tradition. Many people associate vacations with dining out rather than enjoying the sights. They have their favorite bakeries, ice cream shops and candy stores that they must visit. When people quit looking to food as the central part of the vacation, they will be in better health to actually enjoy the attractions, have the energy to take hikes and see the sights that are available.

Sugar is highly esteemed in American society. The ironic thing is that when consumed, this reward only lasts for several seconds, maybe several minutes if a person takes time to savor the sweetness. Then it is gone, but the consequences of the few moments of heavenly bliss remain in our bodies for a more extended period. Please don't tune me out because I am talking about a subject that you find brings comfort in your life. For some people, there is nothing wrong with enjoying a sweet treat on a special occasion. Sugar becomes a problem in our lives when it controls us, causes us health problems, interferes with our lives or is an obsession. You need to carefully evaluate whether or not one piece of candy or a sweet treat will trigger you to overindulge in sugar. For some, abstaining from sugar is the right thing to do to ensure that it does not control you. For others, they can ingest sugar sparingly.

Have you ever taken the time to contemplate what the sweet item you are about to put in your mouth is going to do to your body?

What do the unhealthy treats you ingest do to your body? _____

How can you use visualization as a tool to discourage you from eating sugar knowing what it is going to do to your body? _____

"Watch and pray so that you will not fall into temptation. The spirit is willing, but the flesh is weak." (Matthew 26:41 NIV)
Temptation: the desire to have or do something that you know you should avoid. Something that seduces or has the quality to seduce (1)

Would you say sugar could be a temptation? _____

How does Jesus advise us to deal with temptations? _____

We all have vices. We frequently realize these vices are not suitable for our well-being. For some, these vices are food related. They cause us to gain weight, limit our activity or to have food related health issues. No matter what the vice is, we need to deal with it for us to live fulfilling lives.

Have you ever taken the time to think that sugar, when it is an addiction, is something the devil can use to prevent you from fulfilling your calling and living a joyous life?____ If you do, how is he using it?

_____

Now the serpent was more crafty than any of the wild animals the Lord God had made. He said to the woman, "Did God really say, 'You must not eat from any tree in the garden'?" (Genesis 3:1 NIV) The devil knows each one of our weaknesses and will use them against us. It is to his advantage to keep us sluggish, immobile and unhealthy. When we are not feeling our best, we are unable to fulfill our God-given calling fully.

We need to realize that sugar may be the tool he uses against us.

Do you see sugar interfering with your calling? _____ If so, in what way? _____

   Not all sugars are bad for us. There are two different types of sugar. Natural sugars, which come from fruits and vegetables and are called fructose and glucose. Glucose is essential to our bodies as every cell depends on it for energy. (2) Our bodies can use glucose immediately as fuel. The remainder of the glucose is stored as glycogen in our liver and muscles for further use. The brain and nerve cells depend on glucose, as this is their only energy supply. The body stores excess glucose as fat. Fructose is not as versatile. The body finds fructose harder to break down because the liver is the only place this process occurs. The benefit of getting fructose from fruits is that fruits also contain many other essential nutrients, vitamins, antioxidants and fiber. An advantage of the fiber is that it allows the body to absorb the fructose slowly so that it can break down this sugar. This slow process will not overload our liver or cause the fructose to turn into fat unless we eat excessive amounts of fruit.

   Refined sugars are processed sugars. Our bodies utilize these sugars differently. Refined sugar is digested quickly causing blood sugar to spike. Because of this rapid spike, a person does not experience a full sensation and will continue to consume more food. (4) (5) (6)

   I think we can almost see refined sugar as the Satan of the food world. It deceives our bodies into thinking it needs the sugar rush, it lies to us about its benefits, and it then wreaks havoc in our bodies causing us to have to deal with its consequences: sickness and pain that could be avoided just by abstaining from this terrible vice. We Americans are often fooled into thinking that sugar enhances our lives, rather than hinders it. All one has to do is watch television for half an hour and see the commercials which show us how sugar can transform our fatigue into energy. They try to convince us that sugar will make us happy when we have a bad day, or it is a reward we deserve. We don't often see commercials promoting healthy foods. It is easy to be tricked into thinking we want and need refined sugar in our diet.

   The average American consumes 130 pounds of sugar a year. (7) We are not always aware of how much sugar we are consuming because manufacturers have come up with new ways to disguise sugar in their products. We need to familiarize ourselves with these other names and check the labels for these forms of sugar. We are most familiar with high fructose corn syrup or corn syrup, but there are many others. Here is a list of some of the most common aliases for sugar: fructose (natural sugar from fruits), rice syrup, lactose (natural sugar from milk), sucrose (made from fructose and glucose), barley malt, maltose (sugar made from grain), glucose (simple sugar, product of photosynthesis), fruit juice or dextrose (form of glucose). (8) These added sugars contain empty calories. Empty calories are mostly made of sugars and solid fats and offer little or no nutritional value to our diet. The body is unable to use up all these calories, and so it stores it as fat in the body. In 2010 The National Institute of Health reported that in children between the ages of 2-18, 40 percent of the calories they consumed were considered empty calories. (9)

How does it make you feel to know that you are throwing away your hard earned money to buy foods that have little nutritional value, with high amounts of sugar, which can contribute to increasing weight problems and other health issues? _____

   There is research available saying both, that sugar affects cancer cells and it does not. So let's for a moment play the devil's advocate and say that sugar does not affect the cells. Does this mean that we should go ahead and allow this in our diet and not be concerned with how much we consume? What is one of the high risks of cancer? Obesity. What is one of the leading culprits of obesity? Sugar. Sugar is responsible for making the brain think it is hungry. Therefore, people eat more and then sugar is stored as fat in the body creating a vicious cycle. (10) Statistics show that the average American takes in 20 teaspoons of sugar each day. (11) The excess sugar we take in is turned into body fat, which in turn, leads to many diseases such as heart disease and hypertension, type 2 diabetes, dementia and …cancer. (12) Some of the fat produced from excess sugar, not stored in our fat cells, is stored in the liver, which contributes to non-alcoholic fatty liver disease. The role of the liver is to remove the toxins in our bodies, process the food nutrients and regulate body metabolism. (13) The liver is also responsible for regulating and getting rid of excess sex hormones. Excessive estrogen can be a contributing cause of cancer. (14) When the liver gets overloaded with toxins it fails. Hmmm, sounds like we want to keep our liver healthy to assist our body in preventing sickness, or allowing our body to heal from any illness or disease. So we need to eliminate sugar.

Other research has shown that sugar is taken up by cancer cells at a rate of 10-12 times more than healthy cells. (15) To detect sugar hungry tumor cells the PET (positive emission tomography) scanners use radioactive glucose. A PET scan is one of the most accurate tools for identifying cancer growth. (9)

As I mentioned previously in this book, sugar addictions can be hard to break because of the release of dopamine into the brain. Our bodies crave this "high" sensation and will continue to want to experience this feeling, thus craving more sugar. We need to find replacements, such as exercise, that can release the dopamine into our brains. To break our sugar addictions, we need to detoxify the body. We will be much more likely to break our sugar addiction if we quit cold turkey. Unfortunately, sometimes this comes with withdrawal symptoms. Not only do we have to deal with the physical withdrawal, but also the emotional withdrawal, which at times, can be more significant. The physical withdrawal from sugar usually only lasts a few days. Some of the symptoms may be fatigue, anxiety, irritability, depression, poor sleep, heart palpitations or rapid heartbeat. (16) These withdrawal symptoms are because the toxins are leaving the body while breaking the addiction. Remember, if we go back to eating sugar because we do not like going through the withdrawal, we will have to go through the whole process again the next time we try to quit eating sugar. Rather than focus on the symptoms, focus on how our bodies are ridding themselves of these nasty toxins. Visualize how our bodies are recovering. I find relief when I offer myself a reward for getting through a tough time. Make sure the reward is something that will enhance your healthy lifestyle such as a hike on a favorite trail, a fun activity, or a new book on healthy living. When you look at the positives as you make the changes, and see the good things that are happening in your life, it is much easier to be victorious.

Ways to beat your sugar addiction and eat healthier:

Pray for God to help you overcome your sugar addiction. You need to ask God for the strength to overcome this weakness. Post Bible verses on the refrigerator and pantry shelves so that you are reminded to seek God's assistance in moments of weakness.

Remove foods with refined sugars from your home. You need to get rid of all the foods that will tempt you to eat refined sugar. Clean out your pantry, refrigerator, and freezer.

Adopt new comfort foods. We all like to have a special treat now and then. You need to find something that tastes good and can give you some nutrition when you eat it. Finding a healthy food that you may not always be able to afford as a regular staple can be a good comfort food when you need a treat. Try new healthy recipes and keep the ones that give you comfort in an easy to find place so that you can make it when you need something special.

Find a group of friends to share food ideas. When you have a friend or group of friends to share new recipes with, and try something new, your new lifestyle can be an exciting adventure.

Choose healthy sugars such as fruits. The fiber in the fruit helps to slow the release of glucose into the bloodstream. It also helps to decrease the appetite. Be careful drinking fruit juice. Because there is no fiber, the sugar is released quickly into the bloodstream. Be careful to not overindulge in eating fruit.

Use cacao nibs: Cacao nibs can add chocolate flavor when added to the fruit. You receive the benefits of chocolate without adding sugar to your diet.

Exercise: This will help to lower the extra glucose in the blood. It also helps to decrease the body's resistance to insulin. Exercise will also cause the brain to release dopamine, serotonin, and endorphins, which help to improve your mood and well-being.

Eat proteins and vegetables. Eat adequate amounts of protein and increase your vegetable consumption. Most experts agree that a person should have .36 grams per pound of body weight. Sufficient amounts of protein help to slow the rate of carbohydrate absorption and stabilize the blood sugar. When people lack protein, their bodies can crave sugar and carbohydrates.

Eat smaller quantities of food more frequently. This helps to balance your insulin and control your appetite.

Lose weight or control your weight. Abdominal weight gain increases insulin resistance, and the higher intake of simple sugar adds more calories, which can cause additional weight gain. [17]

Add fermented foods to your meals. Fermented foods provide a bacteria that helps with digestion and detoxing the body so that fructose is not as taxing on the liver. There are several good choices for this including organic yogurt, kimchi, natto, sauerkraut, fermented vegetables and kefir produced from grass-fed milk. [18]

Use natural sugars. Natural sugars have some nutritional value. If you must use some form of sugar in food, use natural sugars. These natural sugars have antioxidants, which help fight cancer. Some of these products are honey, maple syrup, and molasses. However, these should still be used sparingly in your diet. [19]

Use supplements. Vitamins B, C and, zinc, as well as the trace mineral chromium and amino acid L-glutamine help to reduce sugar cravings and symptoms of sugar withdrawal. [16] The mineral chromium helps insulin to control blood glucose and helps with energy production. It also regulates blood sugar, so it does not have the ups and downs. Use 200 mcg once a day, at the start of any meal, to prevent the sugar surges that often leave you reaching for more sugar later. [20]

Reward yourself. Sugar is often a reward for many reasons in a person's life such as: making it through a hard day, celebrating an achievement or having a good workout. Instead of using sugar, find something else that is healthy to reward yourself. These rewards could include a nice walk, watching a movie, or having a healthy meal with a friend. Set up milestones you wish to achieve as you embark on this journey. As you begin to lose weight due to your healthy lifestyle, look forward to buying new clothes.

Do not substitute artificial sweeteners for sugar. Artificial sweeteners have been proven to increase weight gain, cause people to overeat, crave sweets more, trick your body into thinking it is going to get a high-calorie intake, which in turn alters the hunger signal. Many of these sweeteners contain genetically modified ingredients (GMO's) from soy, corn or sugar beets. [21]

Journal your thoughts

Week 5

Day 1: Review Bible verses
Day 2: Reviewing The Code
Day 3: Inspecting The Electric To Meet Code
Day 4: Meats, Eggs And Fish
Antioxidants
Day 5: Removing Toxins From The Temple
Maintaining An Alkaline Diet

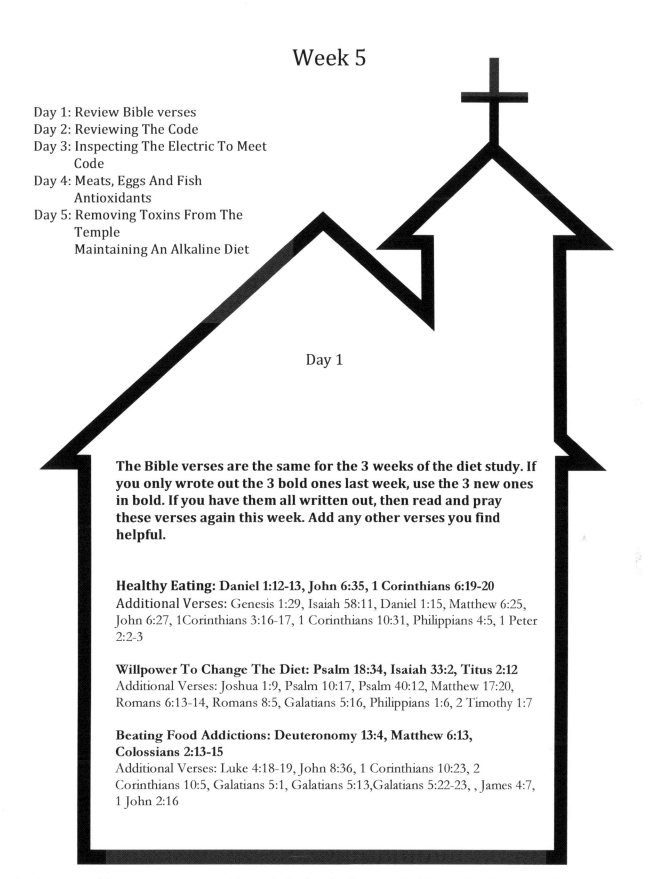

Day 1

The Bible verses are the same for the 3 weeks of the diet study. If you only wrote out the 3 bold ones last week, use the 3 new ones in bold. If you have them all written out, then read and pray these verses again this week. Add any other verses you find helpful.

Healthy Eating: Daniel 1:12-13, John 6:35, 1 Corinthians 6:19-20
Additional Verses: Genesis 1:29, Isaiah 58:11, Daniel 1:15, Matthew 6:25, John 6:27, 1Corinthians 3:16-17, 1 Corinthians 10:31, Philippians 4:5, 1 Peter 2:2-3

Willpower To Change The Diet: Psalm 18:34, Isaiah 33:2, Titus 2:12
Additional Verses: Joshua 1:9, Psalm 10:17, Psalm 40:12, Matthew 17:20, Romans 6:13-14, Romans 8:5, Galatians 5:16, Philippians 1:6, 2 Timothy 1:7

Beating Food Addictions: Deuteronomy 13:4, Matthew 6:13, Colossians 2:13-15
Additional Verses: Luke 4:18-19, John 8:36, 1 Corinthians 10:23, 2 Corinthians 10:5, Galatians 5:1, Galatians 5:13,Galatians 5:22-23, , James 4:7, 1 John 2:16

Assignment: Try one new vegetable or fruit that is discussed this week. If possible bring some to the next meeting and share with the group.

REVIEWING TO MEET CODE
(VITAMINS AND MINERALS IN OUR FOOD)

An electrical code is a set of regulations established by the government. An electrician must adhere to this code when installing the wiring. An inspector will come to the temple and inspect it to make sure that the wiring meets the code.

Nugget of the day: Then God said, "Look! I have given you every seed-bearing plant throughout the earth and all the fruit trees for your food. *(Genesis 1:29 NLT)*

God does not make mistakes. When He created us, He also made sure He provided all we needed to live on His earth. God gave us beautiful, nutritious food that would not only sustain us but also be pleasing to our palate. Why human beings thought they could improve on God's foods is something that baffles me. God added the perfect amount of nutrients to each variety of plants He created. He added no chemicals because He knew they would harm our bodies. As Christians, we are to adhere to God's teachings, and yet many of us miss the Bible verses relating to nourishing our bodies. God felt our physical well-being was essential and He included this frequently in the Bible.

My prayer is that you realize you must take care of your physical body if you are going to be able to fulfill your calling on this earth. God would not have given instructions on how to eat healthy if He did not see it as essential. If you struggle with eating right, ask God for guidance and ask the Holy Spirit to give you the willpower needed to resist the temptation to eat foods that harm your body. Ask that He help break the addiction of food and help recondition your taste buds. Our loving Father knows best, but you cannot reap the benefits of living a good, quality life unless you listen to Him!
****

When an electrician wires a temple, he has to follow specific guidelines so that the temple does not catch fire and the outlets and switches work correctly. Our bodies need a combination of vitamins and minerals to be able to function properly. We cannot nourish our bodies adequately if we do not know what nutrients they need to maintain a healthy state. I have included a list of the nutrients found in the various foods that God has provided for us. Take some time to become familiar with these nutrients. These are God's code for good health.

Dear friend, I hope all is well with you and that you are as healthy in body as you are strong in spirit. (3 John 1:2 NIV) We all know that good health is no accident. It takes hard work to keep our bodies in their optimal state and allow for healing when sickness is present. We cannot live life to the fullest if our bodies are depleted of energy or are sluggish due to receiving the wrong type of fuel. We are each responsible for educating ourselves and making sure that we are physically and spiritually fed on a daily basis, in order to live lives that are pleasing to our loving Father. *Each one should test their own actions. Then they can take pride in themselves alone, without comparing themselves to someone else, for each one should carry their own load. (Galatians 6:4-5 NIV)*

Do you really think that God would have gone to all the trouble to create the vast array of natural foods available to us if He did not believe nutrition was essential to us living healthy lives? Explain.

_____

Are you making sure you are physically and spiritually fed a healthy diet daily? _____

What actions are you taking to ensure you are getting the right nutrition? _____

If God expects us to take pride in ourselves, shouldn't that include taking care of our bodies and minds so that we are as healthy as possible? _____

Are you taking pride in the body and life that God gave you? _____

Studies have shown people who eat diets rich in fruits and vegetables reap many benefits such as lower risks of cancer, heart problems, diabetes and fewer illnesses overall. Each food has its own combination of nutrients that make it unique, just as each one of us is a unique creation in Christ. Because each food has a unique makeup, our bodies do best when we add variety to our diet. By eating a variation of the foods that God has provided for us, we can improve our quality of life.

When preparing meals, there are some guidelines we should follow to ensure our bodies get the proper nutrition at each setting:

- 50% of each meal should consist of vegetables and fruits, and the majority of this section needs to be vegetables. Try to provide a variety of vegetables with different colors and textures to get a variety of nutrients at each meal.
- 25% of the meal should consist of whole and intact grains, quinoa or brown rice.
- The last 25% should be a protein such as fish, organic chicken, beans or nuts.
- Add herbs and spices to the meal to enhance the flavor as well as to add additional health benefits.
- Remember that when using oils to cook the food we need to make sure it is a healthy oil, such as coconut oil. Use olive oil to garnish vegetables that are not heated.
- The beverage of choice should be filtered water.

I have comprised a list of various foods which will provide the nutrients our bodies need for healthy living. There are so many foods God has given us that I cannot list all of them. I have tried to include the most nutritious ones. If there are some new foods on this list you have never tried before, be adventurous. Remember to make healthy living a fun hobby; get excited about trying new foods and finding new recipes. Take time to study the vegetables and fruits before eating them and look at how beautifully God created them. Enjoy the smells and savor the taste, taking time to appreciate how much love God has put into the food that He has prepared for us. The more we appreciate these foods, the more we will want to eat them.

Each vegetable and fruit comes with a unique composition of vitamins and minerals. To help you become more familiar with these, I have included a brief description of the benefits of the most abundant vitamins and minerals we find in our food. When we become familiar with the nutrients our bodies need and the roles each one fulfills, we can become more aware of the foods we need to eat to ensure we are getting the proper nutrition.

Antioxidants: Antioxidants are critical for maintaining the health of our bodies. These antioxidants are chemicals produced by the body or obtained from fruits, vegetables, and grains. These chemicals neutralize the free radicals, which are found in our bodies and can cause damage and promote sickness and disease. Free radicals are highly reactive chemicals, formed when an atom or molecules either loses or gains an electron causing it to be unstable. Our bodies require some free radicals for normal cellular function. However, when there is a high concentration of these free radicals, they damage our cells and cause many health problems. The antioxidants bind to the free radicals neutralizing them and preventing cell damage.

Vitamin A: This vitamin is key to maintaining eye and skin health, promoting proper bone growth and supporting the immune system. It also helps promote cell growth, which helps develop and maintains the heart, lungs, and kidneys. Vitamin A presents with antioxidant properties helping to fight inflammation in our bodies. [1]

Vitamin B: This is called B complex when it has all eight of the B vitamins contained in it. When individualized, each B vitamin has a specific role to fulfill our health. [2]

B1 (Thiamine): This vitamin helps fight stress by protecting the immune system, helps break down simple carbohydrates and helps the body make new cells.

B2 (Riboflavin): This vitamin helps produce red blood cells, works as an antioxidant and may help prevent aging.

B3 (Niacin): This vitamin helps to increase our healthy cholesterol.

B5 (Pantothenic Acid): Helps to manufacture the red blood cells, sex and stress hormones produced by the adrenal glands and maintains a healthy digestive tract.

B6 (Pyridoxine): Vitamin B6, in conjunction with other B vitamins, helps regulate the amino acid level in the body, metabolize our food, and stabilize our blood sugar. It also helps to make antibodies, improve our sleep and moods. B6 helps the body manufacture serotonin, melatonin, and norepinephrine.

B7 (Biotin): This vitamin helps strengthen our nails and promotes healthy hair and skin. It is essential during pregnancy to help promote normal development of the baby and possibly helps with depression and memory loss.

B9 (Folate or Folic acid): Women who are pregnant need this vitamin to help prevent birth defects and assist with the healthy development of the fetus. It may also help with depression and memory loss.

B12 (Cobalamin): This vitamin, in conjunction with B5 and 9, helps produce red blood cells, which protects us from anemia. It also helps iron create hemoglobin. B12 is needed to help maintain a healthy heart, skin, nervous and digestive systems.

Vitamin C (Ascorbic Acid): Vitamin C helps to make collagen, heal wounds, promote the growth and repair of tissues, maintain healthy bones and teeth and helps to absorb iron. [3]

Calcium: This mineral is essential for maintaining good bone, heart, muscle and nerve health. For the body to absorb calcium, it needs vitamin D. [4]

Choline: This micronutrient helps to maintain proper liver, nerve and brain function, energy levels and metabolism. It also helps with muscle movement. [5]

Copper: This trace element helps with the development and maintenance of our immune system, works with iron to help form red blood cells, and aids with iron metabolism. [6]

Vitamin D: This vitamin helps regulate calcium and phosphorus absorption, maintain healthy teeth and bones and regulates insulin levels. It helps with cancer prevention and supports heart, lung, nervous and immune system health. [7]

Vitamin E: This is a powerful antioxidant and may help protect our bodies from many health issues including cancer, vision problems, and memory loss. [8]

Iron: This mineral is an essential component of hemoglobin. Hemoglobin transports oxygen from the lungs to the tissues of the body. [8]

Vitamin K: This vitamin is essential for bone formation and blood clotting which helps prevent excessive bleeding. People who are using blood thinners need to avoid eating too many foods high in vitamin K [8]

Lycopene: This antioxidant helps prevent macular degeneration and cardiovascular disease, lowers bad cholesterol and blood pressure, helps prevent some cancers, and protects the immune system. [8, 9]

Magnesium: Magnesium is essential for bone and teeth health, to regulate blood pressure, convert food into energy, and sustain our heart rhythm. It also supports healthy enzyme, gene, nerve, and muscle function. [10]

Manganese: This trace element helps with forming our bones and connective tissue, and helps with carbohydrate metabolism. [8]

Omega-3 fatty acids: These are essential to maintaining our heart health. Omega -3's help sustain our heart rate, improve blood vessel function, lower blood pressure and decrease inflammation. It may also help with controlling lupus, rheumatoid arthritis, and some cancers. [11]

Phosphorous: This mineral is vital for all cell functions. It is also needed to maintain our energy levels. Phosphorous helps promote strong bones and maintain proper pH. [12]

Potassium: This mineral helps maintain a proper fluid balance in our bodies as well as regulate our blood pressure, muscle contractions, heartbeat, and insulin secretion. [8]

Selenium: This trace mineral helps with maintaining good cognitive function, controls inflammation, helps with fertility and supports the immune system.

Zinc: This essential trace mineral helps maintain our skin, hair, immune system and aids in protein metabolism. [8]

Journal your thoughts

Day 3

INSPECTING THE ELECTRIC
(FRUITS, VEGETABLES, SPICES, HERBS, SEEDS, AND NUTS)

Once the electrician has completed his work, it must be inspected one final time. Everything must meet the legal safety standards (code) of the local government. Anything that does not pass the inspection must be repaired or replaced.

Nugget of the day: Strengthen yourself so that you will live here on earth doing what God wants, not the evil things people want. In the past you wasted too much time doing what nonbelievers enjoy. (1Peter 4:2 NLT)

It is so easy to get caught up in the ways of this world. It is easy to justify our behavior by the way others act. Watch television at night or follow celebrities and our lives seem calm in comparison. We should not compare our lives to the world's standards. We need to look toward Heaven. We should ask ourselves; are we doing what pleases God? On that great day when we meet Him face to face, God will not compare us to anyone else. God will not accept the answer that everyone else did it, so it must be okay. God has given us His set of rules. He sent His Son to instruct us on how to live healthy, fulfilling Christian lives. We have no excuses. God gave us these commands, not to be in control of us, but to provide us with greater freedom. He knows when we live up to His standards our lives will become less worrisome and less complicated. Living lives of sin have us always looking over our shoulder, making it hard to trust others and causing undue stress in our lives. Eating healthy diets enable us to have more energy and do what God has called us to do.

My prayer is that you examine your life using our loving Father's standards and make a sincere effort to improve in areas you have failed in the past. You need to know our Father is a forgiving Dad. He will forgive you for the sins you have committed when you confess to Him and make a sincere effort to change your behavior. Seek God's wisdom and let Him guide you so that you make the correct decisions as to how to live a healthy lifestyle. Ask Him to help you to restore your temple. I pray that you experience the life our loving Father intended for you to live. After all, God does know best, just trust Him!!!

****

To keep our temples safe, we need to have the electrical work inspected to make sure it meets code. If the work is done incorrectly then the wiring could start a fire or shock the inhabitants. Our human temples also need to be inspected to make sure they receive the proper nutrition so that they do not short circuit or run out of energy. For the rest of this week, we will explore the food that we eat and how they can maintain or improve our health. I have provided you with basic nutritional information of various foods so that you can nourish your body correctly. God has given us a nutritional code, which is perfectly balanced with all the nutrients we need for our bodies to perform at their optimal levels. Let's make sure our food source is up to code. I have given suggestions as to how to prepare some of these foods so that you can include them in your diet.

Cruciferous Vegetables: These are classified as superfoods because they offer so much nutrition. They are loaded with vitamins A, C, K, and folic acid. They also provide fiber that is needed in the diet. They are most beneficial when eaten raw, but can be lightly steamed.

Arugula: This plant is an excellent source of fiber and is high in protein. It is also known for decreasing bad cholesterol and improving good cholesterol. Arugula contains the vitamins A, C, and K as well as folate, calcium, iron, phosphorous, potassium and manganese. It contains antioxidants, which help maintain the immune system, strengthens the bones and teeth, supports brain health, and decreases the risk of breast, cervical, colon, and prostate cancers. Since it contains folate, it is excellent for prenatal care. [1] Arugula blends well with other greens to make a healthy salad.

Bok choy: This plant has many antioxidants, vitamins, and minerals, which are essential for maintaining good bone and heart health and decreasing cancer risks. This plant may also help lower blood pressure, improve sleep and reduce inflammation. Some of the vitamins and minerals in bok choy are potassium, vitamin A, calcium, selenium, folate, niacin, and choline. After chopping it up let it sit for 5 minutes before cooking. [2] It tastes best when sautéed with fresh garlic and ginger. I often use bok choy in my green smoothies.

Broccoli: Broccoli is a cruciferous vegetable, which contains cancer-fighting properties. It has sulforaphane, which may detoxify harmful substances in our bodies. The broccoli stalk also has lots of antioxidants, so it is important to include this in the diet. Broccoli may also help with decreasing allergy symptoms and is good for bone health. [3] Broccoli tastes good when steamed and sprinkled with lemon juice or eaten raw with hummus. Broccoli is also an excellent addition to smoothies or salads. The stalks can be used in soups or stews.

Brussels sprouts: These are an excellent source of vitamins B, C, K1, and the minerals manganese, potassium, and choline. They also have sulfur compounds in them, which help to detoxify the body. Brussels sprouts improve heart health and may help prevent some cancers. [4] They can be roasted and served with Parmesan cheese and a small pat of organic butter. They can also be steamed and drizzled with olive oil.

Cabbage: This plant is rich in vitamins K, B, C and the mineral iodine. It also contains sinigrin, which is helpful in preventing some cancers and has potent antioxidant and anti-inflammatory properties. Cabbage is good for maintaining the digestive tract, the heart, the skin and the nervous and endocrine systems. Cabbage juice may help heal ulcers. [5] It is best eaten stir-fried or raw to retain its nutrients. I use cabbage in my smoothies or make a vinegar slaw.

Cauliflower: This is rich in vitamins and minerals, and contains a sulfur compound, which is an excellent cancer-fighting agent. It also has anti-inflammatory properties. Cauliflower helps detoxify our bodies, protect them from ultraviolet radiation, helps maintain our electrolyte balance, maintains our neurological system and strengthens our immune system. (6) Cauliflower is also good for heart health. It works as a substitute for pizza crusts and is delicious when steamed or eaten raw with hummus.

Collard greens: These greens provide us with vitamins A, C, and K as well as the minerals folate, manganese, magnesium, riboflavin and iron. Collard greens are rich in sulfur and have antioxidant and anti-inflammatory benefits for our bodies. Collard greens can lower our cholesterol, help improve bone strength and protect our eyes. (7) The greens help to detoxify our bodies and may help prevent cancer. They are easy to prepare. Steam the greens for 4-5 minutes and then warm 1-teaspoon coconut oil in skillet. Add the greens and sauté and season with salt, pepper and a pinch of cayenne pepper. When done, sprinkle with olive oil and red wine vinegar. Collard greens are also good when used in green smoothies.

Kale: This plant has phytochemicals to prevent tumor growth and helps block cancer-causing agents from affecting the cells. It is another good source to help detoxify the body and provide heart health. (8) Kale is high in fiber and low in calories. It is a good source of iron, vitamins A, C, K, and calcium. Not only is kale good for detoxifying our bodies but it also helps maintain our immune system, liver, eyes, skin, and prevents bone loss. (9) There are different varieties of kale, which have different flavors. Kale is a key ingredient in many green smoothies and is good in salads. To make a kale salad, drizzle olive oil and lemon juice on the kale and let it sit in the refrigerator for 1-2 days. Before serving, add pumpkin seeds, sunflower seeds, and Parmesan cheese.

Radish: Radishes are potent detoxifiers. They have been associated with helping treat cancers due to the detoxifying abilities and the antioxidants they possess. Radishes have been found to be able to kill cancer cells by not allowing the cells to reproduce. (10) Use radishes in salads and smoothies or eat them raw.

Spinach: Spinach is rich in so many vitamins, minerals, and phytonutrients. It is an excellent source of iron as well as potassium, manganese, zinc, magnesium, iron, and calcium. It has carotenoids, which remove free radicals from our bodies before they can cause damage. Spinach also has folate and fiber to help decrease cancer risks. It helps improve eyesight, provides skin protection, maintains healthy blood pressure, helps prevent arteriosclerosis and heart attacks. It also helps our neurological system and bone mineralization as well as promotes healthy fetal development. (11) It tastes better in the colder months when the frost makes the leaves crisper and sweeter. Spinach is best eaten raw, lightly cooked or sautéed. This is one of the best leafy plants to eat. It is an essential ingredient in green smoothies and salads.

Swiss chard: This plant has anti-inflammatory and antioxidant properties. It is rich in calcium and magnesium and supports our bone health. This mixes well with other greens to make a healthy salad.

O*ther vegetables*:
Asparagus: This plant offers many benefits to our bodies. Asparagus is packed with vitamins and minerals including vitamins A, C, E, K, and B6. It also contains folate, iron, chromium, copper, calcium, protein, and fiber. Asparagus is both an anti-inflammatory and antioxidant. It also helps support the heart, improves brain function, is a natural diuretic and regulates blood sugars. (12) It is best stored in the refrigerator with the ends wrapped in a damp towel. One way to prepare this is to steam it. Then add garlic and sprinkle with lemon juice and fresh Parmesan cheese. Another delicious option is to sprinkle with garlic, salt, pepper, and then roast it in the oven at 425 degrees for about 10 minutes.

Beets: Both the root and the greens provide the body with great nutrition. Beets do contain a high amount of sugar and carbohydrate content, so they need to be consumed in small quantities. The beet offers many benefits for our bodies. It has been shown to lower blood pressure, increase stamina during exercise, fight inflammation and help ward off cancer. It is rich in nutrients and fiber, which help ward off osteoporosis, and helps with detoxification. (13) Beets contain betalain, which helps to purify the blood and liver. The green leaves of the beets are healthier than the beet itself. They are higher in iron than spinach. There are studies using the beetroot extract to fight pancreatic, breast and prostate cancer. (14) The greens also provide the body with protein, fiber, phosphorous, zinc, magnesium, potassium, copper and manganese, vitamins A and C, calcium and iron. Beet greens are good in smoothies or sautéed with other greens. When using in smoothies, be careful to use small amounts at first to help develop a taste for them.

Carrots: Carrots contain beta-carotene that may protect cell membranes from toxic damage, slow tumor growth, help slow aging and maintain heart, skin, teeth and gum health. (15) Cooked carrots may have more nutrients and are best steamed or boiled whole to prevent the loss of nutrients. They are also very good eaten raw with hummus or put into salads or smoothies.

Celery: Celery is a low-calorie vegetable. Celery contains antioxidants, which strengthens the immune system. It also works as a diuretic and helps protect the digestive system. It tastes good eaten raw with hummus, in a salad, or sautéed in a stir-fry. (16)

Chili peppers and jalapenos: These peppers contain capsaicin, which may neutralize cancer-causing substances, works as an anti-inflammatory and promotes healthy blood flow. These peppers also help with weight loss. The heat of the peppers may be decreased when cooked. By removing the seeds and white membrane, the peppers lose some of their heat. These peppers add flavor to salsas, tacos, and salads. (18)

Cucumbers: *We remember the fish we ate in Egypt at no cost—also the cucumbers, melons, leeks, onions, and garlic. (Numbers 11:5 NIV)* This vegetable contains vitamins B, C and K, and the minerals copper, potassium, and manganese. Cucumbers are beneficial to us because they help decrease our cancer risks, maintain a healthy digestive system and a healthy weight. They also act as an anti-inflammatory agent and provide the body with antioxidants. (19) Cucumbers enhance the flavor of salads and taste good in smoothies. To make a cucumber salad, add cilantro, olive oil, and lime juice to sliced cucumbers.

Eggplant: Eggplant provides the body with iron, calcium, vitamins B6, C, K, niacin, folic acid, phosphorous, copper, potassium, manganese, and fiber. It helps improve circulation, prevents osteoporosis, increases cognitive function, decreases stress, helps prevent cancer, helps manage diabetes, lowers bad cholesterol, prevents blood clots and promotes heart health. (20) Eggplant is delicious baked, sautéed and served with tomato and mozzarella, or sautéed in vegetable broth with bell peppers and other vegetables. After cooking, drizzle olive oil and lemon juice over it.

Garlic: The phytochemicals in garlic have been shown to halt the formation of nitrosamines. These are carcinogens formed in the stomach. Some studies show that people who have an increased intake of garlic have a lower risk of some cancers, including breast and prostate. (21) Garlic also speeds DNA repair, kills cancer cells, and helps to fight bacteria in our bodies. Crushing the garlic helps release beneficial enzymes. After crushing the garlic, let it sit 15-20 minutes before cooking. This activates the enzymes and releases the sulfur-containing compound that is so beneficial.

Mushrooms: Mushrooms are not true vegetables. They are a fungus, but I have included them in the list because of their many benefits to our health. Mushrooms help strengthen the immune system. They contain lectins, which attack cancerous cells and keeps them from multiplying. Mushrooms have been shown to stop breast cancer tumor growth and inhibit breast cancer metastasis. (22) Research has shown mushrooms help the body to detoxify, slows tumor formation, halts cell mutation, and protects the DNA while leaving healthy cells intact. They also help lower bad cholesterol, increase energy, improve brain function, improve our immunity, provide our bodies with vitamin D and decrease inflammation. (23) Mushrooms taste good in many vegetable dishes, sauces and salads. Many people have a difficult time eating them due to the texture. Cutting them up into very small pieces may help with this issue.

Onions, leeks, scallions, and chives: Onions contain quercetin, which is an antioxidant flavonoid. They help lower cholesterol, thin the blood, fight infections, and help fight asthma as well as hay fever. Onions may also help lower cancer risks. Onions are rich in sulfur-containing compounds, which are essential for detoxing the body, especially helping rid the liver of toxins. Once an onion is cut, it should be used because it does attract bacteria even if stored in the refrigerator. An interesting side note: Onions attract bacteria when cut, so putting one in a jar near the bed of someone with the flu allows the onion to attract the germs and help with healing. [24] Teachers have kept onions in their classrooms during cold and flu season in hopes of keeping their whole class healthy.

Quinoa: Many people classify this food as a grain, but in actuality, it is the seed of a plant. [25] Quinoa is high in protein. It is considered a complete protein because it has all nine essential amino acids. This food also contains iron, B vitamins, vitamin E, calcium, phosphorous, manganese, copper, folate, and antioxidants. It has excellent anti-inflammatory properties. Quinoa is good for energy production, may help to control weight loss, control blood sugar, improve heart health, and support bone health. [25] The seeds should be stored in an airtight container and will last 3-6 months if kept in the refrigerator. Before cooking quinoa, it is best to gently rub them while rinsing the seeds in a fine-meshed strainer. Quinoa is easy to prepare by adding 1 cup of quinoa to 2 cups of water or vegetable broth and bring to a boil. It can be used as a substitute for rice in recipes, used for breakfast cereal, mixed with fruit, seasoned with herbs or made into a salad. Quinoa also tastes great in stir-fry.

Seaweed and other sea vegetables: These vegetables contain beta-carotene, protein and vitamin B12. Seaweed is a cheap and complete source of all known minerals and trace elements found in the ocean. Seaweed is a major player in detoxifying destructive radioactivity in the body. It also contains high levels of iodine, which helps suppress tumor formation and growth. [26] You can grind up seaweed in the blender and pour into a saltshaker or mix with sea salts. Seaweed can be added to smoothies and other dishes. We must use this with caution so that we do not overload our bodies with iodine.

Squash: There are a variety of squash plants. These plants have many antioxidants and anti-inflammatory properties. They contain a large number of vitamins and minerals including vitamins A, C, E, B6, thiamin, folate, magnesium, potassium, copper, calcium, and iron. Squash helps to regulate blood sugars, boosts the immune system, improves lung, bone and eye health, and helps reduce ulcers. [27] The rind has nutrients as well. Squash is a good substitute for pasta and can be used as a replacement for spaghetti or other noodles in recipes. Purchase a spiralizer and use it to make the squash into thin strips resembling noodles.

Sweet Potatoes: These potatoes contain beta-carotene, which may protect DNA in the cell nucleus from cancer-causing chemicals outside the cell membrane. [28] The rich amount of beta-carotene also helps protect the skin from sun damage and is good for eye health. Sweet potatoes contain twice as much fiber as any other potato. [29] These vegetables are good for the heart since they have large amounts of vitamin B6 to help keep the arteries flexible and blood flowing. Sweet potatoes are also high in potassium, which helps with lowering blood pressure and regulating the natural rhythm of the heart. They also help maintain our brain and central nervous system health. Sweet potatoes contain manganese, which helps maintain healthy blood sugar levels. Sweet potatoes are delicious when baked or mashed with cinnamon and organic butter added to them. They can also be cut into thin slices, brushed with coconut oil, seasoned with herbs, salt, and pepper, and then baked in the oven.

Fruits: The Bible specifically lists six fruits in the Bible. These fruits are apples, dates, pomegranates, grapes, figs, and melons.

Remember that although fruit has many benefits, due to the amount of fructose, fruits need to be consumed in moderation to not cause a spike in our blood sugar.

Apples: *Strengthen me with raisins, refresh me with apples, for I am faint with love.* (Song of Solomon 2:5 NIV)

Apples are a good source of fiber, vitamin C, and phytochemicals including quercetin, which helps maintain the nervous system while decreasing the risk of Alzheimer's. They contain pectin, which is a fiber that works as a prebiotic, so it is good for gut health. Other benefits of eating apples may be that they help with heart health, weight loss, and help fight cancer. (31) Apples make a great mid-day snack or taste good in salads.

Apricots: Apricots are rich in fiber, which is helpful in relieving constipation. They contain many of the minerals necessary to maintain good bone health. Some of these minerals are calcium, phosphorous, manganese, iron and copper. The iron also helps prevent anemia, improves heart health, maintains proper fluid balance in our bodies, and helps with detoxification. Apricots have also been found to decrease the risk of cancer. (32) They are very flavorful and can be eaten raw or dried.

Avocados: This fruit has powerful antioxidants that attack free radicals and may help prevent cancer. Avocados are loaded with vitamins C, B5, E, healthy fats, folate, fiber, beta-carotene and high levels of potassium. Avocados are higher in potassium than bananas. This fruit helps lower cholesterol, protects the eyes, may help relieve arthritis symptoms and assist with losing weight. (33) Use avocados to make guacamole, eat with an egg for breakfast or add to a smoothie or salad.

Bananas: This fruit has a high amount of potassium and pectin, as well as antioxidants. They also contain magnesium, vitamins B6 and C. Bananas help with weight loss, protect against developing type 2 diabetes, improve the nervous system and maintain bone and eye health. They also help with white blood cell production. (34) Bananas are a nice addition to a smoothie, taste good in fruit salads or can be eaten plain.

Berries: All berries have phytonutrients and rank higher than most fruits and vegetables in regards to their number of antioxidants. Berries are delicious when eaten plain or make a great addition to smoothies, fruit salads or green salads.

Acai Berries: This berry is considered a super food; rich in healthy mono and polyunsaturated fats as well as fiber. Acai berries are powerful antioxidants. They may also help aid in losing and maintaining weight, improve digestion, improve skin and cell health and boost the immune system. These powerful berries may also help slow aging, increase energy and improve brain function. (35)

Blackberries: These berries are rich in antioxidants. They have been shown to help improve digestion, strengthen the immune system, aid in skin care, maintain bone health, enhance memory and cognition as well as help with weight management. (36)

Strawberries: These berries are high in antioxidants and flavonoids, which suppress an enzyme that damages DNA, and helps inhibit tumor growth. They have quercetin in them, which helps with heart function and cancer prevention. Other benefits include: helping to regulate blood sugar and possibly reducing constipation. (37)

Blueberries: These are high in anthocyanin, which reduces inflammation. They are also a powerful antioxidant. It is reported that blueberries help to protect the brain from degeneration due to aging. These berries have also been shown to decrease cancer risks, including breast cancer. Other benefits include: help with weight loss, good for the skin, improve vision, help digestion and promote good heart health. (38)

Cranberries: They contain vitamin C and dietary fiber as well as being very high in antioxidants. These berries help prevent and fight urinary tract infections, help maintain heart, neurological, and immune system health, help prevent cancer and work as an anti-inflammatory. (39)

Goji berries: These berries have high levels of antioxidants. They improve immune function, fight cancer, maintain skin, protect eye health, increase energy, detoxify the liver and help maintain blood sugar levels. (40) I love to eat goji berries on my salads or put them in power bars.

Cantaloupe: This fruit is loaded with beta-carotene, fiber, vitamins and minerals including vitamins A, C, B6, niacin, the minerals potassium and folic acid. Cantaloupe helps boost our immune system, maintains healthy skin and eyes, helps with stress and anxiety, and helps with arthritis. (41) The seeds of the cantaloupe are also healthy for us to consume. The seeds provide a good amount of plant protein; they are high in fiber and contain vitamins A, C, and E as well as the minerals magnesium, phosphorous and potassium. (42) The seeds can be added to a smoothie or roasted.

Cherries: Cherries have less sugar than most fruits so they are a good snack to eat. Cherries can help improve sleep. One study has shown that drinking a glass of cherry juice 30 minutes after waking up and then another glass 30 minutes before dinner it will help with sleep due to the melatonin they contain. They are also good for improving memory, decreasing osteoarthritis symptoms, help with colon cancer, stroke prevention and help with skin care. (43) Cherries are a great antioxidant and anti-inflammatory. Tart cherries are a better anti-inflammatory than the sweet cherries.

Dates: *Then he gave a loaf of bread, a cake of dates and a cake of raisins to each person in the whole crowd of Israelites, both men and women. And all the people went to their homes. (2 Samuel 6:19 NIV)* Dates contain fiber, potassium, copper, manganese, magnesium and vitamin B6. Dates have been shown to help women have a healthy labor and delivery when eaten for four weeks prior to birth. They also work as an anti-inflammatory, decrease blood pressure, promote heart and digestive health and relieve constipation. This fruit does have high sugar content, so they need to be eaten in small quantities. They are a good substitute for sugar and can be used to make power balls with a variety of nuts and seeds to provide our bodies with energy. (44)
Powerball recipe:
2 cups pitted dates, ½ cup almonds, 2 cups raw cashews, 1 cup figs, 1 tablespoon vanilla, ½ cup raw coconut, ½ cup cacao powder, ½ cup organic peanut butter, 2 teaspoons cinnamon, 1 cup oats ¼ cup flaxseed, 3 tablespoons chia seeds and 1/3 cup water. Walnuts, goji berries, and cacao nibs can also be added to give more flavor to these energy balls. Blend all ingredients in a blender. The mixture should be moist but not sticky. Roll into balls and store in a glass container in the refrigerator. Add extra water as needed, so the mixture is not crumbly.

Figs: *part of a cake of pressed figs and two cakes of raisins. He ate and was revived, for he had not eaten any food or drunk any water for three days and three nights. (1 Samuel 30:12 NIV)*
Then Isaiah said, "Prepare a poultice of figs." They did so and applied it to the boil, and he recovered. (2 Kings 20:7 NIV)
Figs are high in fiber, pectin, vitamins K, and B6. They also contain the minerals copper, potassium, magnesium, and manganese. They help prevent constipation, lower cholesterol, help diabetes, decrease asthma and bronchitis symptoms, and help in the prevention of some cancers. (45) Figs, like dates, have a high sugar content and need to be eaten in small amounts. Figs can be made into a paste and used as a sugar substitute.

Grapefruit: This fruit is rich in vitamin C, antioxidants and lycopene. Grapefruit helps to decrease cholesterol, prevent kidney stones, protect against colon cancer and may help lower risks of some cancers. (46)

Grapes: *If you enter your neighbor's vineyard, you may eat all the grapes you want, but do not put any in your basket. (Deuteronomy 23:24 NIV)* Grapes contain polyphenolic antioxidants including resveratrol, vitamins, and minerals. Resveratrol is a compound that has been found to decrease stroke risks, help protect against cancers of the colon and prostate, heart disease, degenerative nerve disease, Alzheimer's, viral and fungal infections. Other benefits of grapes are that they help maintain blood sugar levels, help with the effects of aging and may help to increase lifespans. Red and purple grapes are the most beneficial. The seeds of the grapes also contain antioxidants that help with protecting cell membrane lipids against oxidative damage, help protect our bodies against infection, heart disease, aging, and cancer. They also strengthen arteries and veins. (47) Grapes are delicious when eaten alone or added to fruit or green salads.

Kiwi: Kiwis are high in nutrients and low in calories. They are high in vitamins A, B6, C (5 times more than an orange) and E, the minerals potassium and copper as well as fiber. They may have many health benefits, which include promoting a healthy heart, lowering blood pressure and aiding in maintaining healthy skin. Kiwis may also improve sleep and help prevent constipation. [48]. This fruit also can help control blood sugar, help with asthma symptoms and promote a healthy colon. Kiwis contain many nutrients in the peel as well, so it too can be used in smoothies or in fruit salads.

Lemons: Lemons contain fiber, many vitamins, including vitamins C, B-complex, as well as the minerals calcium, magnesium, and potassium. It is one of the richest sources of vitamin C. Since lemon juice can be hard on tooth enamel; it is best to dilute the juice with lukewarm water. When drinking lemon water, keep the seeds out of the water since citrus seeds are not good for the body. Avoid adding sugar, honey or other sweeteners as these may reduce the benefits. Drink warm lemon water 15-30 minutes before breakfast for best results. Lemon water boosts the immune system, reduces inflammation by decreasing acidity in the body and removes uric acid in joints. It also flushes out toxins, relieves tooth pain and respiratory issues, helps with throat infections and acts as a blood purifier. Lemons help reduce digestive problems such as bloating and heartburn. Lemons can aid in weight loss, and help reduce bad breath. [49] Oranges and lemons stimulate cancer-killing immune cells. [8] Lemons can be added to smoothies. The rind of organic lemons and oranges are packed with antioxidants and can be used in teas, smoothies or grated in salads. Apply lemon juice to the skin to help reduce scars and dark spots.

Oranges: This fruit offers us fiber, vitamin C, thiamin, folate, and antioxidants. Oranges are good for our digestive system and may help prevent kidney stones, anemia, in addition to improving heart health. [50] They, like lemons, also have cancer-fighting properties.

Papayas: This fruit provides a rich source of vitamin C, flavonoids, B vitamins, folate, potassium, magnesium, copper, and fiber. Papayas help protect against heart disease, and colon cancer, improve the immune system, promote digestive health and are anti-inflammatories. [51] Papayas add flavor to fruit salads.

Pears: Pears are a good source of potassium, fiber, vitamin C, antioxidants, copper, and iron. They are beneficial to the diet because they help with wound repair, cancer prevention, improve circulation and heart health. [52]

Pineapple: The core of the pineapple has more nutrients than the fleshy part. It has the same great taste as the flesh but is a rougher texture. Pineapple has one of the highest sources of bromelain, which works as an anti-inflammatory, cancer fighter, and pain reliever. Pineapple is high in fiber and helps with constipation. It boosts the immune system, helps with circulation and contains manganese, which helps with bone formation. Overdosing on pineapple may cause vomiting, nausea, and headaches. I have given suggestions as to how to prepare some of these foods so that you can include them in your diet. [53,54] Pineapple tastes good in salsa and mixed into fruit salads. Use the core of the pineapple in smoothies.

Pomegranates: *When they reached the Valley of Eshkol, they cut off a branch bearing a single cluster of grapes. Two of them carried it on a pole between them, along with some pomegranates and figs.* (Numbers 13:23 NIV) Pomegranates are another super food. Pomegranates contain many vitamins and minerals, especially vitamins A, C, E, potassium, and folic acid. These fruits have three times as many antioxidants as green tea. Pomegranates may help with fighting prostate and breast cancers. They have been shown to inhibit estrogen synthesis. Other benefits of this fruit include: decreasing the risk of heart attack or stroke, decreasing dental plaque, helping with osteoarthritis, supplying iron to the blood to decrease anemia, and helping to keep the skin healthy. [55] Pomegranates are a great snack or taste good in salads.

Tomatoes: Tomatoes are most beneficial when cooked. Cooked tomatoes increase the amount of lycopene the body can absorb because it breaks down the plant's cell walls. Some lab tests have shown lycopene helps keep cancer cells from growing. Lycopene is a powerful antioxidant. Other foods containing lycopene are watermelon, pink grapefruit, and red bell peppers. Tomatoes are good for maintaining heart, skin, eye and bone health. They act as an anti-inflammatory and may help reduce risks of some neurological diseases including Alzheimer's. [30] Raw tomatoes are good in salads. When cooked, tomatoes are good in chili and squash pastas.

Watermelon: *We remember the fish we ate in Egypt at no cost—also the cucumbers, melons, leeks, onions and garlic. (Numbers 11:5 NIV)* Watermelon has the highest concentration of lycopene in any vegetable or fruit. This helps fight heart disease and some cancers including ovarian cancer. It is rich in calcium to help with bone health and also helps with inflammation in the body. It may also help with detoxifying the kidneys, macular degeneration, and repairing damaged tissue. [56] The rind and seeds also provide nutrition for our bodies. The rind contains chlorophyll as well as the amino acid citrulline. This amino acid is important in maintaining the immune system as well as heart health. The black seeds contain iron, zinc, protein, and fiber. [57] Use the rind and seeds in smoothies. Cold watermelon is refreshing to eat on a hot summer day or when added to a fruit salad.

Legumes and beans

Beans: *"Take wheat and barley, beans and lentils, millet and spelt; put them in a storage jar and use them to make bread for yourself. You are to eat it during the 390 days you lie on your side. (Ezekiel 4:9 NIV)* Beans are high in protein, fiber, folate, and lignans. Beans are especially beneficial for someone consuming a vegan or vegetarian diet because of the protein it adds to their diet. Beans help fight breast and prostate cancers. Other benefits may include their ability to help lower cholesterol, help with weight loss, and manage diabetes. Beans have been found to trigger migraines in some people. [58] There are a variety of types of beans as well as many uses for these beans, which include salads, chili, soups, and sauces.

Oatmeal: Oatmeal provides high levels of fiber, magnesium, and protein. It contains lignans and antioxidants, which protect against heart disease and cancer. The unique fiber in oatmeal helps neutrophils travel to the site of an infection more quickly and allows the body to eliminate bacteria it finds there. [59] It is best to eat steel cut oats. Steel cut oats can be prepared ahead of time and stored in the refrigerator. They taste good when mixed with berries and seeds.

Brown rice: Brown rice is much healthier than white rice. White rice has been refined, and therefore some of its nutritional value has been lost. Brown rice still contains its side hull and bran. Brown rice contains selenium, manganese, naturally occurring oils, antioxidants, and fiber. Because of these nutrients, brown rice helps to prevent colon cancer, stabilize our blood sugar levels, control cholesterol levels and it protects our reproductive and nervous systems. [60]

Lentils: *They brought sleeping mats, cooking pots, serving bowls, wheat and barley, flour and roasted grain, beans, lentils, honey, butter, sheep, goats, and cheese for David and those who were with him. (2 Samuel 17:28-29 NLT)* Lentils contain high concentrations of fiber and folate. They support good heart health, contain iron to increase energy levels, act as a powerful antioxidant, help alkalize the body and help stabilize blood sugar. [61]

Then their father Israel said to them, "If it must be, then do this: Put some of the best products of the land in your bags and take them down to the man as a gift—a little balm and a little honey, some spices and myrrh, some pistachio nuts and almonds. (Genesis 43:11 NIV)

Then the Lord said to Moses, "Take the following fine spices: 500 shekels of liquid myrrh, half as much (that is, 250 shekels) of fragrant cinnamon, 250 shekels of fragrant calamus, 500 shekels of cassia—all according to the sanctuary shekel—and a hin of olive oil. Make these into a sacred anointing oil, a fragrant blend, the work of a perfumer. It will be the sacred anointing oil. (Exodus 30:22-25 NIV)

And she gave the king 120 talents of gold, large quantities of spices, and precious stones. Never again were so many spices brought in as those the queen of Sheba gave to King Solomon. (1 Kings 10:10 NIV)

You are a garden locked up, my sister, my bride; you are a spring enclosed, a sealed fountain. Your plants are an orchard of pomegranates with choice fruits, with henna and nard, nard and saffron, calamus and cinnamon, with every kind of incense tree, with myrrh and aloes and all the finest spices. You are a garden fountain, a well of flowing water streaming down from Lebanon. (Song of Solomon 4:12-15 NIV)

What common thread do you see in each of these verses? _____

Each one of these verses shows how valued herbs, spices, and nuts were to the people in the Bible. There are many other records of people using these plants and seeds for their health and well-being. They were used to make sacred oils and as gifts to kings. They were used for medicine and to provide nutrition.

This is what the Lord says— your Redeemer, the Holy One of Israel: "I am the Lord your God, who teaches you what is good for you and leads you along the paths you should follow. Oh, that you had listened to my commands! Then you would have had peace flowing like a gentle river and righteousness rolling over you like waves in the sea. (Isaiah 48:17-18 NLT)

The Bible tells us we will have peace when we heed God's commands. How does this relate to eating a diet that is pleasing to God? _____

We often say we trust God and want to do what He commands us and yet, we make exceptions. One big exception is in our diet. Rather than making sure we have the proper nutrition to live a healthy lifestyle to have fulfilling lives we justify eating unhealthy food.

Do you believe God has given us direction as to how to eat? _____

If you said yes, do you eat a diet that pleases God? _____

How can you improve in this area? _____

God does not make mistakes. He has provided us with such valuable plants that not only enhance the taste of our food but also provide us with an excellent source of nourishment and health benefits. These herbs and spices are unique and offers us different vitamins, minerals, and essential amino acids, which in turn provide us with energy and strength. These nutrients strengthen our bones, help prevent and heal some illnesses and diseases, boost our immune system and repair cell damage. We need to get back to the basics if we want to live our lives to the fullest. To use these gifts from God, we need to become more familiar with them and how each one can uniquely provide us with specific nutrients necessary in our diet.

Five of the most powerful cancer-fighting spices are turmeric, curcumin, cayenne pepper, oregano, and garlic.

Turmeric: This spice is commonly used in Indian food. It is rich in fiber, B6, potassium and vitamin C as well as manganese and iron. It is a natural, powerful anti-inflammatory, antibiotic, and analgesic. Turmeric's active ingredient is curcumin, which has been shown in studies to slow the growth and spread of tumors. [1] It decreases the time it takes for wound healing, improves digestion, acts as a blood purifier, strengthens ligaments, and helps minimize coughs. It can help decrease arthritis symptoms. It may also lower cholesterol and prevent gas and bloating. It may improve skin conditions, assist with maintaining weight and aid in fat metabolism as well as reduce the side effects of chemotherapy. [2] Turmeric should be a regular additive to our diets. It is recommended to use about 100 to 200 mg (roughly 1-2 teaspoons) daily. Research has shown that when turmeric is used for long periods, it lowers the rates of certain cancers. [3] For increased potency, use the capsule form.

** If a person is on blood thinners, has diabetes, gallbladder problems, stomach issues or are pregnant they should consult their doctor before using turmeric.

Curcumin: This is the active ingredient extracted from turmeric and is very powerful in treating many diseases. Curcumin is not the same spice as turmeric. It is an extract of turmeric, but because turmeric only contains 2-5% of the curcumin, a person needs a significant amount of turmeric to get the benefits of the curcumin. [5] Therefore, it is best used in the extract form. Curcumin is an anti-inflammatory and antioxidant. Some research has shown that it can enhance the effectiveness of chemotherapy drugs [2] and radiation while it protects the healthy cells from their toxic effects. It is also helpful in dealing with cancer, Alzheimer's, osteoporosis, depression, heart disease, rheumatoid arthritis, diabetes, and irritable bowel syndrome. By adding fish oil, olive oil, coconut oil or black pepper to the curcumin the body can use it more readily, and the effect it has on cancer is increased. [6]

Cayenne pepper: This spice contains capsaicin, which may help kill cancer cells. It also has excellent detoxification properties. The hotter the pepper, the better the results. Cayenne has vitamins A, E, B6, C, K, and fiber. It is a good source of vitamin A, partially due to having beta-carotene. Beta-carotene is not only an anti-inflammatory, but it is converted in the body to vitamin A, which is essential for healthy epithelial tissues. The epithelial tissue includes the mucous membranes that line the nasal passages, lungs, intestinal tract and urinary tract. These tissues are the first line of defense of the body against pathogens. This spice may also help in reducing asthma and arthritis. Its antioxidant properties help with preventing free radical damage that can lead to atherosclerosis, colon cancer, heart disease and nerve damage due to diabetic complications. The cardiovascular benefits may include the reduction of blood cholesterol, lower risk of both heart attacks and stroke. The heat of the pepper helps stimulate secretions to clear mucus. [7]

Cayenne pepper enhances the flavor of many vegetable dishes including potatoes and beans. It also tastes good on air-popped organic popcorn.

Garlic: This is a great source of selenium, which may help to protect the body from cancer. It does this by causing the cells to die before having a chance to spread. It has anti-inflammatory, anti-bacterial and antiviral properties. Garlic may also help with improving iron metabolism. It is best to buy garlic that is plump and has unbroken skin. Store it in a cool dark place since it does not have to be refrigerated. When preparing garlic, it is best to chop or crush it to get maximum health benefits. You should wait ten minutes before adding it to any recipe. [8] It is best to add the garlic after the dish is cooked, but if you cannot tolerate raw garlic add it at the end of the cooking time. Garlic is good to sauté with steamed spinach and lemon juice. Add garlic to vegetable smoothies.

Oregano: This herb has potent antioxidant and anti-bacterial properties. It is also a rich source of vitamin K. Oregano also helps with muscle pain, bloating, heart conditions, respiratory tract disorders, toothache and intestinal parasites. There is a study that shows oregano may slow or help prevent breast cancer. [9] Season potatoes, eggs, pizza, pasta, and meat with this spice. It is also good on a variety of vegetables.

Other spices, herbs, and nuts that are essential for our health.

Cinnamon: This is an excellent source of calcium and iron. Cinnamon has anti-clotting agents, which help to prevent clumping of platelets. It also helps stop the growth of bacteria and helps with controlling blood sugar. The scent of cinnamon boosts brain function. Cinnamon is an excellent source of fiber and manganese. It has been found to help with colon health and protect against heart disease. Cinnamon is found to be helpful in fighting flu and colds. [10] Cinnamon is best stored in tightly sealed glass containers in a cool dark place. Ground cinnamon stores for six months and cinnamon sticks last one year. Storing in the refrigerator can increase the shelf life for both. To see if it is fresh, smell it. It should have a sweet smell.

Ginger: Ginger is useful for many medicinal purposes. The most commonly used part of the plant is the root-like stem that grows underground. It is a very potent anti-inflammatory, clears stuffy nose/congestion, cough, and aids with indigestion. Ginger has also been found to help with decreasing toothache pain, swelling, upset stomach, nausea, and relief of cold and flu symptoms. It is very good for helping decrease pain, including pain from osteoarthritis. Ginger helps especially with decreasing knee pain. Ginger also reduces side effects associated with chemotherapy, including dizziness, nausea, vomiting, and cold sweats. [11] It has been found to be helpful in the treatment of several cancers, including ovarian, colorectal, lung, and breast. [12] Ginger is very concentrated, so large amounts are not needed. Use one or two ½ inch slices in a cup of hot water to settle the stomach or mince up a small amount (1 teaspoon full) and swallow it. It has been shown that a slice of ginger cooked in food may help arthritis. Fresh ginger is much better than powder. Make sure the root is firm and smooth. It can be stored in the refrigerator for up to three weeks. Storing it unpeeled in the freezer will help it last six months. It's great to use to make baked apples, add to pureed sweet potatoes with orange juice, use in salad dressing, put in rice dishes or mix into a smoothie.

Peppermint: This herb has many means to improve our health. Its leaves and stems contain menthol, which is used medicinally, in food flavoring and cosmetics. Studies have shown that peppermint helps to decrease headaches, works as a decongestant, soothes sore throats, eases itching and skin irritations from plants. Peppermint has been found to relax muscles of the stomach, which allows bile to flow more freely helping with indigestion. Peppermint helps to relieve gas. Several studies have shown peppermint to be effective in treating irritable bowel syndrome. [13]
**Peppermint should not be given to infants or small children. Do not use if you have gastroesophageal reflux.

Rosemary: This herb stimulates the immune system, increases circulation, and improves digestion. It also helps with increasing blood flow to the brain to improve concentration.
** Fresh rosemary herbs can be stored by trimming their stems, placing them in a glass of water, putting a paper towel or baggie over the glass and storing it in the refrigerator to preserve the herb for a longer period.

Curry powder: This spice contains turmeric, fenugreek, coriander, cinnamon, and ginger. Because of these components, curry powder helps with detoxification, cholesterol management, has anti-cancer benefits and aids in blood sugar control [14]

Aloe vera: This plant has also been called the plant of immortality and the medicine plant. The Egyptians used this plant for treating burns, infections, and parasites. [15] This plant is composed of 95% water, but it is the other 5% that makes it such a potent healer. It has minerals, vitamins, enzymes, glycoproteins, amino acids, and essential oil that have healing properties. The plant can be used externally for burns or skin conditions by cutting off a piece of aloe, slicing it in half and using the gel to soothe the burns. It can also be used to stop itching and take the sting out of bites or sunburn as well as to keep the skin elastic. Aloe can be made into a juice that helps with colitis, peptic ulcers, and digestive tract irritation. Aloe is now being studied for its potential in curing cancer. Research has shown that taking aloe vera with chemotherapy helps improve the quality of life and reduces the side effects. [16] Aloe is good to add to smoothies. Some people have had diarrhea, stomach pain, sick feeling or skin rash noted when ingesting an aloe vera supplement.

Cumin seeds: These are an excellent source of iron, which helps with energy, aids in digestion and immune function. These seeds are also a good source of manganese. They have anti-cancer properties because of their free radical scavenging abilities and ability to help detoxify the liver. You can use cumin seeds to make tea by boiling the seeds and then letting them steep 8-10 minutes. They can also be used to season legumes, brown rice or mixed vegetables. [17]

Flax seeds: These seeds are a great source of omega-3's and antioxidants, as well as a good source of lignans and fiber. Studies show it may help with reducing the risk of breast, endometrial and ovarian cancers. Flax seeds have been shown to help with clearing the skin, enhancing our mood, protecting against radiation, decreasing inflammation and improving joint health. Flax seeds promote healthy blood pressure, are an immune booster, helps with digestive and eye health. The seeds have more nutritional benefit than flax seed oil. [18] When eaten whole the body is unable to digest them. It is best to buy them whole and grind them yourself since the outer shell keeps the fatty acid inside protected. Grind the seeds daily to get the most nutritional value. If you buy them ground, keep them in the freezer to maintain the nutrition value. Whole flaxseed can be stored at room temperature in a dark place for up to one year.

Chia seeds: A great source of omega-3 fatty acids. These seeds are high in antioxidants, help protect the body from free radicals, and contain the minerals calcium, phosphorous, magnesium, and manganese. They are also a good source of fiber, protein, and healthy fats. Chia seeds also contain the phytochemicals quercetin, myricetin, and kaempferol. They have six times more calcium than milk. These seeds have a longer shelf life than most seeds. They can last for up to two years stored in your pantry. Chia seeds are best used after they are ground or soaked. You can use them to replace eggs in a recipe by mixing one tablespoon of seeds with three tablespoons of water and letting them sit for fifteen minutes. Chia seeds can be used as a topping by adding them to many dishes including yogurt, cereal, smoothies, and salads. Chia seeds will become gelatinous when mixed with liquid; so if you prefer them dry, add to the dish right before serving. Chia seeds can also be used as a breading. Mix the seeds with finely ground nuts and spices. [19] A healthy breakfast could consist of a bowl of steel cut oatmeal, berries topped with ground chia seeds, flax seeds, pumpkin seeds and sunflower seeds. Some people report feeling gassy after consuming these seeds. Most of these people find if they soak the seeds before using them, they will not experience gas. Soaking the chia seeds (also called sprouting) helps to increase the nutritional benefits you receive from these seeds and make them easier for the body to digest. Mix 1/3 cup chia seeds and two cups water in a jar and shake for two minutes. Then leave it in the refrigerator overnight. In the morning add to a smoothie or other recipes.

Pumpkin seeds: They are high in magnesium, manganese, copper, zinc, and protein. Pumpkin seeds also have phytosterols and free radical scavenging properties. Pumpkin seeds are good for immune system support and have anti-diabetic effects by regulating insulin. These seeds are rich in phytoestrogens, which increase good cholesterol, decrease blood pressure, joint pain and helps relieve post-menopausal symptoms such as hot flashes. They have anti-inflammatory effects and may help to improve sleep. [20] They are the only seeds that are alkaline-forming. The best way to consume these seeds is raw. If you want to roast them, do it at no higher than 170*F for 15-20 minutes. Sprinkle with Himalayan salt.

Hemp seeds: These contain all 20 amino acids including the 9 amino acids our bodies cannot produce. They are a great source of protein and a rich source of phytonutrients. They are also the richest source of essential polyunsaturated fatty acids. [21] Hemp seeds help to protect our bodies immunity, the bloodstream, tissues, skin, and organs.

Sunflower seeds: These seeds have the highest natural source of vitamin E. One-quarter cup of these seeds will provide almost the entire daily-recommended amount of vitamin E. These seeds also provide protein and fiber, along with magnesium and B vitamins. Sunflower seeds help keep the skin hydrated, smooth and glowing since they contain healthy fat. These seeds also contain selenium, which is an antioxidant. Selenium has been shown to stop the growth of cancerous tumors by keeping the cancer cells from multiplying. Sunflower seeds also contain magnesium, which can help with improving your mood and help when dealing with depression and anxiety. [22]

Almonds: *Then their father Israel said to them, "If it must be, then do this: Put some of the best products of the land in your bags and take them down to the man as a gift—a little balm and a little honey, some spices and myrrh, some pistachio nuts and almonds.* (Genesis 43:11 NIV) These nuts contain a lot of fiber, protein, and healthy fats as well as manganese, magnesium, and vitamin E. Almonds help with good brain function, nourish the nervous system, help with controlling the blood sugar and alkalize the body. Almonds can help reduce our hunger. (23) Almonds provide us with an excellent source of antioxidants. They have phosphorous which helps maintain healthy bones and teeth.

Brazil nuts: These nuts contain protein, which assists in the healing of wounds and cellular growth and repair. They also contain fiber, selenium, zinc, vitamin C, and omega- 3 fatty acids. They help with digestion, maintain a healthy heart, skin, thyroid and immune system, help with hormone balance, and can help prevent constipation. These nuts are high in calories and should be eaten in small amounts. (24)

Cashews: Cashews provide the body with vitamins, minerals, and anti-oxidants, which are required for normal functioning. Cashews contain high levels of copper and proanthocyanidins. (25) Proanthocyanidins are a class of flavonols, which fight against tumor cells by stopping them from dividing further. Cashews may also help prevent colon cancer. Cashews contain low-fat content compared to other nuts and are cholesterol free. The magnesium in them helps lower blood pressure as well as help with bone and nerve health. They help the body utilize iron properly and eliminate free radicals. *"2 handfuls of cashews can be as effective as an antidepressant since the essential amino acid L-tryptophan is broken down into anxiety reducing, snooze inducing niacin. They have the ability to filter ultraviolet rays thus help prevent macular degeneration."* (26)

Hazelnuts: These nuts contain 86% of the daily recommendation of vitamin E as well as magnesium and the B vitamins. These nuts can improve healthy aging, help improve the brain function, work as a powerful antioxidant and promote heart health. (27)

Macadamia nuts: These nuts contain vitamins A and B as well as iron, fiber, folate good fats, and antioxidants. They help maintain our heart health, decrease our appetite, strengthen hair, nails, and skin, improve gut health, and support our bones and nervous system. (28)

Pecans: Pecans contain the minerals manganese, potassium, calcium, iron, magnesium, zinc and selenium as well as vitamins B6, riboflavin, niacin, thiamin, and folate. These nuts are a good source of energy. They also help to decrease bad cholesterol and increase the good cholesterol; they help protect against cancer and protect our skin. (29)

Pine nuts: These nuts are the main ingredient used in pesto. They contain pinolenic acid, which is only found in these nuts. Pinolenic acid helps to make us feel fuller faster, helping with weight loss. They also contain the minerals and vitamins C, D, protein, magnesium, and iron which helps support our bones, boosts our immunity, helps maintain our circulatory and nervous systems and give us a good source of energy. (30)

Pistachios: Many people consider these a nut, although technically they are a seed. Pistachios provide the body with protein, B6, and thiamin. Three ounces daily of these seeds also elevate levels of probiotics in the digestive tract.

Walnuts: These are powerful antioxidants. Walnuts are high in manganese, copper, and biotin and a good source of magnesium. One-quarter of a cup provides us with the daily requirement for omega 3 fats. Consuming these nuts provides us with many health benefits. They help with weight loss, maintain bone health and decrease the risk of osteoporosis, and improve heart health. Some research has shown that two handfuls of these nuts may assist with preventing prostate and breast cancer as well as decrease tumor growth. (31) The phytosterols have been shown to block the estrogen receptors in breast cancer cells. When eating walnuts, make sure to keep the white outer coating on it since up to ninety percent of the antioxidants are found in the skin. (32)

There many other herbs, spices, nuts and seeds that can benefit our health: too many to include in this section. I have tried to share some of the best ones so you can start including them in your diet. I encourage you to continue to explore this area more as you begin to add more foods to your diet and want to enhance flavor and broaden your options.

Don't be afraid to spice up your diet with these foods. Experiment with them, use new spices, nuts, seeds and herbs in your favorite dishes.

Journal your thoughts

Day 4

MEATS, EGGS, AND FISH

Nugget of the day: remember how the Lord your God led you through the wilderness for these forty years, humbling you and testing you to prove your character, and to find out whether or not you would obey his commands. Yes, he humbled you by letting you go hungry and then feeding you with manna, a food previously unknown to you and your ancestors. He did it to teach you that people do not live by bread alone; rather, we live by every word that comes from the mouth of the Lord. (Deuteronomy 8:2-3 NLT)

When we finally give God our lives, He continuously exposes areas that need improvement. It is as if we are an onion and He continues to peel back the layers. Sometimes God gently peels off a layer and lets us ease us into the new change, and other times He quickly rips off the peel and leaves us burning. For many of us, this is frustrating because we feel as if we will never live up to God's expectations. But we need to look at it from God's perspective. God sees us as His children, children He loves very much. He knows we are capable of so much more. God knows our potential, and He does not want us to look back on our lives and say what if... On that great day when we meet our Dad face to face, He wants us to say, "I did my best. I gave you my all, and I became a better person because of following you."

My prayer is that when God exposes your weaknesses rather than feeling as if you are failing, you see it as a challenge. Also, appreciate that our loving Father knows you are capable of so much more. He knows you are capable of doing good in this world and making a difference. Our loving Father knows you better than you know yourself. Take some time to thank our Dad for not giving up on you. Ask Him to give you the strength and knowledge to grow to your full potential.
****

Everything that lives and moves about will be food for you. Just as I gave you the green plants, I now give you everything. (Genesis 9:3 NIV) There is much controversy over whether or not humans should consume meat. Meat provides the much-needed amino acids that our bodies need to make various proteins. Our bodies need protein for many of our bodily functions. If we are going to exclude meat from our diet, we must make sure that we include some other form of protein. Our bodies need approximately .4 grams per pound of body weight daily. Other types of protein include quinoa, beans, lentils, eggs, nuts, green peas, broccoli, leafy greens such as spinach, oatmeal, chia seeds, sunflower seeds, and sesame seeds.

Proteins play very specific and vital roles in maintaining our health. Proteins are in every cell of the body and provide the structure and support for our cells allowing our bodies to move. They also function as antibodies to remove viruses and bacteria. There are messenger proteins, which are hormones that coordinate various biological processes in our systems. Proteins also work as enzymes to assist in the multitude of chemical reactions occurring in our bodies. (1) When we have a protein deficiency, our bodies begin to break down our muscles, experience decreased energy, have an increased risk of injuries when exercising, and increased risk of infection. It can also stunt our growth and slow wound healing. Protein is also essential for pregnant and lactating mothers. [2]

For some people, our bodies function better when we have some meat protein in our diet. However, the type of meat we consume is very important. If we are going to spend money on our food, we want to get the best quality. Meat is not supposed to be the main staple of our meal. It should be about 25% of our plate. The average serving should be 4-6 ounces. When eating meat in the proper proportion, higher quality meats will feed us for several meals. We should be buying our meat for quality, not quantity. The best quality meat is 100% grass-fed beef, venison, grass-fed lamb, wild game or organic, pasture raised and fed poultry.

When you buy beef that is 100% grass fed, this means that the cattle are fed grass their entire lives. Make sure when purchasing meat, you read the label to make sure the cattle were not given a grain option or fed grain at the end of their lives. Grain-fed cattle are often given drugs to help prevent and heal diseases since they are more susceptible to illnesses. They are given hormones to help them mature quicker so that they can be slaughtered sooner, reducing the cost and time to the farmer. Many of the grain fed animals are fed corn and soy, which can be a GMO product. A recent U.S. Department of Agriculture (USDA) inspector's report showed that there were 211 different drug residues contaminating beef sold in the US. It is estimated twenty percent of these drugs may still be in the meat we purchase. [3] Remember that if an animal eats something, you too will consume it when you eat the animal. You are what you eat so only eat the best.

Benefits of Grass-fed Beef vs. Grain-fed Beef: [4, 5]

Grass-fed meat is leaner: This means there is less fat in the meat you consume.

Higher in Omega 3's: These fatty acids are critical to maintaining a healthy heart and nervous system, as well as assisting the body with handling stress.

Provides us with CLA (conjugated linoleic acid): This is a fat that has been shown to reduce the risk of cancer, diabetes, and other immune disorders. It also assists with weight loss and improves brain function.

Helps regulate the omega-6 to omega-3 ratio: The American diet often allows a person to consume too much of the omega-6's, causing an imbalance between the omega 6's and 3's. [6] The grass-fed beef has up to five times as many omega-3's, which help to balance this ratio. [7]

Provides us with more vitamins and trace minerals: Grass-fed meat contains more iron, potassium, calcium, and magnesium as well as vitamins A and E.

Organic chicken: Chickens are fed grain. When the chicken you buy is organic, it means that they are fed organic feed, which cannot be a GMO product. The farmers cannot give the chickens: drugs, antibiotics or hormones and they must be able to go outside. [8] According to one study, these chickens offer us up to 28% more omega-3 fatty acids in our diet. [9] When given the option of getting organic, pasture-raised versus free-range, choose pasture-raised. These chickens are allowed to forage on the food they prefer: grass, seeds, and worms. Their diets are not restricted to grain. [9] It is important to know your meat source. Some farmers know how to do the bare minimal to sell their chickens as free range chickens.

Organic eggs: These eggs offer your body up to 3 times more omega-3 fatty acids, 40% more vitamin A and two times more vitamin E according to some studies. [10] These eggs have also been found to have higher levels of beta-carotene, less cholesterol, and less saturated fat. [11] Conventionally raised eggs have a higher risk of being contaminated with bacteria, such as salmonella. [12]

Fish: Fish is a very good source of lean protein, vitamins A and D and omega-3 fatty acids. Unfortunately, our waters have become polluted with mercury, therefore contaminating our seafood. Because the fish have higher levels of mercury, your fish intake should be limited to twice a week. Taking good probiotics and eating fermented foods can help reduce the effects of mercury on our bodies. (13) The smaller fish have fewer toxins. The best types of fish to include in our diet are wild caught salmon (avoid farm raised), tilapia, shrimp, scallops, sardines and freshwater trout. Wild salmon is high in vitamin D, which may help block the development of blood vessels that feed tumors. It is also rich in omega-3's, which promote heart and eye health, decrease cancer risks, help maintain good brain function as you age, and reduce the risk of depression.

ANTIOXIDANTS

Antioxidants are essential to help maintain a healthy body. They help to combat free radicals that produce oxidation in our bodies. These free radicals are produced in our bodies by natural cell functions such as respiration, inflammation, food metabolism, and as byproducts of cellular reactions. We need some free radicals as they play a role in many cellular processes. The liver produces free radicals to help with detoxification. The white blood cells use these free radicals to get rid of viruses, bacteria, and damaged cells. (1). Some of the external factors are pollution, x-rays, strenuous exercise and smoking.

When we have an excess of free radicals due to an antioxidant imbalance they can damage our bodies causing sickness and disease. When oxidation occurs the when cells gain or lose an electron. (2) The body tries to stabilize these free radicals by stealing an electron from another molecule, that molecule, in turn, must take from another molecule. This chain reaction continues until an antioxidant attaches to the unstable molecule or the reaction decays. (3) This chain reaction is a natural occurrence in our bodies. When these free radicals are produced at high levels so that the body cannot regulate them, oxidative stress occurs. (4) The excess free radicals can cause bodily damage to the cell's DNA, cell membranes, and proteins. Some of the issues that may occur are: the aging process is exacerbated, mutant cells are produced, and tissues are damaged. Some of the diseases that can be related to these free radicals are cancer, arteriosclerosis, heart disease, stroke, diabetes, rheumatoid arthritis, cataracts, Crohn's disease, and ulcers. (5)

Some antioxidants are produced in our body, and others are from external sources such as fresh fruits, vegetables, and herbs. (6) Antioxidants can be found in foods, which contain beta-carotene, other carotenoids, selenium, manganese, lycopene, vitamins C and E. (9) Organic produce appears to have more antioxidants than conventionally grown produce. The fruits and vegetables that have the darker colors are best since many of the antioxidants come from plant pigment. (7) It is important to eat fruits and vegetables of different colors since each color has various health benefits. Lycopene, which provides produce with its pink or red color, is found in tomatoes, watermelon, and pink grapefruit. Beta-carotene makes carrots orange, and anthocyanins make blueberries blue. We need to have at least 3-4 servings of these foods daily.

There are many health benefits to having a diet rich in antioxidants. These benefits include: slowing down of the aging process, healthier skin, boosting our immune system, reducing cancer risks, decreasing the risk of dementia, improving eye and heart health. Some antioxidant-rich foods include artichokes, acai berries, beets, black beans, blackberries, blueberries, carrots, cherries, cilantro, cranberries, dandelion tea, dark chocolate, elderberries, Goji berries, green tea, kale, kidney beans, lentils, pecans, pomegranates, pumpkin seeds, strawberries, tomatoes, and fresh wild caught Alaskan salmon. (2,6) Herbs and spices include cinnamon, cloves, oregano, cumin, basil, ginger, and thyme. (2) When using supplements, you must be careful because high doses of antioxidant supplements may cause health problems due to causing an imbalance between the free radicals and antioxidants or the antioxidants being different than those produced in the body. (8)

Journal your thoughts

REMOVING TOXINS FROM THE TEMPLE
(THE IMPORTANCE OF DETOXING THE BODY)

If our temples have unpleasant odors, a person will find it hard to stay focused and worship.

Then Jesus explained: "My nourishment comes from doing the will of God, who sent me, and from finishing his work. *(John 4:34 NLT)*

Some people that have a whole refrigerator full of food and sit down to eat healthy meals every day, and yet they are starving. Food cannot only serve to feed our body, but it also is a mask to hide our real hunger. We all need God, and we need to know that we have a calling in this world. God is the only One who can nourish our spirits and fill us to help us find our real purpose in life. We deny our selves wholesome food by not accepting that God is the driving force in our lives. To substitute, we have to feed this hunger with "junk food". Junk food can come in many forms: addictions, unhealthy habits, overindulgence, being a workaholic, spending all the time in front of the television. These are only a few of the ways people compensate for their spirits starving and not having the means to fill them. They can become toxic to our bodies and souls. There is no denying there is only One true God. Idols of any sort cannot replace Him. Christians can claim to follow God and accept Jesus as their Savior and not invest the time in feeding their faith. Rather than looking to God, people look to those around them and never get to fulfill their purpose in life. When we do not feed our spirits with the right nutrients, we starve. Our outward appearance may look just fine, but inside our spirit is withering away. We can experience lethargy, pain, lack of energy and depression when we deny our spirit food.

My prayer is that you realize just as your physical body needs to be nourished several times a day, so does your spirit. You cannot feed the spirit one time a week and expect to be able to stay connected to God and hear His call for your life. Spend some time asking for guidance in areas you are starving your spirit. Let God expose areas that are not getting the proper nourishment. If you have not accepted Jesus as your Savior do so today. Ask Jesus to reveal Himself to you. Spend some time seeking Jesus and let Him feed you. It will be the best thing you can do to replenish the nutrients your spirit is craving.

****

We have studied ways to make our bodies become more efficient, have more energy and be healthier. To best put into practice what we have learned, it is essential that we also detox the body periodically. A good detox will rid the bodies of toxins and allow us to use the nutrients we are fueling our bodies with more efficiently, reduces inflammation, increases energy, mental alertness, and aids in weight loss.

Toxins constantly bombard our bodies. Some of these toxins we can control and others we cannot avoid. One report shows that since the beginning of the industrial revolution over eighty thousand toxic chemicals have been released into our environment. Many of these chemicals have not been tested to ensure our safety. [1] These toxins are in our air, water, food, clothing, cleaning supplies, and health and beauty products. Toxins can be a cause of many of our medical problems. Dr. Mark Hyman has listed some of the most common symptoms of having chronic toxicity. These symptoms include: fatigue, muscle aches, joint pain, sinus congestion, post nasal drip, constipation, bloating, gas, diarrhea, foul smelling stool, heartburn, sleep problems, difficulty concentrating, food cravings, water retention, difficulty losing weight, rashes, skin problems, acne, puffy dark circles under the eyes, PMS and bad breath. [1]

God designed our bodies to remove waste from our bodies efficiently. Several systems can do this for us. These systems are the skin, gastrointestinal (liver, gallbladder, colon, and GI tract), lungs, lymphatic (immune system), and urinary (kidneys, bladder, and urethra). [2] Each one has a specific role in keeping our bodies clean, and when one of these becomes congested, it can wreak havoc on the other systems. Our skin eliminates waste through the sweat glands. The urinary tract works as a filter for our blood and removes the waste through urination. Our gastrointestinal tract converts the nutrients the body does not utilize into stool. The liver functions as a filter to break down and remove toxins from our blood and regulates our hormones. The respiratory system eliminates toxins every time we breathe by exhaling carbon dioxide. (3) The lymphatic system is part of the immune system and transports fluids out of the tissues and returns it to the blood. It also rids our bodies of waste, debris, dead blood cells, pathogens, toxins and cancer cells. (4)

No matter how hard we try and avoid all the toxins, we will still be exposed to some of them. Our job is to maintain healthy lifestyles by eliminating as many toxins as we can by eating healthily and taking care of our bodies. This will help us to counterbalance the effects of the toxins we cannot control.

Even this does not always rid our bodies of toxins that cause us to become sluggish and not properly digest our foods. So what else can we do to rid our bodies of some of these toxins? We can do a detox. We need to do this on a regular basis to allow our bodies to operate as optimally as possible. It is recommended we detox two times a year. The detox can last between three days to several weeks. There are several levels of detox.

Some supplements can be used to assist in this process, and there are a variety of detox programs. Detox programs can be very specific or general depending on which program you chose. The primary goal of a detox program is to rid the gut of the debris that the body has stored up in them over time with as little stress as possible. During this time frame, the body must be fueled with nutritious foods that require little effort to break down. Then the toxins need to be flushed out with large amounts of water. To eliminate the stress on the digestive system, remove meats, dairy products, sugar, grains, processed food, and alcohol during the detox. (5)

One form of a detox is to do a juice fast and water diet giving the digestive system a rest. Another simple detox is using the guidelines established in the Daniel Fast, which requires a person to eat only raw fruits, vegetables and vegetable juices while drinking plenty of water to flush out the system. (6) There are many detox recipes available on the Internet. During this time it is also helpful to include a probiotic to help with the digestion while detoxing. Some foods are an excellent source of probiotics. They are yogurt (with active or live cultures) kefir, sauerkraut, kimchi, kombucha, and pickles. Natto can also work as a probiotic for our diet. (7)

Helpful ideas to help detox your body on a regular basis:

- Drink 8-10 glasses of water a day. Using lemon, lime or orange slices in the water is also beneficial. Water not only helps you to stay hydrated, but it also flushes out the toxins.

- Detox the liver by using beets, turmeric, grapefruit, milk thistle, dandelion root, burdock root and green tea in your diet. (8,9) Asparagus helps detox the liver and urinary tract as well as helps with digestion. (10) Green tea also helps clean out the toxins.

- Get regular exercise. Exercise stimulates the cardiovascular system as well as the lymphatic system to help rid your body of toxins. Rebounding on a trampoline or jumping rope is an excellent way to help stimulate the lymphatic system.

- Another way to stimulate the lymphatic system is to take a hot shower for five minutes and then turn on cold water for thirty seconds and repeat three times

- Allow the body to sweat several times a week. You can do this by working out, taking hot baths using Epsom salts, or using a sauna.

- Make sure to eliminate bodily waste by having a bowel movement 1-2 times a day. This is essential to prevent build up in the intestines.

- Take a good probiotic daily.

- Use homemade cleaning supplies instead of store bought to eliminate chemicals in your home. Many of the chemicals can cause toxins to build up in your body.

-     Take time to relax each day and calm your nervous system. Calm bodies help aid in digestion. Perform deep breathing to increase oxygenation of the body. Make sure to get adequate sleep each night so the body can rejuvenate.

-     Get regular massages. This too helps remove toxins from your body. It is essential you drink lots of water after the massage to help flush out the toxins that were mobilized.

-     Eat foods that are known to help detox the body. You should have 8-10 servings of fruits and vegetables a day with the majority of these being from cruciferous vegetables. Garlic and onions are also effective to help detox the body. Use organic and pesticide-free fruits and vegetables whenever possible. Other foods to include are green tea, seeds, and nuts.

-     Avoid eating processed foods including flour and sugar.

-     Use as little medication as possible.

-     Watch the air you breathe. You cannot control all of this, but you can stay away from second-hand smoke, not visit areas that have highly polluted air and fumes. You should avoid using paraffin candles and chemicals in your home.

** If you are under a doctor's care make sure you talk to the doctor before doing a detox to make sure you do not have any restrictions.

MAINTAINING AN ALKALINE DIET

Our bodies have been designed to perform optimally when they are in an alkaline state. We can test the body's alkaline/acid state by checking the pH levels. A neutral pH is 7.0. Optimally the body's blood pH is in the 7.35 to 7.45 range, which maintains a slightly alkaline state. The pH of our bodies will vary depending on our diet and external factors. The organs of the body will also have different pH levels depending on their function. For example, the stomach is highly acidic because it has to break down the food.

The foods we eat vary as to whether they are acidic or alkaline. Due to the changes in our diets from when we were hunters and gathers, to now being buyers of processed food, there has been a significant change in the overall balance of minerals which affects the body's pH. [1] A diet that consists of a higher ratio of alkaline foods and lower amounts of acid-forming foods will enhance our overall performance, giving us more energy and lower our risk of illness and disease.

There is research showing that an alkaline diet may improve our cardiovascular health, bone density, memory and cognition, and reduce the risk of strokes and hypertension. By maintaining a more alkaline state, it may help in reducing the morbidity and mortality from these diseases. [2] Dr. Axe reports that an alkaline diet helps to decrease the calcium accumulation in the urine, decreases muscle spasms and muscle wasting, prevents plaque buildup in the blood vessels, strengthens the immune system, prevents kidney stones and strengthens the bones. It also helps improve the body's ability to absorb minerals and prevent magnesium deficiency. [3] Other research has shown that an alkaline diet can help decrease chronic pain, slow the aging process and help prevent some cancers. An alkaline diet can also assist in the effectiveness of some chemotherapies since some of these agents work best with a higher pH. [4] Produce that is organic and grown in mineral dense soil will have the greater alkaline properties.

The Acid Alkaline Diet consists of 80% of the food being alkaline and 20% acidic for all meals and snacks.

Some of the most common foods that are alkaline in nature:

Beans: Lima and navy beans

Fresh fruits: especially apples, citrus fruits, figs, pumpkins, tomatoes, and watermelon.

Fresh vegetables: Asparagus, avocados, barley grass, broccoli, cabbage, celery, cucumbers, green beans, kale, onions, red beets, spinach, sweet potatoes. These foods are best eaten raw, however, they can be lightly steamed. Cooking vegetables can deplete the minerals, which help maintain an alkaline state.

Green drinks and smoothies: Green plants and grasses have chlorophyll. Chlorophyll helps to restore the blood to an alkaline state.

Herbs: Garlic, ginger, mint,

Herbal Teas

Mushrooms

Nuts and seeds: Almonds, coconut, flax seeds, pumpkin seeds, sesame seeds, and sunflower seeds

Oils: Avocado oil, coconut oil, flax oil, and olive oil

Sprouts

Foods that are acidic: alcohol, artificial sweeteners, caffeinated drinks, eggs, grains, lunch meats, milk, pasta, peanuts, processed cereal, processed foods (most contain high levels of sodium chloride), rice, walnuts, and wheat.

APPLE CIDER VINEGAR

Research continues to provide evidence that apple cider vinegar can offer many health benefits. Therefore, I have included it in this book. To get the health benefits, it must say apple cider vinegar (ACV) with the "mother" on the bottle.

The mother is the sediment on the bottom of the bottle. The mother is the essential part of the vinegar. The mother is the raw enzymes and gut-friendly bacteria that promote healing. The clear vinegar is processed and does not have any of the benefits that raw ACV offers. When introducing ACV into your diet start out slowly and gradually build up to 1-2 tablespoon daily added to 8 ounces of water. Make sure to dilute apple cider vinegar because when taken plain it can be very strong and hard on the esophagus and tooth enamel. It can also be added to tea and made into salad dressing. One of the most common brands on the market is Braggs Organic Apple Cider Vinegar with the Mother.

ACV has many health benefits: [1,2,3,4,5]
- Cider vinegar promotes alkalinity in the body. It is harder for cancer cells to grow in an alkaline body. The gut-friendly bacteria improves the digestive system by helping it to utilize the nutrients more efficiently.
- The pectin in the ACV can help treat diarrhea by forming bulk fibrous matter. It also creates a protective coating for the colon lining and reduces intestinal spasms.

- It prevents indigestion: add 1 teaspoon of ACV and 1 teaspoon of honey to a glass of warm water and drink 30 minutes before eating.
- It acts as a detoxifying agent to the body by helping detox the liver and cleanses the lymph nodes.
- It helps clear sinus drainage.
- It helps stop hiccups.
- It can soothe a sore throat by mixing 1/4 cup ACV and 1/4 cup warm water and then gargling every hour.
- It may decrease swelling by rubbing ACV onto the affected area.
- It may help relieve night leg cramps by taking ACV in water two times a day.
- It helps fight yeast infections. Soak in a bath with 1/2 cup ACV added to the water.
- It helps fight foot and skin fungus by soaking infected area in ACV and water.
- It can increase the body's metabolism, thereby helping with weight loss.
- It may help control blood sugar levels.
- It helps to remove warts. Soak a cotton ball in vinegar and place on the wart with a bandage to keep it on all night. Repeat until the wart falls off. You must be careful as the vinegar can burn the surrounding skin.
- It soothes sunburned skin.

*** Before trying anything new, do your own research. People taking medicine should talk to their physician to make sure it does not interact with their meds. People taking diabetic medication need to speak with their doctors as it can decrease blood sugar levels. [1] Large amounts of ACV for long periods of time could cause harmful effects on your health and can lower your potassium levels and bone density. [2] ACV needs to be diluted in water or juice since it is highly acidic and undiluted ACV can damage tooth enamel, skin, and tissues of the mouth and throat. Each person responds differently to various foods and drinks, and it is crucial you monitor how you react to additions to your diet.

Food for thought:

1. After reading about diet and how important it is to your health, what changes do you want to implement immediately?

2. What areas do you think you need to research more thoroughly?

3. What are some of your short-term goals for improving your diet?

4. What are your long-term goals for improving your diet?

Journal your thoughts

Week 6

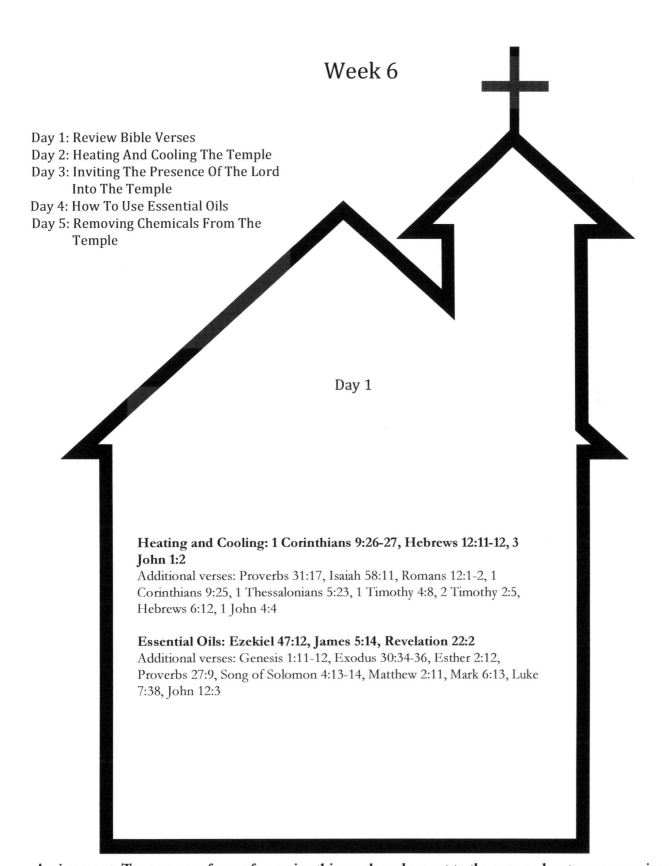

Day 1: Review Bible Verses
Day 2: Heating And Cooling The Temple
Day 3: Inviting The Presence Of The Lord
    Into The Temple
Day 4: How To Use Essential Oils
Day 5: Removing Chemicals From The
    Temple

Day 1

Heating and Cooling: 1 Corinthians 9:26-27, Hebrews 12:11-12, 3 John 1:2
Additional verses: Proverbs 31:17, Isaiah 58:11, Romans 12:1-2, 1 Corinthians 9:25, 1 Thessalonians 5:23, 1 Timothy 4:8, 2 Timothy 2:5, Hebrews 6:12, 1 John 4:4

Essential Oils: Ezekiel 47:12, James 5:14, Revelation 22:2
Additional verses: Genesis 1:11-12, Exodus 30:34-36, Esther 2:12, Proverbs 27:9, Song of Solomon 4:13-14, Matthew 2:11, Mark 6:13, Luke 7:38, John 12:3

Assignment: Try one new form of exercise this week and report to the group about your experience.
Assignment: Research several new oils and their benefits and share with your group. Try one of them in your home.

HEATING AND COOLING THE TEMPLE
(EXERCISE)

A temple needs a proper heating and cooling system so that the congregants are comfortable when worshipping the Lord.

Nugget of the day: Don't you realize that your body is the temple of the Holy Spirit, who lives in you and was given to you by God? You do not belong to yourself, *(1 Corinthians 6:19 NLT)*

This is a verse that is easy to skip over and not take to heart. We all know that we have the Holy Spirit living in us when we accept Jesus, but do you really understand the significance of this? When we possess something beautiful and of value, we take care of it, put it on a shelf to display it properly, or carefully pack it away so that it does not get scratched or dented. However, in the Holy Spirit, we possess something very powerful and sacred. Too often we do not do enough to protect it or value it. We need to take care of our bodies because they house something much more valuable than any material thing we own. Our bodies are a temple, and we should treat them as such. We should respect them and expect others to respect our bodies too. We need to live healthy lifestyles so that our bodies are kept in the best possible physical condition as well. We need to eat healthy to fuel our bodies, and we need to exercise so that our bodies do not break down.

My prayer is that we all take time to appreciate the gift our loving Father has given us; the gift of the Holy Spirit. We need to commit to protecting this gift by taking care of our bodies. Let us realize that proper diet and exercise are not an inconvenience, but a necessity to live quality lives, which allows us to do the Will of our Father to the best of our ability. I pray that we treat our bodies with respect because we are the precious children of God and we deserve what is good. ***For we are God's masterpiece. He has created us anew in Christ Jesus, so we can do the good things he planned for us long ago.*** *(Ephesians 2:10 NLT)*

****

The heating and cooling system in the temple needs to be properly maintained to ensure good indoor air quality and make the building comfortable for the people. Our bodies also need to be maintained. Exercise generates heat in our bodies. The body temperature can be raised as much as three degrees when we exercise. God has given us a cooling system so that our bodies do not overheat. Sweating allows the body to release some of the heat. To keep our bodies efficiently running while exercising, it is imperative that we hydrate it. Drinking water before, during and after exercise is the best way to keep our heating and cooling system running properly.

Exercise is often that dreaded thing we must do in our day because people tell us it is good for us. When we do not see any reason for exercising, lack motivation or have a poor self-image, it makes it hard for us to remain dedicated to exercising on a regular basis. For some of us, our bodies have been a sore subject most of our lives. Our bodies have embarrassed us because people have told us we are too heavy or not beautiful. People often like to point out other's imperfections, so they feel better about themselves. At times, when a person has a poor self-image, they may be afraid to exercise in a place where other people can see them.

What are some of the reasons that you use to keep from exercising? _____

_____

How have others discouraged you from exercising? _____

We need to shed the image that the world projects on us and accept God's truths. We need to see ourselves as God sees us. When we do, we will be able to live our lives more fully. We are not on this earth to please people. We are here to please God. When we struggle with self-image or the inability to break the chains that others have bound us with, we need to ask ourselves the following question: *Am I now trying to win the approval of human beings, or of God? Or am I trying to please people? If I were still trying to please people, I would not be a servant of Christ. (Galatians 1:10 NIV)*

We do not have to be embarrassed to put on a pair of shorts or sweats when working out. We do not need to feel as if our workout is inadequate. If we allow others approval or acceptance of us to interfere with our changing our lifestyles, we will never be able to grow and become the person God has intended for us to become. *Fear of man will prove to be a snare, but whoever trusts in the Lord is kept safe. (Proverbs 29:25 NIV)* God will always approve of us trying to better ourselves and making our temples more efficient to serve Him.

How does it make you feel to know that God is the One you need to please and you should quit trying to win the approval of other people? _____

Isn't it often easier to please God than other people? _____

How can changing your view of exercise make you more willing to do it regularly? _____

_____

If you see exercise as a means to improve stamina so that you can serve God more efficiently will this help motivate you? _____

When we exercise, we need to look at it as a way to get fit, not just as something we are doing to improve our physical appearance. The Bible recognizes that physical strength is a much-needed component of being able to accomplish the plans that God has for us. Without strength and endurance, we will become fatigued and unable to complete our work on this earth. We do not have to spend hours in the gym or perform grueling exercises to be able to do God's work. When we put it into perspective as to why we are exercising, we will be much more inclined to work out on a regular basis. Paul referred to physical training several times in his books. Physical training allows us to do God's work. *"Physical training is good, but training for godliness is much better, promising benefits in this life and in the life to come." (1 Timothy 4:8 NLT)*

Have you ever thought that maybe the reason you are not fulfilling your calling, or in some cases not hearing from God, is because you do not have the energy or strength? _____

If this may be the case for you, what do you plan to do to about this? _____

The hardest part of exercising is the preparation. We often drag ourselves to the gym or slowly walk to the trail, grumbling the whole way as if what we are about to do is painful. We see it as a "have to do" rather than a want to do. After we begin the activity, we realize it is not so bad and wonder why we were complaining about it. Most likely we will start this whole routine over the next day. Exercise should not be that dreaded thing that takes up valuable moments of our time; instead, it should be the activity we look forward to because it enhances our day. Exercise makes the rest of our day productive; it gives us energy, it can change our attitudes, improves our sleep at night and is beneficial to our overall health.

Exercise is not only essential to keep us energized, but also to decrease our risk of diseases, including cancer. Research has shown that regular exercise will cut down the risk of developing cancer as well as preventing its return. (1) Another study showed that the mortality rate of patients diagnosed with cancer was 67 percent lower when they exercised two and half hours per week as compared to the patients who did not exercise. (2)

Overweight women produce and store more estrogen than women who have a good body mass index, which increases the risk of breast cancer. For this reason alone, it is essential to exercise and get into shape. (3) Exercise also helps with improving moods, raises self-esteem and decreases heart disease and diabetes risks.

The American Heart Association recommends 150 minutes a week of moderate exercise to improve cardiovascular health. To lower blood pressure and decrease the risk of heart attack or stroke they recommend forty minutes of aerobic exercise 3-4 times a week. (4) The American Diabetes Association recommends 30 minutes a day, five days a week to improve the body's ability to utilize insulin. (5)

Exercise can also help us recover more quickly when we do face an illness. I can personally attest to the benefits of exercise while recovering from an illness. While receiving chemotherapy, my energy level increased while going through treatment and I lost 60 pounds. I credit this weight loss to both eating a clean diet and working out daily.

If you have not exercised in a while or are battling an illness, this may seem like too much effort. Start slow. Set goals for yourself and work up to the recommended times. Some exercise is better than no exercise. Build in activity throughout the day. Do chores around your house such as gardening and lawn cutting. Park your car farther away in the parking lot, so you have to walk further to the store. Take the stairs rather than the elevator. Get up from your desk every hour and walk around the office. Take a few minutes to do some arm and leg exercises. When watching television, perform an exercise during commercial breaks. Whatever you do, make sure you find time in your day to stay active. Dr. Mercola states that there is substantial evidence that supports sitting for long periods of time increase the risk of disease and mortality even when maintaining a healthy lifestyle. (6)

Exercise is classified as moderate or vigorous. Moderate exercise consists of walking, yoga, and doing activities such as mowing the lawn or gardening. Vigorous workouts include jogging, swimming, and bicycling. Exercise is also classified as aerobic and anaerobic. Both types are important. Aerobic activities focus on improving cardiovascular endurance, and anaerobic activities improve muscle strength.

There are many exercise programs available, and each promoter will tell you why theirs is the best. Many will try to convince you that only their program can offer you all the activity needed to keep the body healthy. I believe, like diet, each one of us has unique needs, and no cookie-cutter exercise program works for everyone. People benefit from a variety of programs depending on their season of life. I change my routine up quite regularly. I get bored quickly, and when I am doing the same thing each day, I burn out and quit exercising altogether. I also need to change my exercise routine depending on how my body is responding and how I am feeling during a particular period.

In the spring and summer months, I enjoy the outdoors and would much rather take a hike on a trail, so I spend much of my summer hiking. Hiking not only gives me the benefits of the exercise, but I also get the benefits of the sunshine. While walking, I put on my praise music and can spend some uninterrupted prayer time with God. It is often during this time that God clears my head and helps me find answers and gives me solutions to problems I am facing. I have found that no matter where I am exercising, in my home, the gym or on a trail, when I spend time in prayer and praise the time passes quickly. I have also spent time walking the trails with a friend. Not only do I reap the benefits of the exercise, but also enjoy good conversation and can share my faith. By doing some form of exercise with our friends, it is an excellent way to "kill two birds with one stone." Too often people choose to visit by eating at a restaurant or sitting around snacking and this can lead to weight problems. Exercise is a healthy alternative.

If exercise is something you find hard to do or get motivated to begin, enlist the help of a friend. It is easier to do something when you are accountable to another person. For me, even on the days I do not want to walk, it is nice to have a friend reminding me of the importance of keeping active.

You can do exercise in your home, at a community center, or you can pay for a gym membership. Many gyms are inexpensive and are open 24/7 and offer a variety of classes at no additional charge. Most exercise routines can be done at home. There are a variety of television programs and websites where you can find workout routines. A person can utilize surrounding parks and neighborhood trails or just walk around their neighborhood.

If a doctor is treating you for a medical condition you need to consult with him or her first.
Because there are many types of exercises a person can do, take some time to explore what works best for you and which offers you the most benefit. Mix and match workouts to stimulate different muscle groups and to improve metabolism. When we do one type of activity, the body becomes accustomed to the routine, and we do not benefit as much from the exercise. The body becomes efficient at performing the routine and burns

fewer calories. Changing up the routine also helps to keep our brains sharp.

Here is a listing of some of the exercises you can explore:

Strength training: Strength training is an integral part of your exercise routine. You should do this at least two times a week. It will help you lose unwanted body fat and prevent age-related muscle loss. Strength training also improves the cardiovascular system and stresses our bones, which helps to prevent osteoporosis by increasing bone density. The increase in muscle mass will help enhance the body's metabolism. There are several ways to do this type of training. You can use body weight (such as pushups, squats, wall pushes), resistive tubing or band exercises, free weights or machines. Before beginning to exercise, warm up with stretching and 10 minutes of aerobics. Make sure to do the exercises correctly to prevent injury. Lifting excessive weights can cause you to lose control and stress the joints or injure the muscles.

There are different weight training programs you can do depending on the results you want to obtain. If a person wants to increase muscle mass and strength then they should do no more than 8-10 repetitions per set using a weight that will fatigue the muscle. When using weight training to tone and condition the muscles, you should do 10-12 reps per set. When you can do more reps with one weight, then increase the amount of weight next time. Weight training should be done 2-3 days a week and cardio training the other days. To train effectively there needs to be a recovery period to allow the muscles to heal between sessions. Therefore weight training should be done every other day or work different muscles groups on opposite days. [7,8]

Yoga: This program helps people focus on their breathing technique as well as improve strength and flexibility. Deep breathing is an essential component of good health. It can enhance a person's posture and improve lymphatic flow. Another benefit of yoga is that it can be relaxing and help focus the mind. It can be performed at different levels so that people with low energy or weak muscles can do a modified version until they build up their strength.

HITT: (High-intensity interval training) This type of training requires a person to perform bouts of high-intensity exercise followed by recovery periods of low-intensity exercise. This program focuses on getting the heart rate up and burning fat in less time. After completing the routine, it can improve the person's metabolism for up to 48 hours. Most of the HITT routines are done using only a person's body weight and can be performed anywhere. Most of the programs take less than 30 minutes to complete. [9]

Zumba, barre and other classes: Many gyms and community centers offer a variety of classes. Check the site directory to see what the center provides. For some people, working out with a group can be highly motivating. Zumba is a dance fitness program, which has choreographed moves done to music. It is a full body workout and helps burn calories. Barre classes help improve posture, balance, and strength combining techniques from ballet, yoga, and Pilates. It uses a barre as a prop to maintain balance while doing the exercises.

Swimming: Swimming works all the muscle groups and is an excellent aerobic activity. The benefits of swimming are increased endurance, improved muscle strength, and cardiovascular fitness. The buoyancy of the water alleviates some of the strain on the joints, so it is good for people who have painful joints.

Walking: This is an excellent activity especially for someone just starting to exercise. Try and keep a brisk pace for a good cardiovascular workout. Brisk walking helps maintain a healthy bodyweight, strengthens the bones and muscles, is a good cardiovascular exercise and improves balance, coordination and a person's mood. Be careful when using a treadmill. Treadmills can alter gait patterns, so if you can walk on a trail or path, you will have a more natural gait. Another advantage to walking on trails or in neighborhoods is that the terrain varies from flat to hilly and can challenge the cardiovascular system. The HITT program can be done in combination with your walking program.

Bicycling and jogging: These programs offer the same benefits as walking. They can be a more intense exercise for the cardiovascular system. Therefore, they are excellent aerobic activities. Some people find these activities refreshing, and they look forward to doing them.

Stretching: This is important to do with all the exercise programs and becomes more important as our bodies age and become less flexible. Stretching before and after exercise helps reduce injuries.

Balance Training: It is always good to incorporate some balance exercises. These exercises can help strengthen the lower extremities as well as improve our agility. As we get older, balance can become more of an issue. Performing activities to maintain our balance can be helpful to decrease the chance of falling as we age.

Video Game programs: For people who enjoy video games there are now many active game systems, which can challenge you physically. The WII® and Kinect® systems offer many options.

Ways to develop an exercise program that works for you:

Pick an activity that interests you: You will be more motivated to exercise when you enjoy what you are doing.

Find the time of day that works best for you: I like to work out first thing in the morning. Before going to work, I can spend time doing my exercises. I feel it helps me to be more alert at my job. You will have to determine what time of day works best for you. Some people like to exercise in the evening because they find it helps them unwind after a busy day.

Stick with it: Your body needs time to adapt to exercise. At first, it is hard to get into the routine, but as your body gets used to training, it begins to crave it. It may take several weeks before you want to exercise and it is no longer a chore.

Work out with an exercise buddy: It helps to have encouragement. When you have a partner, it is not as easy to miss a training session. They help to hold you accountable for exercising regularly.

Use the time for prayer and or worship: You get the benefits of both exercise and God. I know that I can focus more clearly on God when I am active. Some of my best writing comes to me when I am working out.

Hire a trainer: Trainers can give you motivation and guidelines, especially when you are just starting out. They will teach you the proper way to do the exercises and vary your program, so you work all the muscle groups. Using a trainer is another way to be accountable for following through with an exercise program.

Set small, achievable goals: It is much easier to be motivated to exercise when you see results. If the goals are long term, and you don't see change, it will be hard to stay motivated.

Don't compare yourself to others: Everyone has to start at the beginning. People that can perform the routines and make it look easy most likely started where you did, at the beginning. When you expect to complete the exercise routine like someone else, you can get discouraged.

Keep an exercise log: Record your progress. When you do not feel productive or hit a peak, it is nice to be able to go back and see that you have made progress from where you started. It is easy to forget what your baseline was if you do not record it.

Look at how exercise improves your life: Take note as to how your quality of life improves. Sleep, energy, and productivity can all be enhanced with exercise. When you see the benefits in your life, you will be much more prone to continue your routine.

Food for thought:

1. What types of exercise are you interested in doing?

2. What time of day would work best for your schedule?

3. Do you have a friend that would be interested in exercising with you?

4. What are your goals for exercising?

Journal your thoughts

INVITING THE PRESENCE OF THE LORD INTO THE TEMPLE
(OILS AND INCENSE WERE USED IN BIBLICAL TIMES)

Oils and incense were used in Biblical times for religious rituals, anointing the sick, and helping to heal the sick.

Nugget of the day: Daniel said to the guard, "please give us this test for 10 days; don't give us anything but vegetables to eat and water to drink. After 10 days compare how we look with all the other young men look who eat the kings food. See for yourself and then decide how you want to treat us, your servants." (Daniel 1:11-13 NLT)

Isn't it amazing? God gave us all the instructions on how to live the most productive lives possible. It is all here in the Bible. Too often, we think we can do so much better than God. He gives us foods that fuel the body, herbs, spices, and oils that help with healing and commandments that keep chaos out of our world. These are guidelines for healthy living and building strong interpersonal relationships that when followed makes for good, clean stress-free life. And yet people continue to think we know more than God. We believe we can make foods from chemicals that will fuel the body more efficiently, alter the plants He gave us so we can make them bigger, treat every symptom with manmade drugs, make our own rules and allow everyone to do their own thing. We think we can live in a me-centered world and do what makes us happy. Many people think they can live sedentary lives with no adverse effects. Look where all of our "improvements" have gotten us. More people are overweight and struggle with health issues. Don't you wonder what God must be thinking about all this? He knows if we would just listen to Him our lives and our world would be so much better.

My prayer is that you realize God did not give you the Bible to dictate your life. In actuality, it allows you to live a full, healthy, God-centered life that would give you less stress and more pleasure in this world. I pray you ask God for guidance on how to de-stress your life so you can live the way He intended for you to live. You need to realize your body is a temple for God.

****

Then the Lord said to Moses, "Gather fragrant spices—resin droplets, mollusk shell, and galbanum—and mix these fragrant spices with pure frankincense, weighed out in equal amounts. Using the usual techniques of the incense maker, blend the spices together and sprinkle them with salt to produce a pure and holy incense. Grind some of the mixture into a very fine powder and put it in front of the Ark of the Covenant, where I will meet with you in the Tabernacle. You must treat this incense as most holy. Never use this formula to make this incense for yourselves. It is reserved for the Lord, and you must treat it as holy. Anyone who makes incense like this for personal use will be cut off from the community." (Exodus 30:34-38 NLT) Frankincense is an essential oil still used today for its healing properties. It has anti-inflammatory, local anesthetic, and antifungal properties. Research has also shown it may help with fighting cancer. (1) Besides its health benefits, frankincense is used during worship or a person's quiet time to draw closer to God. The book of Revelation also mentions the use of incense during prayer. *Then another angel with a gold incense burner came and stood at the altar. And a great amount of incense was given to him to mix with the prayers of God's people as an offering on the gold altar before the throne. The smoke of the incense, mixed with the prayers of God's holy people, ascended up to God from the altar where the angel had poured them out. (Revelations 8:3-4 NLT)*

The oils used today are not the same as those in Biblical times. They did not have the same technology to extract the oils that we do now. They used oils that they could extract from the plant, but they also used other parts of the plants for healing and everyday uses. For example, frankincense in its resin form was used for perfume and incense as well as healing; cedar wood was also made into perfumes. (2) People used aloe plants for skin conditions and constipation. The entire anise plant (seeds, leaves, and stems) was used for getting rid of fevers.

Have you ever taken the time to contemplate that God created this world with such precision and purpose, not leaving out any detail? He gave us all the essential things we need to help us live healthy lives: spiritually, physically, emotionally and mentally. God has also provided us with a means to heal our bodies when we encounter illness or disease. Take some time to appreciate the love that God invested in us when He created this world.

Many of us read the Bible, take bits and pieces of it and apply it to our lives, but seldom do we heed all of God's advice. I don't know about you, but the more I study healthy living, the more I realize just how great our God is and how much information He packed into the Bible. He included all aspects of healthy living in the Bible. Along with diet, God also gave us essential oils. They are frequently mentioned in the Bible. God intended for oils to be used, and He gave us this insight in both the Old and New Testaments. *Fruit trees of all kinds will grow on both banks of the river. Their leaves will not wither, nor will their fruit fail. Every month they will bear fruit, because the water from the sanctuary flows to them. Their fruit will serve for food and their leaves for healing." (Ezekiel 47:12 NIV)* The last chapter of the last book of the Bible refers to these oils. *On each side of the river stood the tree of life, bearing twelve crops of fruit, yielding its fruit every month. And the leaves of the tree are for the healing of the nations." (Revelation 22:2 NIV)*

Have you taken the time to really think about how important God's creation of trees and plants are to our survival? _____

God began the first chapter of the first book (Genesis 1:29) with this information, and He ended the last chapter of the last book with this information (Revelation 22:2).

How do these verses impact you? _____

I guess God wanted to remind us just how imperative it is that we eat well and that we can use oils for healing while living on this earth. He also shows us that He would provide us with similar types of food and oils in Heaven.

Take a look at how essential oils were used in the Bible to get a clearer understanding as to just how potent these oils can be. Oils and fragrant incenses are mentioned in over 200 verses. The Levite priests were in charge of diagnosing and healing disease through prayer and anointing with oils. (3) There are over 600 references in the Bible to essential oils and the aromatic plants from which they are extracted. (4) At least 33 different essential oils or aromatic oil-producing plants are mentioned in the Bible (4) There are 76 verses about anointing with oil. (5) There are 14 principle oils listed that were used by people in the Bible. The oils listed are myrrh, frankincense, calamus, cedarwood, cinnamon, cassia, galbanum, onycha, spikenard, hyssop, sandalwood, myrtle, cypress, and rose of sharon. (4)

The first time many of us were introduced to essential oils in our lives was when we heard the Christmas story for the first time. Frankincense and myrrh became part of our vocabulary before we ever knew what they were. *On coming to the house, they saw the child with his mother Mary, and they bowed down and worshiped him. Then they opened their treasures and presented him with gifts of gold, frankincense and myrrh. (Matthew 2:11-12 NIV)*

The magi could have brought Jesus any gift they chose. And yet they decided on these because they knew how valuable these oils were and that these oils were significant enough to give to the King. When Jesus was older and His time on this earth was drawing to a close, Mary anointed Jesus with expensive oil. *Then Mary took a twelve-ounce jar of expensive perfume made from essence of nard, and she anointed Jesus' feet with it, wiping his feet with her hair. The house was filled with the fragrance. (John 12:3 NLT)* Jesus understood the significance of this oil and appreciated the gift. *Jesus replied, "Leave her alone. She did this in preparation for my burial. You will always have the poor among you, but you will not always have me." (John 12:7-8 NLT)*

The people who lived in the Biblical times valued oils. They understood that oils had many useful purposes and used them for spiritual cleansing and purification from sin: *Then Moses said to Aaron, "Take your censer and put incense in it, along with burning coals from the altar, and hurry to the assembly to make atonement for them. Wrath has come out from the Lord; the plague has started." So Aaron did as Moses said, and ran into the midst of the assembly. The plague had already started among the people, but Aaron offered the incense and made atonement for them. (Numbers 16:46-47 NIV)* Oils were used to honor God: *Then the Lord said to Moses, "Take fragrant spices—gum resin, onycha and galbanum—and pure frankincense, all in equal amounts, and make a fragrant blend of incense, the work of a perfumer. It is to be salted and pure and sacred. Grind some of it to powder and place it in front of the ark of the covenant law in the tent of meeting, where I will meet with you. It shall be most holy to you. (Exodus 30:34-36 (NIV)* They also used these oils as perfume and to improve their moods: *Perfume and incense bring joy to the heart, and the pleasantness of a friend springs from their heartfelt advice (Proverbs 27:9 NIV)*

The Bible associates healing of the sick with the anointing of the oils. *They drove out many demons and anointed many sick people with oil and healed them. (Mark 6:13 (NIV)* **Is anyone among you sick? Let them call the elders of the church to pray over them and anoint them with oil in the name of the Lord.** *(James 5:14-16 NIV)* God does not waste space in His Word. He only includes what we need to know while on this earth. We need to take time to understand that essential oils have a place in all of our lives.

Food for thought:

1. Do you have a new appreciation for the essential oils and all they can do?

2. What stands out to you in regards to essential oils and what they can do for us?

3. What smells do you find to be effective in calming you, increasing your energy level or bringing a smile to your face?

Journal your thoughts

HOW TO USE ESSENTIAL OILS

Essential oils have many uses in our lives today. They can be used to improve focus, assist in healing, and for cleaning.

Nugget of the day: My child, pay attention to what I say. Listen carefully to my words. Don't lose sight of them. Let them penetrate deep into your heart, for they bring life to those who find them, and healing to their whole body. (Proverbs 4:20-22 NLT)

To whom do you listen? Do you listen to the people around you or do you listen to our loving Father? At times, it seems so much easier to talk to other people and get their advice. But have you noticed that you can talk to five different people and get five different answers? Although people who love us want to help us, their solutions are often based on their life experiences and what benefits them. When we face struggles, we need to go straight to the source and talk to our Dad. He will never steer us wrong because He truly knows what we need. He knows what our future holds, and He knows how our actions will affect those around us. Before you speak to others when they seek your guidance, consult with your Dad. Don't talk freely on your own accord, as it may not be God's will.

My prayer is that you seek our loving Father when faced with struggles. I pray you are patient and wait for a response before you act. There may be a reason God is slow to answer. You need to trust Him and know He will never guide you wrong when you truly listen to Him. When you do speak with others, pray first with them so that God's will prevails. After all, Father knows best!!!

****

How often do you smell a particular smell and it takes you back to another time? Maybe it reminds you of a childhood memory and brings back the good old days. Aromas are important for more reasons than just memories. Aromas can improve a mood, enhance sleep, increase focus and assist in healing. Essential oils are highly concentrated plant components and have been used for thousands of years. These oils serve so many functions and can provide so many benefits to enhance healthy living. Some of these benefits include: using them for relaxation, improving our health, making health and beauty products, improving our skin conditions and for cleaning our homes. They serve many purposes including medicinal, personal care, aromatherapy, and cleaning. Using essential oils in your home to replace scented candles is an excellent way to not only keep your home smelling good but also keep the toxins out. Most candles are made of paraffin wax, which creates highly toxic benzene and toluene when burned (both are known carcinogens). In fact, the toxins released from paraffin candles are the same as those found in diesel fuel fumes. [1] If you want to use candles, use beeswax candles, which are natural air cleaners and produce negative ions.

Essential oils are not actually oils. They do not contain the fatty acids that make up oil. These oils are made from extracting different parts of the plants. It takes enormous amounts of a plant to make the oil. For example, it takes 250 pounds of lavender plants to make 16 ounces of this oil. [2] This chapter is written to help you become familiar with a few of the many benefits these oils can provide in your life. I encourage you to do more research into the many different types of oils and all the benefits they can provide.

Tips for using oils:

1. Use high-quality therapeutic grade oil: pure, medicinal and steam distilled.

2. Most oils need to be applied to the skin using a medium such as a carrier oil or water. Many of the oils are highly concentrated and need to be diluted so as not to cause skin irritation or reactions. Lavender, German chamomile, tea tree, sandalwood, and rose geranium do not need to be diluted.

3. Talk to your doctor if you have any health concerns or issues using the oils. Before using a essential oil,

research the benefits as well as any contraindications. There are some circumstances when a person should not use particular oils. If you are allergic to the plant the oil is extracted from; you will be allergic to the oil.

4. There is a difference between fragrance oils and essential oils. If it says fragrance or perfume, it is not a natural essential oil. Fragrance oils are artificially created and have chemicals in them

5. Be cautious when using oils around infants or children and check all the precautions. Do not use undiluted essential oils on a baby or child because their skin is delicate and much more sensitive to the oils.

6. Avoid certain oils while pregnant or nursing. Some of these include jasmine, lemongrass, nutmeg, cinnamon, anise (aniseed), chamomile, sage, and cedar wood. (2) Before using oils during pregnancy, do your research to make sure they are safe for you to use.

Diffusing the oils: Essential oils can be diffused several ways.

Diffusers: There are different types of diffusers. Some use water, and others us a fan with oil placed on a filter. I keep a diffuser in each room and use a variety of oils in them.

Cotton balls: Place several drops of oil on cotton balls and put them in your car vents. This is extremely helpful when driving long distances because the oil can help energize you. Eucalyptus in your car can help clear your congestion.

Plugins: These can be purchased online and will diffuse the oils in your home or car.

Furnace Filter: Place several drops on your furnace filter to help give the whole house a clean smell.

Bathwater: When taking a bath, place several drops of oil in the tub.

Aromatherapy necklaces, bracelets or pendants: They can be worn when going out and wanting the benefit of essential oil. Some parents find that when their children use essential oil while at school, it calms them or helps to improve their focus.

Reed diffusers: These use a glass vase. Place carrier oil in the vase and add several drops of an essential oil. Place reed diffuser sticks in the vase. If you use a vase with a narrow opening, the aroma will last longer.

Benefits of some commonly used oils: Before using these oils, you should consult an essential oil specialist to learn all the contraindications and proper ways to use these oils. I have included a small list of oils for you to become familiar with and to show you how valuable these oils can be in your life.

Cinnamon: Cinnamon oil helps to stimulate brain function, improve circulation, relieve depression, control blood sugar and sugar cravings, boost the immune system and fight viruses. (3)

Cloves: This oil is an antiseptic and can help improve oral infections and canker sores. It is also beneficial for boosting your immune system, improving respiratory problems, easing bug bites, earaches, and skin problems. They can be used in your home to get rid of fleas or mosquitoes. (4)

Eucalyptus: This oil is known for its decongestive abilities. It is very useful for clearing up congestion and helping you breathe at night when you have a cold.

Frankincense: There is a reason the wise men brought this oil to the Baby Jesus. Not only does it help a person meditate and improve their spiritual connection, but it also has potent medicinal properties. The University of Leicester researchers in the U.K. have brought to our attention that the wise men brought medicine to the Baby Jesus when they presented Him with frankincense. Along with many of its healing properties, it shows promise in treating ovarian cancer. (5) Frankincense can help in healing many illnesses because of its anti-inflammatory properties. It is associated with boosting immunity, fighting infections, arthritis, colds and respiratory problems, digestive disorders, healing skin cuts and scarring, improving oral and uterine health. (5, 6) Frankincense is not recommended for pregnant women or nursing mothers. It can be used in diffusers, on the skin or by placing 2-3 drops under the tongue.

Grapefruit: This oil helps with migraines, improves the lymphatic system, helps treat acne, boosts the immune system, helps stimulate the brain, decreases cramps, eases stress and depression, helps remove toxins in the body and can be used as a deodorant. (7)

Lavender: This oil is excellent for relaxing and helping fall asleep at night. If you do not have a diffuser, you can put several drops in bath water or on your pillow to get a good night's sleep. It is also a good oil to put in your bath to relax after a stressful day.

Lemon: Lemon oil helps reduce stress, boosts the immune system, helps with asthma, aids in weight loss and helps with stomach problems. (8) It is also known for its ability to stimulate lymph drainage and as a bug repellant. (9)
*If used on the skin it is best to stay out of the sun for 12-24 hours after use due to skin becoming photosensitive.

Oregano: Oregano oil helps clear up respiratory problems, is a potent antioxidant, helps rid the body of infections, improves skin conditions and decreases arthritis pain and flu symptoms. (10)

Peppermint: This oil relieves nausea, can be an analgesic for muscle aches and pains and can help with migraines. It is also useful for helping increase focus, boost energy and decrease stress. Some teachers use this oil to help students do better on their tests. Do not use on children under 30 months. (11)

Roman chamomile: This oil helps to relieve anxiety, insomnia, and stress. It also is an anti-inflammatory, aids in digestion, may promote heart health and ease arthritis pain. (12)

Rosemary: This oil has been shown to normalize low blood pressure. (13) It also helps fight cancer, decreases inflammation, improves mental clarity and overcomes fatigue. It may also help with hair regrowth.
* This oil can increase blood pressure so should not be used if you have high blood pressure. (14)

Sandalwood: Sandalwood works as an antiseptic, anti-inflammatory, improves memory, helps with skin care, boosts the immune system and helps decrease spasms. (15)

Tea Tree: This oil is known for its ability to heal wounds, fight acne, gets rid of nail fungus, an antiseptic for minor cuts and as a natural deodorant. (16)

*** Remember many oils need to be diluted before using. You must read the labels and see how the manufacturer recommends you use the oil. Some oils cannot be ingested. Not all oils are of the same therapeutic grade and can cause problems for the user. Research any oil you want to use to see what precautions or contraindications accompany the use of these oils. If you are receiving medical attention, make sure your doctor is aware of the oils you are using.

Besides using essential oils for health reasons, there are many other ways to use these oils to eliminate chemicals that are dangerous to your health.

Cleaning: Lemon and tea tree oil are great natural disinfectants.

Mosquito repellant: Lemongrass, citronella and eucalyptus oils mixed with 1 teaspoon of coconut oil can be used on the skin to ward off mosquitos.

Eliminate odors: Use essential oils in the laundry, in vacuum cleaners, trashcans and in diffusers around the house.

Natural perfume: Apply several drops of your favorite oil on the wrists.

Eliminate mold: Tea tree oil is good for eliminating mold.

Ward off mice and ants: Place cotton balls with peppermint oil near areas that you have a problem with mice or ants.

Food for thought:

1. Were you surprised to learn that essential oils are well documented in the Bible?

2. What essential oils do you want to use in your home?

3. Do you see the value of using these essential oils?

4. What aromas are soothing and comforting to you?

Journal your thoughts

Day 5

REMOVING CHEMICALS FROM THE TEMPLE
(HEALTH AND BEAUTY)

We have worked very hard at rebuilding our temples. We need to make sure that we are also eliminating the chemicals that can be toxic and harmful to our newly designed temples.

Nugget of the day: This is what the Lord says—your Redeemer, the Holy One of Israel: "I am the Lord your God, who teaches you what is good for you and leads you along the paths you should follow. Oh, that you had listened to my commands! Then you would have had peace flowing like a gentle river and righteousness rolling over you like waves in the sea. (Isaiah 48:17-18 NLT)

As a parent, there are times that I am frustrated while watching my grown children doing something that will cause them added stress to their lives even though there is a more straightforward solution. Rather than listen to me, they want to prove they are independent and don't need my advice. It is hard for a parent to stand back and watch when we know how to help our children. God must be frustrated a lot. He has many children in this world trying to prove they can make it on their own and don't need Him to guide them. God does not want us to live in a state of unrest. He wants us to have peace and joy in our lives. The problem is that we are often too hardheaded to heed His advice and follow His direction. God even made it simple for us. He gave us the Bible, an entire book on how to find joy, how to get along with people, how to stay out of trouble and how to keep our bodies and minds healthy. Yet, we continually try and prove we can live our lives differently. The results are frustration, unhappiness, unhealthy bodies, and unnecessary struggles. Can't you just imagine God sitting on His throne shaking His head and asking the same question we earthly parents ask: when will they learn to listen to me?

My prayer is that you realize our loving Father does know best. He knows just what you need and when we need it. I pray that you adhere as closely as possible to the teachings of the Bible. Understand that God did not give you rules just to exert His authority, but to allow you to live a joyful and peace-filled life. So take some time to pray for guidance and the ability to submit to our Heavenly Father. You will find that when you trust God, your life will become less complicated.

****

When trying to keep contaminants out of our bodies, we must take into consideration that the skin absorbs many toxins. The skin is the largest organ of the body and very porous. If you want to rid your body of toxins, you need to not only consider what you put in your body but also what you put on your body. Some of the chemicals can disrupt your hormone balance. It is important to read labels and become educated as to which ingredients you should avoid when selecting body care products. Many of the products used have dyes in them, use synthetic fragrances and preservatives, and are made from petroleum derivatives. If the name of the ingredient is too hard to pronounce or the label reminds you of chemistry class, try a different product. There are so many ingredients you should try and avoid. You need to do your research about the products you use to be an educated consumer. Some of the ingredients to try and avoid in your beauty products are olefin sulfonate, mineral oil, synthetic fragrances, cocoamidopropyl betaine, triclosan, sodium lauroyl sarcosinate, potassium cocoyl glutamate, sulfates, parabens, and phenoxyethanol. [1,2] I have listed some recipes to help you begin your journey of healthy living. The Internet offers many ideas and recipes for clean living.

Hair and Skin Conditioner: Massage coconut oil into your hair before going to bed. Coconut oil also works like a gel on hair to spike it or give it some body. Coconut oil is also an excellent skin conditioner, makeup remover, wound healer, and eases razor burns.

Homemade Shampoo: 1 Tablespoon baking soda and 1 cup of water. Put into a bottle and shake before using. Do not use every day because it can cause dryness to the scalp.

Another Shampoo: ½ cup water, ½ cup Castile liquid soap, 1 teaspoon vegetable oil or glycerine. If you want a scent, add a few drops of essential oil. Mix well and put in a bottle. Do not use vegetable oil if your hair is oily.

Hair Conditioner: 1 Tablespoon apple cider vinegar and 1 cup hot water.
There are many other recipes for natural shampoo and conditioners on the Internet.

Detox Bath: Fill a tub with water and use 2 cups Epsom salt, 2 cups sea salt and 1/2 cup baking soda. Add several drops of lavender or frankincense essential oil. Soak in the tub for 20 minutes to help remove toxins from the body. The essential oils help to decrease stress.

Homemade deodorant:
Mix baking soda (only Arm and Hammer since others contain aluminum) and lemon juice.
Often after adopting a healthy diet, deodorant is no longer needed.

Another Deodorant Recipe
Ingredients:
8 Tbsp. Coconut oil in solid form
1/4 cup baking soda
1/4 cup arrowroot powder or cornstarch
Directions: Combine baking soda and cornstarch or arrowroot powder. Then add the coconut oil and mix so that it looks like the consistency of the deodorant you buy. If it is too moist add more cornstarch. This mixture can be put in old deodorant dispensers or stored in another container.

Homemade toothpaste:
Mix equal parts of Arm and Hammer baking soda and coconut oil with several drops of peppermint extract.

Teeth whitening
Turn a piece of banana peel inside out and rub it on the area you want to treat. As you knead, the nutrients will be absorbed into the teeth. Then brush your teeth.

Acne, pimples and brown spots: Take a piece of banana peel and turn inside out and rub it on the affected area until the peel becomes brown (few minutes). As the skin dries, it will absorb the nutrients from the skin. Do not wash the skin for 30 minutes. Let the nutrients soak into the skin.

Remove brown spots or highlight your hair: Lemon juice can be used on the skin to remove sunspots or highlight your hair.

Soothe sunburns: Use apple cider vinegar and apply with a washcloth or add 1 cup to your bath water.

Lip-gloss: Use coconut oil.

Coconut Oil Moisturizer: Place 2 cups of coconut oil in a mixer and whip it. Add several drops of essential oil. Then place in a jar and use as a lotion.

Avocado Honey Face Mask: Use 1 fully ripened avocado with skin and seed removed, 1-tablespoon honey. Mash the avocado and add honey until well mixed. Apply to the skin and let stay for 10-15 minutes. Rinse your face with lukewarm water and pat dry. This mask is perfect for dry skin.

Body Scrub: Mix 1-tablespoon chia seeds, ¼ cup coconut oil and 1 teaspoon lemon juice together and store in a container. To apply, dampen your face or body and apply in a circular motion. Let sit for 2 minutes and then remove with a wet towel.

Poison Ivy and bug bites salve: Make a paste out of baking soda and apple cider vinegar. Apply to the affected area. It will dry up the poison ivy and stop the itch.

Food for thought:

1. What are some changes you can make right now to eliminate using unnecessary chemicals on your body?

Journal your thoughts

Week 7

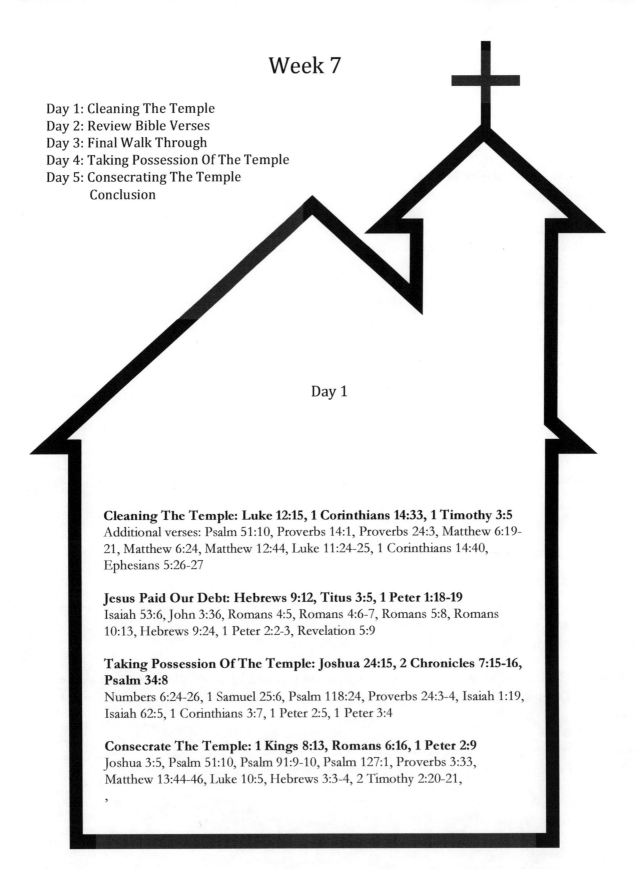

Day 1

Cleaning The Temple: Luke 12:15, 1 Corinthians 14:33, 1 Timothy 3:5
Additional verses: Psalm 51:10, Proverbs 14:1, Proverbs 24:3, Matthew 6:19-21, Matthew 6:24, Matthew 12:44, Luke 11:24-25, 1 Corinthians 14:40, Ephesians 5:26-27

Jesus Paid Our Debt: Hebrews 9:12, Titus 3:5, 1 Peter 1:18-19
Isaiah 53:6, John 3:36, Romans 4:5, Romans 4:6-7, Romans 5:8, Romans 10:13, Hebrews 9:24, 1 Peter 2:2-3, Revelation 5:9

Taking Possession Of The Temple: Joshua 24:15, 2 Chronicles 7:15-16, Psalm 34:8
Numbers 6:24-26, 1 Samuel 25:6, Psalm 118:24, Proverbs 24:3-4, Isaiah 1:19, Isaiah 62:5, 1 Corinthians 3:7, 1 Peter 2:5, 1 Peter 3:4

Consecrate The Temple: 1 Kings 8:13, Romans 6:16, 1 Peter 2:9
Joshua 3:5, Psalm 51:10, Psalm 91:9-10, Psalm 127:1, Proverbs 3:33, Matthew 13:44-46, Luke 10:5, Hebrews 3:3-4, 2 Timothy 2:20-21,

,

Assignment: Try one homemade cleaning supply and report to your class what the effects were in your home

CLEANING THE TEMPLE
(CLEANING AND DECLUTTERING THE HOME)

Construction is a messy job. It is best to clean up as you go along. This way the mess does become overwhelming and hinder yours or the other workers' ability to complete the project.

Nugget of the day: You say, 'I am rich. I have everything I want. I don't need a thing!' And you don't realize that you are wretched and miserable and poor and blind and naked. So I advise you to buy gold from me—gold that has been purified by fire. Then you will be rich. Also buy white garments from me so you will not be shamed by your nakedness, and ointment for your eyes so you will be able to see. *(Revelations 3:17-18 NLT)*

This world loves to give us a false sense of security. The world tells us we are nobodies if we don't drive a nice car, live in a big house or have designer clothes. There is nothing wrong with having nice things as long as we understand these things do not define us. What truly matters is our faith and how we live our lives. What if people could see straight into one another's souls? What would others see in your soul? Is your soul nicely clad, pure in thoughts, clean in actions or is your soul tattered with impure thoughts and dark with sin? God sees our soul. He does not even look at our outer appearance. On that great day when we meet Him face to face, we will stand before Him baring our souls.

My prayer is that we all prioritize our lives. We remove things that bog us down and obstruct us from living healthy lives. I pray you realize that God loves you regardless of your material wealth. Ask God to help you remove obstacles that obstruct your relationship with Him. Decluttering our lives of material things is freeing and allows us to focus on what is important. Vow to stay committed to our loving Father. To borrow my favorite quote from the movie God's Not Dead "Sometimes the devil allows people to live a life free of trouble because he doesn't want them turning to God. Their sin is like a jail cell, except it is all nice and comfy and there doesn't seem to be any reason to leave. The door's wide open. Till one day, time runs out, and the cell door slams shut, and suddenly it's too late." (1)
****

We all know what clutter can do in a temple. The build-up of clutter and debris can happen quickly and without much warning. While we are remodeling our temples, we need to make sure to keep this mess under control so that we can continue to build. If the distractions become too much, we will not be able to continue working on our temples. Every so often we need to stop and work on cleaning up our rooms.

For if a man cannot manage his own household, how can he take care of God's church? (1 Timothy 3:5 NLT) We often do not take the time to realize how our homes can affect our moods, the relationships with our family, our ability to spend time in God's Word and respond to our callings. When we are at peace, the immune system has a greater ability to fight and heal us. Taking care of our homes requires us to establish our priorities. We need to make decisions as to whether our house is going to be calm and peaceful or chaotic. No one intentionally decides that his or her house is going to be chaotic. We all want to have a home that is inviting and can allow us to relax after a hectic day. We need to make conscious decisions as to how our homes look. The décor, the knick-knacks that we set around our homes, and the clutter can affect how we feel. We have to ask ourselves who are we trying to impress with the way our home looks? This may seem like a trivial question, but whom are you trying to impress? Too often people believe the look of their home determines their self-worth and how others see them. Instead of going for comfort, people design their homes to look as if it is something out of a magazine. Rather than being able to relax, they are worried about the formal appearance of their home. Then there is the other extreme, where people believe the more they have the better off they appear. *Then he said, "Beware! Guard against every kind of greed. Life is not measured by how much you own. (Luke 12:15 NLT)*

People tend to collect "stuff". At first, a collection or hobby can be fun, but some times it takes over our homes and life. What once was fun and relaxing now becomes a chore to manage. Clutter can cause us to become distracted and take away from the things that should be a priority in our lives: things such as spending time in God's presence and restoring our bodies. We need to evaluate our colors and patterns in our homes. Sometimes the colors we choose to paint our rooms can be fun and exciting initially, but eventually prove to be too stimulating for us to relax fully. If we truly want to allow ourselves, family members and guests to find our homes warm and inviting, we need to take an honest look at how our homes are set up. Our homes can be an unsuspecting cause of chaos in our lives, putting our brains and family on overload. Research has shown there is a link between depression, stress, anxiety and clutter. When a family is used to the clutter they do not always recognize the correlation because the clutter has been part of their home life for awhile.

Take some time to walk through your house, as a visitor might and try and see the home with a fresh set of eyes.

When you enter your home, does it look warm and inviting so that you want to relax or do you feel as if you are in a display home and everything needs to be kept in perfect order. Rather than being able to relax, do you feel as if you need to be formal and/or straighten anything that is out of order?

_____

Look around. Does the clutter or amount of knick-knacks that are displayed easily distract you? _ Are your eyes constantly moving around the room so that you are unable to focus on another person or the task at hand?

Do you feel as if you have to spend time rearranging to make room for more stuff? _____

How are your color choices and patterns affecting you? Sometimes bright colors are fun and exciting, but when the newness wears off they can be over stimulating. Take a look around and see how the colors affect your mood.

I can personally attest to how a house can affect life. I was a collector. I loved to collect many different things and displayed them in every room. I became a slave to my home. Rather than enjoy it, I felt as if I constantly had to dust and clean it. I always had to make room for new pieces I brought into my home. It was a constant battle to keep up with everything I owned. I got to a point where I no longer enjoyed the things, instead I felt obligated to keep building the collections and finding new places to display them. I always felt as if I was in constant motion in my house. Between raising three boys and having to keep up with a chaotic house it was hard to relax. Nine years ago all this changed. I made the changes gradually. At first, it was hard to declutter and let go of my possessions, but as time went on it became easier and more freeing. I was finally able to clean my house in a few hours instead of it taking days.

I now look forward to coming home and enjoy being there. I know I will be able to relax. I still have knick-knacks that mean something to me, but they are neatly displayed. I have repainted my rooms so that the colors are bold and warm. I use Himalayan salt lamps, which are not only beneficial for my health but also give a warm glow to the room. I have oil diffusers in each room so that I enjoy the smell. My home is no longer a place of chaos, but a haven that I look forward to at the end of the day and miss when I am gone.

Not only do colors and décor affect our well-being, but smells also play a role in this. What odors or smells would a visitor notice? _____

Can you think of ways materialism has controlled your home life and/or you personally? _____

_____

If the answer is yes, what can you do about it? _____

Remember change does not occur overnight. Do not attempt to make drastic changes quickly or you may revert to your old habits. The sooner you release yourself from the bonds of materialism, the sooner you will be able to direct your attention to the things that really matter.

Not only do our décor and clutter affect our healthy lifestyles, but also what we use to clean our homes can have a significant impact on our health. We need to be careful as to how we clean our houses so that we are not polluting them with toxins. The media tells us that everything should be convenient. The store shelves are stocked with many cleaning supplies that we are told will make our lives much easier, but they are toxic. Many chemicals in our kitchens and bathrooms have been shown to cause health problems. They should be eliminated if possible.

Create in me a clean heart, O God. Renew a loyal spirit within me. (Psalm 51:10 NLT) As we recite this verse let's not only pray for a clean heart but a clean home; a home that renews our energy and gives us peace. In order to live in a relaxing home, we need it to be clean. This requires us to use some cleaning supplies. Store bought cleaning supplies can be expensive, and they contain many toxic chemicals. Many of the chemicals are known or are suspected carcinogens. If we are eating healthy and keeping chemicals out of our diet, we should also keep them out of our homes. We must be cautious of products that claim to be "green", "biodegradable" or "natural". There are not many regulations, and so these labels can be used loosely. Manufacturers are not obligated by U.S. law to list all ingredients in consumer products. Therefore, many substances can be used that cause people with allergies or respiratory problems to present with symptoms such as headaches, lung irritations, cough, watery eyes, and sneezing. [2,3] One study revealed that using cleaning sprays has the same effect on a person's health as smoking a pack of cigarettes every day. [4] The women in the study had a decreased lung capacity and increased rate of asthma. Another study showed that nurses who cleaned surfaces with disinfectants regularly had a significant increase in lung disease. [5]

Many commercial product containers have WARNING or DANGER written on the label. All one has to do is read the container to see the range of adverse effects these chemicals can have on your body. These side effects can vary from acute symptoms such as respiratory problems, skin and eye irritations to chronic problems with the lungs, hormone disruption, heart problems and even cancer. Bathroom cleaning products, for example, can cause light-headedness, dizziness and breathing difficulty. Some companies make safe, natural cleaning products, but you need to do your homework before using them to make sure the product is safe.

Although these chemicals may be convenient and advertise that they require less work to clean our homes, we are compromising our health. Which is more important: using a little elbow grease and keeping our bodies free from toxic chemicals or saving a few minutes and exposing ourselves to health hazards? You need to choose health over convenience, and homemade products will accomplish this. I have found that homemade products do just as good, if not a better job without the harmful chemicals. They do not take any more time to get the same results.

It is not difficult to make your cleaning supplies. Many of them can be made in a short period of time. I bought spray bottles with different color lids to hold my cleaners. I then labeled them with the name and ingredients. I have included my labels for your use.

Shopping List for making cleaning supplies:
Spray bottles
Funnel
Rubbing alcohol
Dawn dish soap
Cornstarch
Olive oil
Lemon juice
White vinegar
Baking soda
Ivory soap
Borax
Washing soda
Hydrogen peroxide
Cream of tartar

A couple of drops of essential oils can be added to the cleaners to give your home a pleasant smell.

Glass cleaner:
1/4 cup rubbing alcohol
1 Tbsp. cornstarch
2 cups warm water
Pour all into a bottle and shake well.

Dusting spray:
2 tsp. olive oil
1 tsp. lemon juice
1/4 cup white vinegar
1-cup warm water
Pour all into a bottle and shake well.

Tub and shower cleaner:
1 part vinegar
1 part Dawn
Heat the vinegar so that the ingredients mix together. Spray on the tub or shower and let sit for several minutes and then rinse. For heavy soap scum, allow the mixture to sit on the area for a longer time.

Lime buildup on faucets:
Cut a lemon and rub it on the faucet. Let it sit overnight and then wipe with a damp cloth.

All-purpose cleaner:
2 tsp. baking soda
4 Tbsp. Dawn
1 1/2 cup water
Spray and wipe

Cabinet and wood floor cleaner:
1 part vinegar
1 part water
Few drops olive oil
Spray and wipe

Stove cleaner:
1 Tbsp. of salt
1 Tbsp. of baking soda
1 Tbsp. of water
Mix to form a paste. Use a cloth dipped in the paste to clean the stove.

Pots and Pans:
Baking soda works well to clean most pots and pans. Mix baking soda with water to make a paste and then let it sit for several minutes before scrubbing the pot or pan.
If this does not work, place 1-cup vinegar and some water into the pan and bring it to a boil. Then remove the pan and add 3 Tablespoons of baking soda. After it is done fizzing, drain the excess liquid and scrub with the remaining paste.

Unclog your sink:
Pour ½ cup vinegar and 1/2 box baking soda down the drain

Put the plug in the drain and hold in place until it stops fizzing
Wait 30 minutes and then pour boiling water down the drain and the sink should drain. If it does not work the first time repeat this process.

Laundry detergent:
Soap Nuts: These nuts are actually berries, found in the Himalayans, and they contain soap in them. Soap nuts are gentle on the skin, so they are a good alternative for people with sensitive skin. I use them for my laundry and get good results. This is an inexpensive alternative to buying laundry detergent. 4-5 nuts are placed in a muslin bag and can be reused for 4-5 loads. The soap nuts can be ordered on the Internet.

Homemade Laundry detergent:
1 bar of Ivory soap
1 box of washing soda
1 box of Borax
Heat 4 cups of water in a pan just before it boils. When done, shave the Ivory soap into the water and stir until dissolved. Fill a 5-gallon bucket with 3 gallons of hot water and mix in the Ivory soap mixture and stir. Then add 1 cup washing soda and 1/2 cup borax and stir. Let it sit overnight and then pour into cleaned out detergent bottles.

Granite counter cleaner:
3 drops Dawn dish soap
1/4 cup rubbing alcohol
1 cup water
Several drops essential oil (optional to give good smell) After cleaning, buff the countertop with a dry rag.

Whiten clothes
Add 1/2 cup lemon juice to the rinse cycle

Carpet cleaner:
Pour a small amount of white vinegar onto the carpet to cover the stain.
Sprinkle baking soda over the stain. Let this bubble up and absorb the stain. Rub away the stain with a damp white cloth.

Weed Killer:
1-gallon vinegar
2 cups Epsom salt
¼ cup Dawn dish soap
Mix and spray

Car window de-icer:
2/3 cup vinegar
1/3 cup water
Spray on car windows and melt away the ice.

Grout cleaner:
Lemon juice
1-2 teaspoons cream of tartar
Mix to make a paste and then use a toothbrush to apply. Rinse off the paste.

Dirt and Rust stains:
Lemon juice mixed with salt will help remove these stains.

Air fresheners:
Air fresheners and candles can be very toxic to our bodies.
I like to use essential oil diffusers in my rooms. These are easy to use. The diffusers can be bought online or at most health food store. Be sure to use pure essential oils

In my car, I put essential oil on cotton balls and put it in the vent. So when the air blows out of the vent, I can clean the air. There are also diffusers for the car that you can purchase.

Baking soda is also very good at removing odors.

Garbage disposal:
Use cut lemons to rid the disposal of any odors.

Cream of tartar (a natural bleach)
Use a few tablespoons of cream of tartar with hot water or hydrogen peroxide to clean any rusty drains, stains in sinks or in aluminum pans that are discolored.

Porcelain sink, tub, and commode: Rub the porcelain surfaces with cream of tartar to get rid of the stains.

Fabric stain: Mix a few teaspoons of cream of tartar with some glycerin and then spray on the stain.

Dishwasher: Use vinegar in the rinse dispenser to get rid of streaks and spots.

Walls: Mix 1cup vinegar to a gallon of water and then clean with a rag.

Hydrogen Peroxide: This works as a disinfectant and as a bleach substitute. It can be used on cutting boards, to clean refrigerators, bathrooms and on grout. To use on grout, scrub with a toothbrush along the lines.

Clean silver: Boil water in a large pot, getting the water as hot as possible. Remove it from the heat and place tinfoil in the bottom of the pot. Next put the silver in the pot and then pour baking soda over it. It will fizz, and the tarnish will be removed. It works well, getting into all the crevices. Then wash the silver with soapy water to remove the film. This technique requires no elbow grease.

***Whenever trying a new cleaning supply, it is best to try on an inconspicuous area first to make sure it will not leave a spot or harm the fabric. Make sure to read all cleaning instructions in owner's manuals or consult with the manufacturer of the product you are cleaning if you are unsure of the precautions of using certain ingredients.

Food for thought:

1. Do you see the value of eliminating cleaning products that can be hazardous from your household?

2. What are you going to do to do to decrease the number of chemicals in your home?

Journal your thoughts

I AM F.E.D.

Glass Cleaner

¼ cup rubbing alcohol
1 Tablespoon cornstarch
2 cups warm water

I AM F.E.D.

Dusting Spray

2 teaspoons Olive Oil
1 teaspoon lemon juice
¼ cup white vinegar
1 cup warm water

I AM F.E.D.

Tub and Shower Cleaner

1 part vinegar
1 part Dawn dish soap
Spray on and let sit for a short period on time
and then wipe and rinse off.

I AM F.E.D.

All Purpose Cleaner

2 Teaspoons baking soda
4 Tablespoons white vinegar
½ teaspoon dawn
1 ½ cups water

I AM F.E.D.

Homemade Laundry detergent:
1 bar of Ivory soap
1 box of washing soda
1 box of Borax
Heat 4 cups of water in a pan just before it boils. When done shave the Ivory soap into the water and stir until dissolved. Fill a 5-gallon bucket with 3 gallons of hot water and mix in the Ivory Soap mixture and stir. Then add 1 cup washing soda and 1/2 cup borax and stir. Let sit overnight and then pour into cleaned out detergent bottles.

I AM F.E.D.

Car window de-icer:
2/3 vinegar
1/3 water
Spray on car windows and melt away the ice.

I AM F.E.D.

Weed Killer:
1 gallon vinegar
2 cups Epsom salt
¼ cup Dawn dish soap
Mix and spray

I AM F.E.D.

Cabinet and wood floor cleaner:
1 part vinegar
1 part water
Few drops olive oil
Spray and wipe

133

FINAL WALK-THROUGH
(REVIEWING YOUR GOALS)

Before the owner accepts the completed job, there is a final walk through. Each part of the temple must be inspected to check for any problems. If there are problems, the builder addresses them before giving the temple the seal of completion.

Nugget of the day: And so, dear brothers and sisters, I plead with you to give your bodies to God because of all he has done for you. Let them be a living and holy sacrifice—the kind he will find acceptable. This is truly the way to worship him. *(Romans 12:1 NLT)*

What holds you back from completely surrendering your life to God? The devil loves to mess with our heads. He loves for us to feel inadequate as if we have made so many mistakes or have so many flaws that God would not want us to witness for Him. And yet, it is the struggles and mistakes that have given us all a testimony. We all sin, and we all have battles to fight in our lives. When we emerge victorious from these conflicts, we can testify how great our God is. God knows we are not perfect. He knows each one of us will make mistakes in our lives and God still chooses to love each one of us. God does not give up on us. He keeps giving us signs that He is with us and He loves us. Until we breathe our last breath, God will be at our side, pushing us to grow as Christians and be the best we can be. He continues to expose areas in our lives that need improving upon so that we mature and draw closer to God. If you have not accepted Jesus as your Savior, He will lead you to the cross.. If God does not give up on us, then we surely should not.

My prayer is that you accept the fact that God loves you, not for what you do, but for who you are: His beloved child. Completely surrender your life to our Lord. Ask Him for forgiveness for mistakes you have made and then leave those mistakes at the cross. Quit carrying them with you and letting them take away the joy your Father wants you to experience in this life. Be willing to share your testimony with whoever will listen. Each one of us has a unique story, a story that God has given us. Be proud of who you are and bask in the love that your loving Father showers on you each day.
****

Let's take a walk through our temple that we have worked so hard on constructing. We need to take time to appreciate all the hard work we have done these past weeks. We also need to reevaluate any areas that need further work. Don't be discouraged; no building is ever really complete. The remodeling of your temple was a huge undertaking. You had to address many issues and make changes that are hard to make. This temple is a work in progress.

The same is true with our lives. We will always have areas on which we can improve. It seems when we get through one significant change; we find another area that needs work. We need to embrace these challenges. It is God's way of helping us draw nearer to Him. If we get too comfortable in life and do not have to rely on God for our strength, our relationships with Him often falter. When there are no challenges in life, it is easy to think we can handle life on our own.

You should embrace the new challenges because God knows you have more potential and are capable of fulfilling your calling. He wants to push you to be the best you can be. God loves to see you grow and become a stronger Christians. He also knows each one of us individually and understands how hard some of these changes are for us to make and appreciates the effort we exert to build our temples more pleasing to Him. God knows how hard we must strive to live godly lives as opposed to living ungodly lives that many people in this world embrace and glorify. Keep up the good fight.

Take some time to review the work you did to remodel the inside of your temple. Spend some time revisiting the goals you developed when drawing up the blueprints. Inspect each area that was built and appreciate the accomplishments. Big or small, you need to celebrate these achievements. If there are areas that still need some work, be honest with yourself about the work that you need to do. By addressing the issues that still need improvements, you can have a plan in place to keep moving forward. When goals are written down, there is a better chance you will achieve them. If you are doing this study in a small group, take this week to celebrate together. Congratulate each other on a job well done.

INTERIOR OF THE TEMPLE: Lives are complicated. When the inside of the temple is not in order, there is chaos in your life. Forgiveness, repentance, strongholds, and unrest can wreak havoc. Many things can cause you to be unhappy or hinder your growth. Take time to appreciate how much you have improved upon in this study and address any issues that need work.

INTERIOR WALLS: You need boundaries in your life so that you can accomplish your goals.
Goals accomplished:

Work that needs to be done:

FLOOR: When you hold onto negative strongholds, you can lose focus of your calling. You need to believe God's truths and not the enemy's lies.
Goals accomplished:

Work that needs to be done:

CEILING: A positive attitude can make all the difference as to how you live your life. We can make it through the tough times and draw closer to God.
Goal accomplished:

Work that needs to be done:

SANCTUARY: Stress wreaks havoc on our lives. It causes our physical bodies pain, and it can cause us mental anguish. We need to restore peace and decrease the stress in our lives.
Goal Accomplished:

Work that needs to be done:

CHAPEL AND VESTIBULE: You can make changes in your life, but if you do not find contentment or have time to rest and rejuvenate, you can still struggle.

Goals accomplished:

Work that needs to be done:

POWER SOURCE: You need the power to make your home warm and comfortable. By eating healthy, your temple is more energy efficient.

Goals accomplished:

Work that needs to be done:

HEATING AND COOLING: Exercise is essential to keeping your body in good shape. It is also crucial in helping to fight and prevent a variety of illnesses.

Goal accomplished:

Work that needs to be done:

REMOVAL OF CHEMICALS AND TOXINS FROM THE TEMPLE: There are many things in your environment that you are unable to control. It is imperative to control the things that you can control in your life so that your body is healthier.

Goals accomplished:

Work that needs to be done:

Remember to celebrate the victories. Do not give up on making changes in your life. When you trust God, He will continue to give you strength to make changes and help you to continue to grow in faith and improve your lifestyle. *And I am certain that God, who began the good work within you, will continue his work until it is finally finished on the day when Christ Jesus returns.* (Philippians 1:6 NLT)

Journal your thoughts

Day 4

TAKING POSSESSION OF THE TEMPLE **(YOU NOW HAVE THE BASICS TO LIVE A HEALTHY LIFESTYLE)**

Once the work is complete, the builder gives the keys to the new owner. This is a special day when the owner finally takes possession of the building.

Nugget of the day: The Lord had said to Abram, "Leave your native country, your relatives, and your father's family, and go to the land that I will show you. I will make you into a great nation. I will bless you and make you famous, and you will be a blessing to others. *(Genesis 12:1-2 NLT)*

It is so easy to have the misconception that when we follow God and His calling, life will be easy. Often the opposite is true. When we listen to Him, we have to step out of our comfort zone and do something with which we are not familiar requiring us to lean on God for strength. Following our calling can become an emotional roller coaster. One moment we are confident we can accomplish the task with God's guidance. The next moment we doubt whether or not we have the ability and question if God is going to help us. It can be frustrating as we muddle through blindly, taking the next step of faith hoping we are moving in the right direction. As we go along, there are periods of silence when God does not speak. Instead, He allows us to learn to trust Him and to have to struggle with finding the right way. If following our calling were easy, we would assume it was us who accomplished the work. We would never get to see how active God is in our lives and we would never learn how to trust God to guide us through this world. We would not stay in communication with Him and learn to speak to Him or include Him in our lives. There are many blessings when we dedicate our lives to Him. When we see how God can use us with all our imperfections and weaknesses to do the impossible, we have to stand in awe of how much interest He takes in each one of us. We get to hear Him speak to us and guide us. It is in these times we see God's role as a loving Father.

My prayer is that you realize God has a calling for your life. This calling may not be easy, and it may force you to take a leap of faith into areas you have never been. I pray you embrace the challenge and take the

136

time along the way to appreciate all God is doing in your life. Use this time to draw closer to our Dad. God's calling will give you more rewards and joy than you can ever experience when you try and go at life alone without Him to guide you. God will show you His glory when you accept His calling.
****

By now I hope that you are in awe of how great and knowledgeable our loving Father truly is. I hope that you, like me, are realizing that God has given us the keys to living successful and productive lives. It is up to us as to whether or not we accept these keys and heed God's advice so we can live the lives He has intended for us. The more I study the Bible, the more I realize that God has provided for all of His children from the beginning of time. He has given us a book of life's instructions to show us how to live fulfilling lives and to make the most out of our time here on this earth. God taught us the importance of having and maintaining a relationship with Him. He has also spoken about the importance of having and restoring relationships with one another. God has taught us how to have peace and joy in our lives, maintain the health of our bodies through nutrition and oils and also about the importance of exercise to keep our bodies fit. If we truly believe that God has a plan for our lives, then we also have to believe He has given us the means with which to fulfill this plan. However, just like anything we do, to be successful, we must do our part. Sitting back and waiting for God to work is not the answer. God has also given us free will. It is up to us to answer the calling and make an effort to be successful. He never promised us that it would be easy to fulfill our callings, but He has promised us blessings when we stay committed to fulfilling them.

I too have grown in my faith and have learned to trust God. I first worked on changing my lifestyle and now have embarked on a new career. I am doing my best to heed His call. I have found that one of the hardest things in life to do is to surrender to God and be faithful in believing His promises. At times, I struggled with surrendering to His Will, and my writing was delayed because of this. He and I had many battles, and I let my mind fill with self-doubt. God was patient with me. He listened to my fears. In the end, God showed me that He was and is in charge. He was on this journey with me, and He will remain faithful even when I falter. This book was as much for me as it is for other readers. God has used this book to draw me closer to Him, strengthen my relationship and to teach me that I must look straight up instead of straight ahead when I need help. I hope you have learned to look up for your strength. I also hope that you are learning to trust God with your calling even when you do not see the immediate fruits of your labor. When God calls, He delivers on His promises, and He will not disappoint us. Too often, we miss out on seeing His glory because we quit before we complete the task He has put before us.

As you have worked through this Bible study have you seen God more active in your life? __ In what ways?

_____

In what ways has God spoken to you through this study and throughout your journey? _____

_____

In what ways has God challenged you to trust Him more thoroughly and turn over your struggles to Him?

_____

Have there been times during this study that you felt as if things were overwhelming and you could not make changes? _____ In what areas did you think you could not overcome the challenge?

_____

How has God shown you that with His help you could not only overcome these challenges but that you can also address new challenges? _____

We cannot be successful in life if our bodies are not in the best shape possible. Whatever stage of life we are in, we must maintain our bodies, so we have the energy and stamina to get through our days.

Throughout this journey we have talked about our bodies being God's temple. Do you take this to heart and try and live your life accordingly? _____

In what areas do you think you still need to improve to give God the honor and glory He truly deserves? (Remember we are all human and we will never be perfect. There will always be areas of our lives on which we can improve. When we are aware of these areas, we can focus on them and ask the Holy Spirit to help us improve.) _____

_____

Take a moment to pray and ask God for His wisdom to help you become more aware of these areas and to guide you to make changes.

We have a responsibility as Christians to stay true to our faith and lead a life that brings others closer to our loving Father. *But those who hope in the Lord will renew their strength. They will soar on wings like eagles; they will run and not grow weary, they will walk and not be faint. (Isaiah 40:31 NIV)*

How have you found renewed strength in the Lord as you have worked on improving your lifestyle?

_____

Have seen God's hand in restoring your temple not only physically but also spiritually and emotionally?

_____

There is so much to see and do in this world. So many adventures await you. It would be a shame to miss out because you do not have the energy and stamina to participate in everything God has planned for you. *We do not want you to become lazy, but to imitate those who through faith and patience inherit what has been promised. (Hebrews 6:12 NIV)* I often witness people sitting on the sidelines watching as others enjoy all life has to offer. They miss out because they have difficulty moving, find it hard to breath when they exert energy or do not have the endurance to walk very far. I see the hurt in their eyes, the embarrassment on their faces and the sadness in their demeanors because they are missing out. I know people who have dreams and callings and yet do not have the energy to fulfill them. Life is too short to miss out on all the opportunities God has provided for us in this world. *And so, dear brothers and sisters, I plead with you to give your bodies to God because of all he has done for you. Let them be a living and holy sacrifice—the kind he will find acceptable. This is truly the way to worship him. (Romans 12:1 NLT)*

As you have worked through this study, has your calling become clearer, and if so how?

_____

Are you now ready and able to fulfill your calling, or are there physical, emotional or mental barriers that need to be broken down first? _____

If you are still waiting for God to give you a new calling, do not be discouraged. Maybe your calling right now is to continue to work on the areas you are still struggling with, so you are prepared when He calls you. As you embark on this new stage of life, focus on God and let Him give you strength. Maybe you had tried to exercise before but were unable to stick with it, or life overwhelmed you. Take some time to pray to God and keep your eyes focused on Him as He guides you on this new journey.

I wish you the very best as you continue on your journey in life. If you have not already given your life to God, I pray that you do. I have seen what God is capable of doing when we trust Him and allow Him to take control. Life becomes an adventure and God can amaze us with all He is capable of doing. If this study has drawn you closer to our loving Father and you are learning to trust Him more with your life, then God has used this book for His glory. There is no sweeter joy than to be in love with our God and have a relationship with Him.

Remember you belong to God, my dear children. You have already won a victory over those people, because the Spirit who lives in you is greater than the spirit who lives in the world. (1 John 4:4 NLT)

Journal your thoughts

Day 5

CONSECRATING THE TEMPLE
(DEDICATING YOUR HARD WORK TO GOD)

Temples are dedicated to God when they are debt free. Until the debt is paid off, the building is blessed. Consecration is the transfer of ownership.

Nugget of the day: I heard a loud shout from the throne, saying, "Look, God's home is now among his people! He will live with them, and they will be his people. God himself will be with them. (Revelation 21:3 NLT)

Research has shown that we need exercise to maintain our physical health. The same is true for our spiritual health. We must spend time in our spiritual gym. We need to flex our muscles of faith, so they grow stronger. We need to spend time performing endurance training as we go through the trials of this life so we can run the good race. We want to finish with arms raised in victory as we cross the finish line, look directly into the eyes of God and hear those glorious words "well done good and faithful servant". On that great day, we will not regret one moment of our spiritual training. All the trials we faced will have been worth the pain and suffering when we realize it prepared us to enjoy eternity in paradise. Every moment spent flexing our spiritual muscles and strengthening our faith will be worth the sacrifice of earthly pleasures to see God's glory first hand.

My prayer is that you realize if you want to enjoy all the promises God has given you, you need to live a Christian life. You need to stay in the Word and need to live by the rules God has given you. Work on your resistance training to stand against immoral values of this world, strengthen your faith and run the good race. To train, you must have a daily faith routine. This routine will allow you to grow in your relationship with our loving Father. On that great day when you meet our Dad face to face, all this training will have been worth it.

****

Congratulations! If you are reading this chapter, you have worked hard on rebuilding and remodeling your temple to make it pleasing to God. It is time to celebrate your accomplishments and enjoy the temple you have built. All the hard work is worth it when we finally get to move into our new temple. We get to stand and marvel at all that has been done and appreciate the time and effort it took to build such a beautiful temple. We can now consecrate the temple that we have worked so hard on to rebuild.

We cannot consecrate a temple unless it is debt free. The Good News is that we are debt free! The blood of Christ has paid our debt. *With his own blood—not the blood of goats and calves—he entered the Most Holy Place once for all time and secured our redemption forever.* (Hebrews 9:12 NLT) We have been given a gift we should cherish forever. The gift of salvation is something that will never grow old or become outdated. It is the only thing we will take with us when we leave our present body and join our Heavenly Father. When we accepted Christ, we gave Him our life.

By consecrating our temples, we turn our lives over to God. Our body is no longer our own. *Don't you realize that your body is the temple of the Holy Spirit, who lives in you and was given to you by God? You do not belong to yourself, for God bought you with a high price. So you must honor God with your body.* (1 Corinthians 6:19-20 NLT)

Spend some time reflecting on the meaning of this Bible verse. How are you going to allow it be a guide as to how you live your life? _____

Making changes in our lives is not always easy. We have been conditioned into believing we should be independent and live our lives the way we want to live. This is the human way of thinking. This independence has often gotten us into trouble and caused us heartache and many complications. It is when we surrender our lives, seek God's guidance, and live according to the Bible's commands that we see all that God is capable of doing in our lives. Many of us miss seeing God's blessings because we are too hardheaded to surrender and allow Him direct access to our hearts. *Then Joshua told the people, "Purify yourselves, for tomorrow the Lord will do great wonders among you."* (Joshua 3:5 NLT) When we let other people or worldly things influence our lives, we miss out on our real purpose. We also need to be on guard to not allow Satan to steal our joy. Satan wants us to miss out on seeing God's glory and reaping the benefits of following Jesus. *The thief's purpose is to steal and kill and destroy. My purpose is to give them a rich and satisfying life.* (John 10:10 NLT)

God's ways are so much better than our ways. We are foolish not to let Him be in charge. By consecrating our temples, we are telling God we want Him to be in control. My prayer for you is that if you have trouble surrendering your life to God, you make the time to spend in His presence and ask Him to help you overcome your fears. Ask God to give you the courage to live the life only He can provide you. As you conclude this study, commit to staying connected to God. Include Him in every battle, decision, and celebration. Let Him be the first One you speak to in the morning and the last One you wish a good night. Making a conscious effort to keep God ever present in your life will keep you on the right path. When you stumble, your prayer life will get you back on track.

And so, dear brothers and sisters, I plead with you to give your bodies to God because of all he has done for you. Let them be a living and holy sacrifice—the kind he will find acceptable. This is truly the way to worship him. Don't copy the behavior and customs of this world, but let God transform you into a new person by changing the way you think. Then you will learn to know God's will for you, which is good and pleasing and perfect. (Romans 12:1-2 NLT) As this study comes to a close, take this time to do just as Paul has asked. Consecrate your body to Christ. Know that you are now living for Him. In doing so, you will promise to try and keep your body, mind, and soul in the best shape so that you can fulfill your calling and enjoy the life God has prepared for you. Spend some time alone with God thanking Him for helping you achieve all you have these past thirteen weeks. Enjoy this time with Him. If you are doing this study in a small group, have a ceremony to consecrate your newly renovated temple and then spend some time celebrating your accomplishments as a group.

Dear Heavenly Father,
Let this temple, which You have helped me rebuild, be a holy place. My temple is debt free thanks to the blood of Christ. I am now able to consecrate this temple. Help me to live the life You chose for me many years before I was even born. Give me the strength and stamina to fight the good fight and run the race that you have set before me. On this day I consecrate this temple in your name. I pray that I may be a person that helps to draw others close to you. Let me be a light that shines in this dark world and let others know that I am a

Christian by my actions. I vow to try and keep this temple to the best of my abilities; physically, mentally and emotionally sound. My life is a gift from You, the Creator of the universe and I want to honor you in all I do. I dedicate my service to You, almighty God, through Jesus Christ our Lord. Amen

CONCLUSION

In conclusion, I want to thank you for your dedication. This was an intense study, and it required you to explore many areas of your life and to address issues that were not always comfortable to address. There were changes that you made, and are still in the process of making, that took a lot of work and at times were very trying. There may have also been some changes that have already been reversed. Know there will be setbacks, but with God's help, you will get back on track. I want to encourage you to continue the fight to live a life that is pleasing to God. Continue to restore your temple. Until that great day when you meet our loving Father face to face, He will continue to push you to your limits. When you clear one hurdle, God will make you aware of another obstacle that is interfering with your relationship with Him and keeping you from fulfilling your calling. *And I am certain that God, who began the good work within you, will continue his work until it is finally finished on the day when Christ Jesus returns.* (Philippians 1:6NLT) He loves us too much not to keep working with us and helping us to grow closer to Him.

For some readers, you have seen immense changes in your lifestyle and are seeing the rewards of the time and effort you have invested. I pray that you continue to live the lifestyle you have adopted and continue to see improvement. For others, this may have been your first attempt at changing your lifestyle. This information can be overwhelming, and it may take you some time to process all that you have studied. This book may have been a seed planted to give you the desire to make the changes necessary to live a healthy life. Take some time to go through the chapters again and work through them at a slower pace. Be patient with yourself and enjoy the journey of growing and improving your life. Know that it is okay to take more time. You may not have completed all you set out to do, but if you stay the course, change will come.

I pray that this book has given you the information you need to continue to work on your temple. There is no better way to thank our loving Father for all He is doing and will do in your life than to make your temple pleasing to Him. Healthy living, when adopted as a lifestyle, should not be a chore or something to dread. Instead, it should give you energy and excite you so that you want to continue along this path. There is so much to do in this world, so many places to go and people to meet that you need to be in optimal health so that you can enjoy all the opportunities God is providing for you.

The purpose of this study is to serve as a guide and ignite a fire in you so that you want to delve deeper into many of the subjects presented. This book is just the first leg of your journey. There is so much more to learn and so many new things to try. I hope that you have accepted this new way of life as a rewarding hobby. A hobby you can enjoy and possibly share with others. I hope that you now have a hunger to learn more. Review your journaling and research the areas you highlighted along the way so that you can continue to grow.

You should now feel empowered to take responsibility for your health. We all have choices and decisions to make that will affect our well-being. No one knows you better than you know yourself. No one doctor or other health professional has all the answers. You need to be an advocate for yourself. Some of the things that work for one person may not work for another. God created us as unique individuals. Because we are unique, we all have different needs and different opinions. Rather than just listening to another person, do your research, pray about your options and then make an informed decision as to how you are going to improve or maintain your health.

I want to reiterate that the information I have shared in this book is something I found that worked for me and helped with improving my lifestyle. I hope I have shed some light on options that are available to you for enhancing your lifestyle. It is now your responsibility to determine what is best for you.

More than anything else, I pray each of you has come to know our loving Father in a more personal way. I hope that you have renewed your faith in God. I want you to feel His presence and know just how much He loves you. For those of you who already have a good relationship with God, I pray it has grown stronger and reached a new level of intimacy. There is nothing better in this world than to know the love of our Father. It is so important that you develop a deeper trust in God so that you can hear His voice and follow His calling for you amidst all the chaos of this world. It is not always easy to follow God, but the rewards outweigh the struggles. We have become so accustomed to doing things on our own and being independent that it takes energy and blind faith to give God our lives and let Him guide us. On those days when doubt and fear fill your mind, and you cannot find rest, I pray that you feel God's strong arms holding and comforting you. This world is a hard place to maneuver through without leaning on God and allowing Him to guide you. The more you trust Him, and lean into Him for support, the more you can accomplish. Our Father does know best. From the beginning, God has provided for you to meet all your needs and allow you to complete your calling successfully. God touched on every aspect of living a healthy life when He gave the earthly authors the words to pen in the Bible.

I thank you, the reader, for choosing this Bible study and allowing me to share my remarkable journey with you. Although it is not one I would have chosen for myself, I now know that God had a plan and He has always been in control. God has chosen a path for you as well. It may not be what you had planned, but trusting Him will surpass your highest expectations. Some are fortunate enough to understand God's plan in their life while on this earth and for others it will not be clear until we meet our loving Father face to face. It will be at that moment you will realize your earthly battles were well worth the fight. We will finally understand God's plan for our lives with the ultimate goal being to join Him in eternity. Until that day when we meet our loving Father, stand in awe of all His glory and realize just how well orchestrated our lives were, I urge you to continue *to fight the good fight, run the race, keep the faith and fix your eyes on the prize*. It will all be worth it when we hear those glorious words *"well done good and faithful servant"* (Matthew 25:23 NIV)!!!

In conclusion, I pray that God continues to guide you on your journey. Let Him give you the strength to withstand the temptations of this world and live the life He has designed specifically for you. I pray you can accept His love and walk through life knowing you are God's special child. He has called you by name, and He will never leave you.

Eating Habits questionnaire

If you are going to change your eating habits to improve your diet, you need to become aware of your eating patterns and food consumption. Take time to evaluate what and when you are eating. If possible keep a log of your food intake for the week and then review what you are eating.

1. How many times during the week do you eat meals at home?

2. How many times a week did you eat fast food?

3. How many times a week did you go to a sit-down restaurant?

3b. How many times did you order healthy choices?

4. How many meals do you eat a day?

5. What does your breakfast primarily consist of?

6. What does your lunch consist of?

7. What does your dinner consist of?

8. How often do you snack throughout the day?

9. What do your snacks consist of?

10. What emotions cause you to eat more frequently and/or unhealthy foods?

11. What emotions cause you to eat less?

12. How often do you drink soda? Diet soda? Water? Sports drinks? Juice? Tea? Coffee?

12b. Do you add anything to your drinks (sugar, creamer etc.)?

13. What time do you stop eating at night?

14. Do you eat when you are full?

15. What are your go- to foods for comfort?

16. What are your eating habits at parties?

17. When do you grocery shop?

18. Do you use a list or buy spontaneously?

If possible make copies of this and record your daily food consumption for 1 week

Day:	What did you eat and drink?
Breakfast	
Snack	
Lunch	
Snack	
Dinner	
Snack	
Other	

What toxins and chemicals are you exposed to everyday?

We need to take the time to look at our lives and see what potential toxins and chemicals we come in contact with each day. We are often unaware of how much we are exposed to on a regular basis. Many of us feel as if we have created a safe environment in our homes and in our lives. Until we take the time to survey our lives, we do not realize how many chemicals we are exposed to every day.

Take some time to evaluate how many of these potential toxins can be found in your everyday life. Not all of the products we use are toxic. We need to look at the labels and sometimes do additional research. We are all exposed to some toxins and chemicals in our everyday lives. Not all can be avoided. If we want to maintain our health, we need to change the things we can change. Some of these things will be addressed in this book. In other areas, you may need to do some research to try and determine what changes you can make to improve your living conditions.

Rate how often you are exposed to these toxins. Use the following rating scale.
0= never
1= seldom
2=weekly
3=daily

In your home do you use:
Air fresheners or plug-ins ____
Candles ____
Dryer sheets ____
Conventional cleaning supplies ____
Shower spray every time you shower? ____
Ammonia or bleach to clean ____
Do you park your car in a garage attached to the house? ____
Do you have mold or untreated water damage in your house? ____
Has your home been flooded? ____
Do you smoke or are you exposed to second hand smoke? ____
Do you use pesticides, herbicides or other chemicals on your plants and in your home? __
Do you use paint, wood stains or preservatives on a regular basis? ____
Are you exposed to chemicals when working on a hobby? ____
Are exposed to new carpet or furniture? ____

Health and beauty: How often do you use:
Cosmetics ____
Cologne or perfume ____
Deodorant ____
Antibacterial soap ____
Scented soaps, detergents or potpourri ____
Products to dye or perm your hair ____
Acrylic nail polish ____
Take prescription drugs? ____
Do you have mercury fillings in your mouth? ____

Diet: How often do you…
Eat fast food? ____
Eat non-organic fruits and vegetables? ____

Eat frozen meals? ____
Eat conventional meats and dairy products? ____
Cook with vegetable or canola oil? ____
Use artificial sweeteners? ____
Eat foods with food coloring or dyes? ____
Eat microwave popcorn? ____
Eat canned foods? ____
Store or heat up food in plastic containers or wrap? ____
Do you drink tap water? ____

Workplace:
Do you work in a place that has a damp or mildew smell? ____
Are you exposed to chemicals and/or dyes? ____

REFERENCES

TRUSTING THE ARCHITECT

(1) Freddrick. "Hematidrosis." *Wikipedia*. Wikimedia Foundation, n.d. Web. 28 Dec. 2016.

LAYING THE FLOOR

(1) "Humor Therapy, Therapeutic Benefits of Laughter, Laughter Therapy, Laughter, Stress Hormones, Immune Function, T-cells, Gamma-interferon, B-cells, Endorphins, Alternative Medicine, Integrative Medicine." *Humor Therapy, Therapeutic Benefits of Laughter, Laughter Therapy, Laughter, Stress Hormones, Immune Function, T-cells, Gamma-interferon, B-cells, Endorphins, Alternative Medicine, Integrative Medicine*. N.p., n.d. Web. 17 Feb. 2017. <http://www.holistic-online.com/Humor_Therapy/humor_therapy_benefits.htm>.

(2) Schoenfeld, T. J., P. Rada, P. R. Pieruzzini, B. Hsueh, and E. Gould. "Physical Exercise Prevents Stress-Induced Activation of Granule Neurons and Enhances Local Inhibitory Mechanisms in the Dentate Gyrus." *Journal of Neuroscience* 33.18 (2013): 7770-7777. Web.

(3) "10 Superfoods That Reduce Stress." *Mercola.com*. N.p., 27 Apr. 2015. Web. 10 Feb. 2017.

(4) http://www.mayoclinic.org/healthy-lifestyle/stress-management/in-depth/stress-relief/art-20044456

THE SANCTUARY

(1) Salleh, Mohd. Razali. "Life Event, Stress and Illness." *The Malaysian Journal of Medical Sciences : MJMS*. Penerbit Universiti Sains Malaysia, Oct. 2008. Web. 05 Jan. 2017.

(2) https://www.psychology.org.a"Understanding and Managing Stress." Australian Psychology Society, 2012. Web.u/Assets/Files/StressTipSheet.pdf

THE VESTIBULE

(1) N.p., n.d. Web. <http://www.answers.com/Q/How_many_verses_are_there_in_the_Bible_about_money>.

THE CHAPEL

(1) "Brain Basics: Understanding Sleep." *National Institute of Neurological Disorders and Stroke*. U.S. Department of Health and Human Services, n.d. Web. 01 July 2017. <https://www.ninds.nih.gov/Disorders/Patient-Caregiver-Education/Understanding-Sleep>.

(2) "Healthy Sleep Cycles Balance Hormones and Burn Fat." *NaturalNews*. N.p., n.d. Web. 04 July 2017. <http://www.naturalnews.com/031101_sleep_hormones.html>.

(3) "11 Signs You're Sleep Deprived." *Health.com*. N.p., n.d. Web. 04 July 2017. <http://www.health.com/health/gallery/0,,20906153,00.html#you-think-you-ve-fallen-asleep-at-the-wheel-0>.

(4) *American Psychological Association*. American Psychological Association, n.d. Web. 04 July 2017. <http://www.apa.org/topics/sleep/why.aspx>.

(5) Publications, Harvard Health. "Blue Light Has a Dark Side." *Harvard Health*. N.p., n.d. Web. 04 July 2017. <http://www.health.harvard.edu/staying-healthy/blue-light-has-a-dark-side>.

(6) "Do You Sleep on an "Organic" Mattress?" *Dr. Axe*. N.p., 16 June 2017. Web. 04 July 2017. <https://draxe.com/organic-mattresses-and-how-to-pick-the-healthiest-bed/>.

(7) Ebrahim, I. O., C. M. Shapiro, A. J. Williams, and P. B. Fenwick. "Alcohol and Sleep I: Effects on Normal Sleep." *Alcoholism, Clinical and Experimental Research*. U.S. National Library of Medicine, Apr. 2013. Web. 04 July 2017. <https://www.ncbi.nlm.nih.gov/pubmed/23347102>.

(8) "What Are the Five Worst Foods for Sleep?" *Mercola.com*. N.p., n.d. Web. 04 July 2017. <http://articles.mercola.com/sites/articles/archive/2013/05/02/worst-sleep-foods.aspx>.

(9) McLaughlin, August. "Foods That Increase Serotonin and Induce Sleep." *LIVESTRONG.COM*. Leaf Group, 21 May 2015. Web. 04 July 2017. <http://www.livestrong.com/article/294169-foods-that-increase-serotonin-and-induce-sleep/>.

(10) "Study: Physical Activity Impacts Overall Quality of Sleep." *National Sleep Foundation*. N.p., n.d. Web. 05 July 2017. <https://sleepfoundation.org/sleep-news/study-physical-activity-impacts-overall-quality-sleep>.

(11) "9 Foods to Help You Sleep." *EatingWell*. EatingWell, 17 Nov. 2011. Web. 04 July 2017. <http://www.eatingwell.com/article/32617/9-foods-to-help-you-sleep/>.

(12) LD, Kristin Kirkpatrick MS RD. "5 Foods That Help You Sleep." *Health Essentials from Cleveland Clinic*. N.p., 12 July 2016. Web. 04 July 2017. <https://health.clevelandclinic.org/2014/06/5-foods-that-help-you-sleep/>.

REWIRING THE TEMPLE

(1) Klein, Sarah, and Copyright Health Magazine 2011. *CNN*. Cable News Network, 30 Mar. 2010. Web. 15 Mar. 2017. <http://www.cnn.com/2010/HEALTH/03/28/fatty.foods.brain/index.html>.

(2) "How to Stop Food Cravings and Prevent Addictions." *Mercola.com*. N.p., n.d. Web. 15 Mar. 2017. <http://articles.mercola.com/sites/articles/archive/2011/02/25/cant-beat-food-cravings-four-steps-to-help-you-kick-your-addictions.aspx>.

(3) N.p., n.d. Web. <http://bodyecology.com/articles/the-top-3-most-addicting-foods-why-they%E2%80%99re-destroying-your-health-and-how-to-get-your-kids-off-them>.

(4) Pratt, Steven, and Kathy Matthews. *Superfoods Rx: Fourteen Foods That Will Change Your Life*. New York: Harper Paperback, 2005. Print. page 11

(5) "Obesity Rates & Trends Overview." *Obesity Rates & Trends Overview: The State of Obesity*. N.p., n.d. Web. 15 Mar. 2017. <http://stateofobesity.org/obesity-rates-trends-overview/>.

(6) "Cancer Prevention Diet." *Cancer Prevention Diet: How to Lower Your Risk with Cancer-Fighting Foods*. N.p., n.d. Web. 15 Mar. 2017. <http://www.helpguide.org/articles/diet-weight-loss/anti-cancer-diet.htm>.

(7) "Antioxidants and Cancer Prevention." *National Cancer Institute*. N.p., n.d. Web. 15 Mar. 2017. <http://www.cancer.gov/about-cancer/causes-prevention/risk/diet/antioxidants-fact-sheet>.

(8) "Color Me Healthy - Eating for a Rainbow of Benefits." *Today's Dietitian*. N.p., n.d. Web. 15 Mar. 2017. <http://www.todaysdietitian.com/newarchives/110308p34.shtml>.

(9) "Water – The Most Vital Nutrient - Me & My Body." *Me and My Body*, www.meandmybody.com/browse_topic.php?topicId=22&all=1.

CONSERVING OUR ENERGY

(1) N.p., n.d. Web. <http://whole9life.com/wp-content/uploads/2010/12/whole9-produce-guide.pdf+>.

(2) "Healthy Eating with the Seasons." *Healthy Eating with the Seasons*. N.p., n.d. Web. 15 Mar. 2017. <http://www.whfoods.com/genpage.php?tname=faq&dbid=28>.

(3) Lee, Rebecca. "Consumer Reports: 'Natural' Food Labels Misleading Consumers." *CBS News*, CBS Interactive, 27 Jan. 2016, www.cbsnews.com/news/natural-food-labeling-misleading-consumer-reports-fda-lacks-regulations/.

(4) "It Says It's USDA Organic? That Doesn't Mean It's Non GMO." Wondergressive. N.p., 16 Feb. 2014. Web. 15 Mar. 2017.

<http://wondergressive.com/organic-not-non-gmo/>.
(5) "Are Frozen Vegetables Healthy? - Ask Dr. Weil." *DrWeil.com*. N.p., 03 Dec. 2016. Web. 15 Mar. 2017. <https://www.drweil.com/diet-nutrition/nutrition/are-frozen-vegetables-healthy/>.
(6) "Grass Fed Natural Beef." *American Grass Fed Beef*. N.p., n.d. Web. 15 Mar. 2017. <https://www.americangrassfedbeef.com/grass-fed-natural-beef.asp>.
(7) "Eat Wild - Basics." *Eat Wild - Basics*. N.p., n.d. Web. 15 Mar. 2017. <http://www.eatwild.com/basics.html>.
(8) "Finding the Best Seafood for Your Health and the Earth." *Mercola.com*. N.p., n.d. Web. 15 Mar. 2017. <http://articles.mercola.com/sites/articles/archive/2015/06/01/best-seafood.aspx>.

CLEANING, STORING AND PREPARING FOOD
(1) "How to Store Food Without Using Toxic Plastics." *Mercola.com*. N.p., n.d. Web. 16 Mar. 2017. <http://articles.mercola.com/sites/articles/archive/2011/11/16/practical-options-to-store-your-food-without-contaminating-them-with-plastics.aspx>.
(2) Duvauchelle, Joshua. "What Are the Dangers of Plastic Food Storage Containers?" *LIVESTRONG.COM*. Leaf Group, 27 Jan. 2015. Web. 16 Mar. 2017. <http://www.livestrong.com/article/173172-what-are-the-dangers-of-plastic-food-storage-containers/>.
(3) "Killer Cookware: The Dangers of Teflon." *Healthy Holistic Living*. N.p., 08 July 2014. Web. 16 Mar. 2017. <http://www.healthy-holistic-living.com/dangers-of-teflon.html>.
(4) "Non-Stick Cookware Dangers & How to Choose the Best Cookware." *Mercola.com*. N.p., n.d. Web. 16 Mar. 2017. <http://www.mercola.com/Downloads/bonus/dangers-of-nonstick-cookware/report.htm>.

USING THE RIGHT GAUGE WIRE
(1) "American Academy of Environmental Medicine (AAEM)." *American Academy of Environmental Medicine (AAEM)*. N.p., n.d. Web. 16 Mar. 2017. <https://www.aaemonline.org/gmo.php>.
(2) Smith, Jeffrey. "10 Reasons to Avoid GMOs." *Institute for Responsible Technology*. N.p., 15 Jan. 2017. Web. 16 Mar. 2017. c
(3) "More Good News for Organic!" *Cornucopia Institute*. N.p., 06 Jan. 2017. Web. 16 Mar. 2017. <https://www.cornucopia.org/2017/01/good-news-organic/>.
(4) Barański, Marcin, Dominika Średnicka-Tober, Nikolaos Volakakis, Chris Seal, Roy Sanderson, Gavin B. Stewart, Charles Benbrook, Bruno Biavati, Emilia Markellou, Charilaos Giotis, Joanna Gromadzka-Ostrowska, Ewa Rembiałkowska, Krystyna Skwarło-Sońta, Raija Tahvonen, Dagmar Janovská, Urs Niggli, Philippe Nicot, and Carlo Leifert. "Higher Antioxidant and Lower Cadmium Concentrations and Lower Incidence of Pesticide Residues in Organically Grown Crops: A Systematic Literature Review and Meta-analyses | British Journal of Nutrition." *Cambridge Core*. Cambridge University Press, 15 July 2014. Web. 16 Mar. 2017. <https://www.cambridge.org/core/journals/british-journal-of-nutrition/article/higher-antioxidant-and-lower-cadmium-concentrations-and-lower-incidence-of-pesticide-residues-in-organically-grown-crops-a-systematic-literature-review-and-meta-analyses/33F09637EAE6C4ED119E0C4BFFE2D5B1>.
(5) N.p., n.d. Web. <http://www.drweil.com/drw/u/ALB00035/The-Dirty-Dozen-Foods-You-Should-Always-Buy-Organic.html>.
(6) "10 Organic Foods That Are Worth the Money." *Mercola.com*. N.p., n.d. Web. 16 Mar. 2017. <http://articles.mercola.com/sites/articles/archive/2010/11/20/10-organic-foods-that-are-worth-the-money.aspx>.

COOKING WITH OIL
(1) "Healthy Cooking Oils - The Ultimate Guide." *Authority Nutrition*. N.p., 18 Aug. 2016. Web. 14 Mar. 2017. <https://authoritynutrition.com/healthy-cooking-oils/>.
(2) Dannie, Marie. "Is Coconut Oil Good for Frying on High Temperature Cooking?" *LIVESTRONG.COM*, Leaf Group, 3 Oct. 2017, www.livestrong.com/article/446041-is-coconut-oil-good-for-frying-on-high-temperature-cooking/.
(3) "Countless Coconut Oil Uses and Health Benefits." *Mercola.com*. N.p., n.d. Web. 14 Mar. 2017. <http://articles.mercola.com/sites/articles/archive/2013/11/18/coconut-oil-uses.aspx>.
(4) "20 Coconut Oil Benefits (#5 Is Life-Saving)." *Dr. Axe*. N.p., 12 May 2016. Web. 14 Mar. 2017. <https://draxe.com/coconut-oil-benefits/>.
(5) Www.gulosolutions.com, Gulo Solutions LLC -. "American Society for Nutrition." *American Society for Nutrition - Coconut Oil*. N.p., n.d. Web. 14 Mar. 2017. <http://www.nutrition.org/asn-blog/2009/07/coconut-oil/>.
(6) "10 Impressive Health Benefits of Coconut Oil." *Authority Nutrition*. N.p., 01 Sept. 2016. Web. 19 Mar. 2017. <https://authoritynutrition.com/top-10-evidence-based-health-benefits-of-coconut-oil/>.
(7) "Is Coconut Oil Bad for Your Cholesterol?" *Dr. Mark Hyman*, 26 June 2017, drhyman.com/blog/2016/04/06/is-coconut-oil-bad-for-your-cholesterol/.
(8) "Coconut Health Benefits for Heart Health | Dr. Sinatra." *Heart Health Vitamins, Supplements & Advice*. N.p., n.d. Web. 14 Mar. 2017. <https://www.drsinatra.com/coconut-health-benefits-for-heart-health>.
(9) "Coconut Oil Pulling Benefits and My How-to Guide." *Dr. Axe*. N.p., 06 Dec. 2016. Web. 14 Mar. 2017. https://draxe.com/oil-pulling-coconut-oil/
(10) "Vast Majority of Olive Oil Is Adulterated." *Mercola.com*, articles.mercola.com/sites/articles/archive/2016/12/17/fake-olive-oil.aspx.
(11) "Olive Oil Benefits for Your Heart & Brain." *Dr. Axe*. N.p., 02 Dec. 2016. Web. 14 Mar. 2017. <https://draxe.com/olive-oil-benefits/>.
(12) "11 Surprising Benefits of Olive Oil." *Organic Facts*. N.p., 01 Mar. 2017. Web. 14 Mar. 2017. <https://www.organicfacts.net/health-benefits/oils/health-benefits-of-olive-oil.html>.
(13) "Chemistry and Health of Olive Oil Phenolics." *Critical Reviews in Food Science and Nutrition*. U.S. National Library of Medicine, n.d. Web. 14 Mar. 2017. <https://www.ncbi.nlm.nih.gov/pubmed/19093267>.
(14) "6 Reasons Why Vegetable Oils Can Be Harmful." *Authority Nutrition*. N.p., 18 Aug. 2016. Web. 14 Mar. 2017. <https://authoritynutrition.com/6-reasons-why-vegetable-oils-are-toxic/>.
(15) Hyman, Dr. Mark. "Dr. Mark Hyman: Why Vegetable Oils Should Not Be Part of Your Diet." *EcoWatch*. N.p., 27 June 2016. Web. 14 Mar. 2017. <http://www.ecowatch.com/dr-mark-hyman-why-vegetable-oils-should-not-be-part-of-your-diet-1882164589.html>.
(16) "Stop Using Canola Oil Immediately!" *Dr. Axe*. N.p., 20 Dec. 2016. Web. 19 Mar. 2017. <https://draxe.com/canola-oil-gm/>.
(17) "Trans Fat: Avoid This Cholesterol Double Whammy." *Mayo Clinic*. N.p., n.d. Web. 19 Mar. 2017. <http://www.mayoclinic.org/diseases-conditions/high-blood-cholesterol/in-depth/trans-fat/art-20046114>.

QUALITY CONTROL
(1) "5 Ways to Keep BPA Out of Your Food." *Mercola.com*. N.p., n.d. Web. 17 Mar. 2017. <http://articles.mercola.com/sites/articles/archive/2008/10/07/5-ways-to-keep-bpa-out-of-your-food.aspx>.
(2) Admin. "Cacao Vs. Cocoa: Are You Eating The Healthiest Chocolate?" *Healthy Info Network*, 24 Dec. 2017, healthyinfonetwork.com/2017/12/24/cacao-vs-cocoa-eating-healthiest-chocolate/.
(3) "92% Of Restaurant Meals Have Too Many Calories: Study." *Time*, Time, time.com/4187120/restaurant-meals-fast-food-calories/.
(4) Fisk, Michelle. "Fast Food & Bad Health Side Effects." *LIVESTRONG.COM*. Leaf Group, 20 Apr. 2015. Web. 17 Mar. 2017. <http://www.livestrong.com/article/353199-fast-food-bad-health-side-effects/>.
(5) "7 Foods to Avoid That Sabotage Your Healthy Diet." *Mercola.com*. N.p., n.d. Web. 17 Mar. 2017. <http://articles.mercola.com/sites/articles/archive/2015/07/01/7-healthy-foods-to-avoid.aspx>.
(6) Babe, Food. "Why Microwave Popcorn Is An Absolute Health Nightmare." *Food Babe*. N.p., 27 Dec. 2014. Web. 17 Mar. 2017. <http://foodbabe.com/2013/11/12/microwave-popcorn/>.
(7) "The Health Risks of Eating Conventionally-Grown Potatoes." *Livingmaxwell: A Guide to Organic Food & Drink*. N.p., 03 Sept. 2014. Web. 18 Mar. 2017.

<http://livingmaxwell.com/health-risks-conventional-potatoes>.

(8) Network, Pesticide Action. *What's On My Food :: Pesticides on Potatoes*. N.p., n.d. Web. 16 July 2017. <http://www.whatsonmyfood.org/food.jsp?food=PO>.

(9) "13 Ways That Sugary Soda Is Bad For Your Health." *Authority Nutrition*. N.p., 18 Aug. 2016. Web. 17 Mar. 2017. <https://authoritynutrition.com/13-ways-sugary-soda-is-bad-for-you/>.

(10) Price, Annie. "Are You Accidentally Ingesting This Kidney-Damaging Rust Inhibitor?" *Dr. Axe*, 20 June 2017, draxe.com/phosphoric-acid/.

(11) "Sugar and Cancer Growth Research." *Dr. Sircus*. N.p., 10 Dec. 2016. Web. 17 Mar. 2017. <http://drsircus.com/medicine/cancer/sugar-cancer-growth-research>.

(12) "The 76 Dangers of Sugar." *The Healthy Advocate*. N.p., 20 Sept. 2013. Web. 17 Mar. 2017. <http://thehealthyadvocate.com/2011/03/29/the-76-dangers-of-sugar/>.

(13) "Artificial Sweeteners -- More Dangerous than You Ever Imagined." *Mercola.com*, articles.mercola.com/sites/articles/archive/2009/10/13/artificial-sweeteners-more-dangerous-than-you-ever-imagined.aspx.

(14) Shell, Ellen Ruppel. "Artificial Sweeteners May Change Our Gut Bacteria in Dangerous Ways." *Scientific American*. N.p., 05 Mar. 2015. Web. 17 Mar. 2017. <https://www.scientificamerican.com/article/artificial-sweeteners-may-change-our-gut-bacteria-in-dangerous-ways/>.

(15) "21 'Health' Foods You Should Never Eat." *Dr. Axe*. N.p., 30 Oct. 2016. Web. 18 Mar. 2017. <https://draxe.com/health-foods-you-should-never-eat/?utm_source=nurture&utm_medium=email&utm_campaign=nurture>.

(16) "Top 6 Essential Health Benefits of Sea Salt." *Dr. Axe*. N.p., 30 Jan. 2017. Web. 18 Mar. 2017. <https://draxe.com/10-benefits-celtic-sea-salt-himalayan-salt/>.

(17) "Avoid This If You Want to Keep Your Thyroid Healthy." *Mercola.com*, articles.mercola.com/sites/articles/archive/2009/09/05/Another-Poison-Hiding-in-Your-Environment.aspx.

(18) Rose, Gianna. "Why Isn't White Bread Good for You?" *LIVESTRONG.COM*. Leaf Group, 28 Jan. 2015. Web. 18 Mar. 2017. <http://www.livestrong.com/article/343850-why-isnt-white-bread-good-for-you/>.

(19) "The Top 10 Worst Food Ingredients to Avoid Like The Plague." *REALfarmacy.com*. N.p., 04 Aug. 2016. Web. 18 Mar. 2017. <http://www.realfarmacy.com/worst-ingredients/>.

(20) "Food Dyes: A Rainbow of Risks." *Food Dyes: A Rainbow of Risks | Center for Science in the Public Interest*. N.p., n.d. Web. 16 July 2017. <https://cspinet.org/resource/food-dyes-rainbow-risks>.

(21) "A Sweet Problem: Princeton Researchers Find That High-Fructose Corn Syrup Prompts Considerably More Weight Gain." *Princeton University*, The Trustees of Princeton University, www.princeton.edu/news/2010/03/22/sweet-problem-princeton-researchers-find-high-fructose-corn-syrup-prompts

(22) "How High Fructose Corn Syrup Destroys Your Body (It's NOT a Pretty Picture)." *Dr. Axe*. N.p., 23 Nov. 2016. Web. 17 Mar. 2017.

(23) Juhasz, Francine. "Other Names for MSG or Monosodium Glutamate." *LIVESTRONG.COM*. Leaf Group, 15 Apr. 2015. Web. 16 July 2017. <http://www.livestrong.com/article/377482-other-names-for-msg-or-monosodium-glutamate/>.

(24) "A Possible Cause of Alzheimer's Dementia – Industrial Soy Foods." *Medical Hypotheses*, Churchill Livingstone, 7 Dec. 2013, www.sciencedirect.com/science/article/pii/S0306987713005628.

(25) *The Doctor Within*. N.p., n.d. Web. 18 Mar. 2017. <http://www.thedoctorwithin.com/soy/magic-bean/>.

(26) "The Whole Soy Story: The Dark Side of America's Favorite Health Food." *Mercola.com*. N.p., n.d. Web. 16 July 2017. <http://articles.mercola.com/sites/articles/archive/2008/07/17/the-whole-soy-story-the-dark-side-of-america-s-favorite-health-food.aspx>.

(27) "The Truth About Soy Foods: Can Soy Damage Your Health?" *Mercola.com*. N.p., n.d. Web. 18 Mar. 2017. <http://articles.mercola.com/sites/articles/archive/2010/09/18/soy-can-damage-your-health.aspx>.

JUICING AND SMOOTHIES

(1) Lawenda, M.D. Brian D., and About Brian D. Lawenda, M.D.I Am an Integrative Oncologist. I Trained at Massachusetts General Hospital (Harvard Medical School) in Radiation Oncology and through Stanford-UCLA (Helms Medical Institute) in Medical Acupuncture. I Am the Founder of Integrat. "Juicing." *Integrative Oncology Essentials*. N.p., 24 Jan. 2014. Web. 19 Mar. 2017. <https://integrativeoncology-essentials.com/2014/01/juicing-and-blending-anticancer-turbocharging/juicing/>.

(2) "Juicing vs. Blending: Everything You Need to Know." *Reboot With Joe*. N.p., 26 Jan. 2017. Web. 19 Mar. 2017. <http://www.rebootwithjoe.com/juicing-vs-blending-facts/>.

(3) "Juicing vs. Blending: Which One Is Better?" *FOOD MATTERS®*, Food Matters, 31 Jan. 2018, www.foodmatters.com/article/juicing-vs-blending-which-one-is-better.

(4) N.p., n.d. Web. <http://articles.mercola.com/sites/articles/archive/2011/11/13/benefits-of-juicing.aspx+http://www.all-about-juicing.com/best-fruits-and-vegetables.html+>.

THE DANGER OF SUGAR

(1) "Temptation - Dictionary Definition." *Vocabulary.com*. N.p., n.d. Web. 01 Apr. 2017. <https://www.vocabulary.com/dictionary/temptation>.

(2) "Endurance Sports Nutrition: The Body's Fuel Sources." *Human-Kinetics*, www.humankinetics.com/excerpts/excerpts/the-bodyrsquos-fuel-sources.

(3) Traister, Jeffrey. "The Function of Disaccharides." *LIVESTRONG.COM*, Leaf Group, 3 Oct. 2017, www.livestrong.com/article/535273-the-function-of-disaccharides/.

(4) "Natural vs. Refined Sugars: What's the Difference? | CTCA." *CancerCenter.com*. N.p., 30 July 2014. Web. 01 Apr. 2017. <http://www.cancercenter.com/discussions/blog/natural-vs-refined-sugars-whats-the-difference/>.

(5) "10 Disturbing Reasons Why Sugar Is Bad For You." *Authority Nutrition*. N.p., 18 Aug. 2016. Web. 01 Apr. 2017. <https://authoritynutrition.com/10-disturbing-reasons-why-sugar-is-bad/>.

(6) "Natural vs Processed Sugars." *Organics.org*. N.p., 10 Feb. 2017. Web. 01 Apr. 2017. <http://organics.org/natural-vs-processed-sugars/>.

(7) Welsh, Jennifer. "The Terrifying Truth About How Much Sugar Americans Eat [INFOGRAPHIC]." *Business Insider*. Business Insider, 11 Sept. 2012. Web. 01 Apr. 2017. <http://www.businessinsider.com/how-much-sugar-americans-eat-infographic-2012-9>.

(8) Espat, Adelina. "Does Sugar Cause Cancer? | MD Anderson Cancer Center." *Does Sugar Cause Cancer? | MD Anderson Cancer Center*. N.p., n.d. Web. 01 Apr. 2017. <https://www.mdanderson.org/publications/focused-on-health/may-2015/FOH-cancer-love-sugar.html>.

(9) "5 Reasons Cancer and Sugar Are Best Friends." *5 Reasons Cancer and Sugar Are Best Friends*. N.p., n.d. Web. 01 Apr. 2017. <http://beatcancer.org/2014/03/5-reasons-cancer-and-sugar-are-best-friends/>.

(10) Norris, Jeffrey. "Sugar Is a Poison, Says UCSF Obesity Expert." *UC San Francisco*. N.p., 25 June 2009. Web. 01 Apr. 2017. <https://www.ucsf.edu/news/2009/06/8187/obesity-and-metabolic-syndrome-driven-fructose-sugar-diet>.

(11) "Frequently Asked Questions About Sugar." *Frequently Asked Questions About Sugar*. N.p., n.d. Web. 01 Apr. 2017. <http://www.heart.org/HEARTORG/HealthyLiving/HealthyEating/HealthyDietGoals/Frequently-Asked-Questions-About-Sugar_UCM_306725_Article.jsp#.WN8mk1dIFEw>.

(12) "How Bad Is Sugar for Your Liver and Brain?" *Mercola.com*. N.p., n.d. Web. 01 Apr. 2017. <http://articles.mercola.com/sites/articles/archive/2016/01/13/sugar-destroys-liver-brain.aspx>.

(13) N.p., n.d. Web. <https://www.betterhealth.vic.gov.au/health/conditionsandtreatments/liver>.

(14) "The Liver's Role in Hormone Balance Newsletter." *Women's International Pharmacy*. N.p., n.d. Web. 01 Apr. 2017.

<http://www.womensinternational.com/connections/liver.html>.

(15) "What Are Empty Calories?" *What Are Empty Calories? | Natural Balance Foods*. N.p., n.d. Web. 01 Apr. 2017. <https://www.naturalbalancefoods.co.uk/community/healthy-living/what-are-empty-calories/>.

(16) Haas, Elson M., Daniella Chace, and .. *The New Detox Diet: The Complete Guide for Lifelong Vitality with Recipes, Menus, and Detox Plans*. Berkeley, CA: Celestial Arts, 2004. Print.

(17) "Sugar and Cancer." *EatRight - Oncology Nutrition, a Dietetic Practice of the Academy of Nutrition and Dietetics*. N.p., n.d. Web. 01 Apr. 2017. <https://www.oncologynutrition.org/erfc/healthy-nutrition-now/sugar-and-cancer/>.

(18) "What Happens in Your Body When You Eat Too Much Sugar?" *Mercola.com*. N.p., n.d. Web. 01 Apr. 2017. <http://articles.mercola.com/sugar-side-effects.aspx>.

(19) Seward, Marc. "5 Surprising Benefits of Maple Syrup." *Healthy Focus*. N.p., 20 Feb. 2017. Web. 01 Apr. 2017. <https://healthyfocus.org/benefits-of-maple-syrup/>.

(20) "Easy Ways to Kick Your Sugar Addiction." *The Dr. Oz Show*. N.p., n.d. Web. 01 Apr. 2017. <http://www.doctoroz.com/article/kick-your-sugar-addiction>.

(21) "Trying To Lose Weight? Stay Away From Artificial Sweeteners." *Rodale's Organic Life*. N.p., 23 Oct. 2015. Web. 01 Apr. 2017. <http://www.rodalesorganiclife.com/food/trying-lose-weight-stay-away-artificial-sweeteners>.

REVIEWING THE CODE

(1) "Office of Dietary Supplements - Vitamin A." *National Institutes of Health*. U.S. Department of Health and Human Services, n.d. Web. 21 Apr. 2017. <https://ods.od.nih.gov/factsheets/VitaminA-HealthProfessional/>.

(2) McDermott, By Nicole. "The Benefits of Vitamin B Complex." *Life by Daily Burn*. N.p., 14 July 2016. Web. 21 Apr. 2017. <http://dailyburn.com/life/health/benefits-vitamin-b-complex/>.

(3) "Vitamin C (Ascorbic Acid)." *University of Maryland Medical Center*. N.p., n.d. Web. 21 Apr. 2017. <http://www.umm.edu/health/medical/altmed/supplement/vitamin-c-ascorbic-acid>.

(4) "Calcium and Calcium Supplements: Achieving the Right Balance." *Mayo Clinic*. Mayo Foundation for Medical Education and Research, 05 Aug. 2015. Web. 21 Apr. 2017. <http://www.mayoclinic.org/healthy-lifestyle/nutrition-and-healthy-eating/in-depth/calcium-supplements/art-20047097>.

(5) "What Is Choline? Big Benefits & Signs of a Deficiency." *Dr. Axe*. N.p., 29 Mar. 2017. Web. 21 Apr. 2017. <https://draxe.com/what-is-choline/>.

(6) "Copper." *Linus Pauling Institute*. N.p., 03 Jan. 2017. Web. 21 Apr. 2017. <http://lpi.oregonstate.edu/mic/minerals/copper>.

(7) Ware, Megan. "Vitamin D: Health Benefits, Facts and Research." *Medical News Today*. MediLexicon International, n.d. Web. 21 Apr. 2017. <http://www.medicalnewstoday.com/articles/161618.php>.

(8) *Fight Back with Food*. New York, NY: Reader's Digest Association, 2007. Print.

(9) Anonymous. "How Lycopene Helps Protect Against Cancer." *The Physicians Committee*. N.p., 20 Apr. 2016. Web. 21 Apr. 2017. <http://www.pcrm.org/health/cancer-resources/diet-cancer/nutrition/how-lycopene-helps-protect-against-cancer>.

(10) "10 Evidence-Based Health Benefits of Magnesium." *Authority Nutrition*. N.p., 17 Aug. 2016. Web. 21 Apr. 2017. <https://authoritynutrition.com/10-proven-magnesium-benefits/>.

(11) "Omega-3 Fatty Acids: An Essential Contribution." *The Nutrition Source*. N.p., 26 May 2015. Web. 21 Apr. 2017. <https://www.hsph.harvard.edu/nutritionsource/omega-3-fats/>.

(12) *Phosphorus*. N.p., n.d. Web. 21 Apr. 2017. <http://www.whfoods.com/genpage.php?tname=nutrient&dbid=127>.

(13) Ware, Megan. "What Are the Health Benefits of Selenium?" *Medical News Today*. MediLexicon International, 19 Jan. 2015. Web. 21 Apr. 2017. <http://www.medicalnewstoday.com/articles/287842.php>.

INSPECTING THE ELECTRIC CODE

(1) "10 Interesting Benefits of Arugula." *Organic Facts*. N.p., 13 Feb. 2017. Web. 08 Apr. 2017. <https://www.organicfacts.net/health-benefits/vegetable/health-benefits-of-arugula.html>.

(2) Ware, Megan. "The Health Benefits of Bok Choy." *Medical News Today*. MediLexicon International, n.d. Web. 08 Apr. 2017. <http://www.medicalnewstoday.com/articles/280948.php>.

(3) "9 Health Benefits of Broccoli." *9 Health Benefits Of Broccoli | Care2 Healthy Living*. N.p., n.d. Web. 08 Apr. 2017. <http://www.care2.com/greenliving/love-it-or-hate-it-broccoli-is-good-for-you.html>

(4) "What Are the Benefits of Eating Brussels Sprouts?" *Mercola.com*. N.p., n.d. Web. 08 Apr. 2017. <http://articles.mercola.com/sites/articles/archive/2014/11/16/benefits-brussels-sprouts.aspx>.

(5) "13 Amazing Benefits of Cabbage." *Organic Facts*. N.p., 28 Feb. 2017. Web. 08 Apr. 2017. <https://www.organicfacts.net/health-benefits/vegetable/health-benefits-of-cabbage.html>.

(6) "Top 20 Benefits of Cauliflower." *Organic Facts*. N.p., 28 Feb. 2017. Web. 08 Apr. 2017. <https://www.organicfacts.net/health-benefits/vegetable/health-benefits-of-cauliflower.html>.

(7) "What Are Collard Greens Good For?" *Mercola.com*. N.p., n.d. Web. 08 Apr. 2017. <http://foodfacts.mercola.com/collard-greens.html>.

(8) Administrator. "Cancer Fighting Foods/Spices - Welcome To Cancer Cure Foundation." *Cancer Fighting Foods/Spices - Welcome To Cancer Cure Foundation*. N.p., n.d. Web. 08 Apr. 2017. <http://www.cancure.org/12-links-page/37-cancer-fighting-foods-spices>.

(9) Lewis, Alison. "Top 10 Health Benefits of Eating Kale." *Mindbodygreen*. N.p., 02 Apr. 2012. Web. 08 Apr. 2017. <https://www.mindbodygreen.com/0-4408/Top-10-Health-Benefits-of-Eating-Kale.html>.

(10) "20 Surprising Benefits Of Radish." *Organic Facts*. N.p., 10 Mar. 2017. Web. 08 Apr. 2017. <https://www.organicfacts.net/health-benefits/vegetable/health-benefits-of-radish.html>.

(11) "15 Impressive Benefits of Spinach." *Organic Facts*. N.p., 29 Mar. 2017. Web. 08 Apr. 2017. <https://www.organicfacts.net/health-benefits/vegetable/health-benefits-of-spinach.html>.

(12) "5 Powerful Health Benefits of Asparagus You Probably Didn't Know." *EatingWell*. N.p., n.d. Web. 08 Apr. 2017. <http://www.eatingwell.com/blogs/health_blog/5_powerful_health_benefits_of_asparagus_you_probably_didn_t_know>.

(13) "Six Amazing Health Benefits of Eating Beets." *Mercola.com*. N.p., n.d. Web. 08 Apr. 2017. <http://articles.mercola.com/sites/articles/archive/2014/01/25/beets-health-benefits.aspx>.

(14) Kapadia, G. J., G. S. Rao, C. Ramachandran, A. Iida, N. Suzuki, and H. Tokuda. "Synergistic Cytotoxicity of Red Beetroot (Beta Vulgaris L.) Extract with Doxorubicin in Human Pancreatic, Breast and Prostate Cancer Cell Lines." *Journal of Complementary & Integrative Medicine*. U.S. National Library of Medicine, 26 June 2013. Web. 08 Apr. 2017. <https://www.ncbi.nlm.nih.gov/pubmed/23828331>.

(15) "10 Benefits of Carrots: The Crunchy Powerfood." *10 Benefits Of Carrots | Care2 Healthy Living*. N.p., n.d. Web. 08 Apr. 2017. <http://www.care2.com/greenliving/10-benefits-of-carrots.html>.

(16) N.p., n.d. Web. <http://www.whfoods.com/genpage.php?tname=foodspice&dbid=140>.

(17) Writer, Leaf Group. "What Are the Health Benefits of Jalapeno Peppers?" *Healthy Eating | SF Gate*. SF Gate, 01 Sept. 2012. Web. 08 Apr. 2017. <http://healthyeating.sfgate.com/health-benefits-jalapeno-peppers-4880.html>.

(18) Writer, Leaf Group. "What Are the Health Benefits of Jalapeno Peppers?" *Healthy Eating | SF Gate*. SF Gate, 01 Sept. 2012. Web. 08 Apr. 2017. <http://healthyeating.sfgate.com/health-benefits-jalapeno-peppers-4880.html>.

(19) "9 Amazing Health Benefits of Cucumbers." *Mercola.com*. N.p., n.d. Web. 08 Apr. 2017. <http://articles.mercola.com/sites/articles/archive/2014/08/23/health-benefits-cucumbers.aspx>.

(20) "10 Amazing Benefits of Eggplant." *Organic Facts*. N.p., 28 Feb. 2017. Web. 08 Apr. 2017. <https://www.organicfacts.net/health-benefits/vegetable/health-benefits-of-eggplant.html>.

(21) "Garlic and Cancer Prevention." *National Cancer Institute*. N.p., n.d. Web. 08 Apr. 2017. <http://www.cancer.gov/about-cancer/causes-prevention/risk/diet/garlic-fact-sheet>.

(22) https://www.ncbi.nlm.nih.gov/pmc/articles/PMC3339609/

(23) "Mushrooms' Surprising Immunity-Boosting Benefits." *Dr. Axe*. N.p., 01 July 2015. Web. 08 Apr. 2017. <https://draxe.com/mushroom-nutrition-benefits/>.

(24) Thompson, Jennifer. "Jennifer Thompson." *Jennifer Thompson*. Jennifer Thompson Http://healthybliss.net/bliss/wp-content/uploads/2014/11/hb_logo_01.png, 31 Dec. 2015. Web. 08 Apr. 2017. <http://healthybliss.net/healing-power-of-onions-can-onions-absorb-bacteria-viruses-and-flu/>.

(25) Mateljan, George. *The World's Healthiest Foods: Essential Guide for the Healthiest Way of Eating*. Seattle, WA: George Mateljan Foundation, 2007. Print.

(26) "The Importance of Minerals and Trace Elements for Health and Cancer Prevention." *The Importance of Minerals and Trace Elements for Health and Cancer Prevention*. N.p., n.d. Web. 08 Apr. 2017. <http://www.healingcancernaturally.com/importance-minerals-trace-elements.html>.

(27) "7 Amazing Benefits of Squash." *Organic Facts*. N.p., 28 Feb. 2017. Web. 08 Apr. 2017. <https://www.organicfacts.net/health-benefits/fruit/squash.html>.

(28) "NCI Says What You Eat Can Hurt You or It Can Help You Fight Cancer. List of Foods with Cancer-fighting Properties Follows." *Cancer Survivors Network*. N.p., n.d. Web. 08 Apr. 2017. <https://csn.cancer.org/node/236257>.

(29) "5 Huge Health Benefits of Sweet Potatoes." *NaturalNews*. N.p., n.d. Web. 08 Apr. 2017. <http://www.naturalnews.com/035739_sweet_potatoes_beta-carotene_nutrients.html>.

(30) "Tomato Nutrition Helps You Fight Cancer & Inflammation." *Dr. Axe*. N.p., 10 July 2015. Web. 08 Apr. 2017. <https://draxe.com/tomato-nutrition/>.

(31) "10 Impressive Health Benefits of Apples." *Authority Nutrition*. N.p., 22 Aug. 2016. Web. 08 Apr. 2017. <https://authoritynutrition.com/10-health-benefits-of-apples/>.

(32) "10 Impressive Benefits of Apricots." *Organic Facts*. N.p., 29 Mar. 2017. Web. 08 Apr. 2017. <https://www.organicfacts.net/health-benefits/fruit/apricots.html>.

(33) "12 Proven Health Benefits of Avocado." *Authority Nutrition*. N.p., 18 Aug. 2016. Web. 08 Apr. 2017. <https://authoritynutrition.com/12-proven-benefits-of-avocado/>.

(34) Szalay, Jessie. "Bananas: Health Benefits, Risks & Nutrition Facts." *LiveScience*. Purch, 29 Sept. 2014. Web. 08 Apr. 2017. <http://www.livescience.com/45005-banana-nutrition-facts.html>.

(35) "12 Health Benefits of Acai Berries." *Dr. Group's Healthy Living Articles*. N.p., 05 Oct. 2015. Web. 08 Apr. 2017. <http://www.globalhealingcenter.com/natural-health/benefits-of-acai/>.

(36) "15 Best Benefits of Blackberry." *Organic Facts*. N.p., 28 Feb. 2017. Web. 08 Apr. 2017. <https://www.organicfacts.net/health-benefits/fruit/blackberries.html>.

(37) Ware, Megan. "Strawberries: Health Benefits, Nutritional Breakdown." *Medical News Today*. MediLexicon International, n.d. Web. 08 Apr. 2017. <http://www.medicalnewstoday.com/articles/271285.php>.

(38) "7 Health Benefits of Blueberries." *Dr. Axe*. N.p., 30 Mar. 2017. Web. 08 Apr. 2017. <https://draxe.com/health-benefits-blueberries/>.

(39) N.p., n.d. Web. <http://www.nutrition-and-you.com/cranberries.html>.

(40) "Goji Berries: Antioxidant & Anti-inflammatory Superfruit." *Dr. Axe*. N.p., 29 Mar. 2017. Web. 08 Apr. 2017. <https://draxe.com/goji-berry-benefits/>.

(41) "7 Important Benefits of Cantaloupe." *Organic Facts*. N.p., 29 Mar. 2017. Web. 09 Apr. 2017. <https://www.organicfacts.net/health-benefits/fruit/health-benefits-of-cantaloupe.html>.

(42) Boucher, Kristen, Health & Organic Wellbeing (H.O.W) Says, Zirah1 Says, Kristen Boucher Says, Lori Says, Sharon Says, Joni Says, Sonia C. Says, Linda Says, Modesto Caldera Zapata Says, Nilesh Says, Marla Says, Nym Says, Tim Says, Jessie Says, Daniel Says, Garba Inusa Says, Heba Says, and Jan Lopez Says. "3 Health Benefits of Cantaloupe Seeds." *MIX Wellness*. N.p., 12 May 2016. Web. 09 Apr. 2017. <https://mixwellness.com/health-benefits-of-cantaloupe-seeds/>.

(43) "11 Health Benefits of Cherries." *11 Health Benefits Of Cherries | Care2 Healthy Living*. N.p., n.d. Web. 09 Apr. 2017. <http://www.care2.com/greenliving/11-health-benefits-of-the-beautiful-cherry.html>.

(44) "Health Benefits of Dates - Over 7 Reasons to Eat a Date Fruit." *Natural Society*. N.p., 03 Feb. 2015. Web. 09 Apr. 2017. <http://naturalsociety.com/health-benefits-of-dates-7-reasons-eat-date-fruit/>.

(45) "15 Best Benefits of Figs or Anjeer." *Organic Facts*. N.p., 10 Mar. 2017. Web. 09 Apr. 2017. <https://www.organicfacts.net/health-benefits/fruit/health-benefits-of-figs-or-anjeer.html>.

(46) "The 20 Healthiest Fruits on the Planet." *Authority Nutrition*. N.p., 03 Oct. 2016. Web. 09 Apr. 2017. <https://authoritynutrition.com/20-healthiest-fruits/>.

(47) "Grapes Nutrition Facts and Health Benefits." *Nutrition And You.com*. N.p., n.d. Web. 09 Apr. 2017. <http://www.nutrition-and-you.com/grapes.html>.

(48) Ware, Megan. "Kiwifruit: Health Benefits, Nutritional Breakdown." *Medical News Today*. MediLexicon International, n.d. Web. 09 Apr. 2017. <http://www.medicalnewstoday.com/articles/271232.php?page=2>.

(49) "Top 10 Health Benefits of Lemon Water." *Health And Love Page*. N.p., n.d. Web. 09 Apr. 2017. <http://www.healthandlovepage.com/top-10-health-benefits-lemon-water>.

(50) "Oranges 101: Nutrition Facts and Health Benefits." *Authority Nutrition*. N.p., n.d. Web. 09 Apr. 2017. <https://authoritynutrition.com/foods/oranges/>.

(51) "Papaya." *Papaya*. N.p., n.d. Web. 09 Apr. 2017. <http://www.whfoods.com/genpage.php?tname=foodspice&dbid=47>.

(52) "11 Surprising Benefits of Pears." *Organic Facts*. N.p., 13 Feb. 2017. Web. 09 Apr. 2017. <https://www.organicfacts.net/health-benefits/fruit/pears.html>.

(53) "11 Amazing Benefits of Pineapples." *Organic Facts*. N.p., 02 Feb. 2017. Web. 09 Apr. 2017. <https://www.organicfacts.net/health-benefits/fruit/pineapples.html>.

(54) "6 Bromelain Benefits, Side Effects and Dosage." *Dr. Axe*. N.p., 29 Mar. 2017. Web. 09 Apr. 2017. <https://draxe.com/6-unbelievable-health-benefits-bromelain/>.

(55) "7 Amazing Benefits of Pomegranates." *Organic Facts*. N.p., 10 Mar. 2017. Web. 09 Apr. 2017. <https://www.organicfacts.net/health-benefits/fruit/health-benefits-of-pomegranate.html>.

(56) "9 Amazing Benefits of Watermelon." *Organic Facts*. N.p., 13 Feb. 2017. Web. 09 Apr. 2017. <https://www.organicfacts.net/health-benefits/fruit/watermelon.html>.

(57) "6 Watermelon Facts That Might Surprise You." *Mercola.com*. N.p., n.d. Web. 09 Apr. 2017. <http://articles.mercola.com/sites/articles/archive/2014/07/21/watermelon-nutrition.aspx>.

(58) Jung, Alyssa. "5 Health Benefits of Beans and 5 Surprising Risks | Reader's Digest." *Reader's Digest*. N.p., 06 Mar. 2014. Web. 09 Apr. 2017. <http://www.rd.com/health/conditions/health-benefits-of-beans/>.

(59) "Oats." *Oats*. N.p., n.d. Web. 09 Apr. 2017. <http://www.whfoods.com/genpage.php?tname=foodspice&dbid=54>.

(60) "10 Reasons Why Brown Rice Is the Healthy Choice." *VegKitchen*. N.p., 06 Nov. 2016. Web. 09 Apr. 2017. <http://www.vegkitchen.com/nutrition/10-reasons-why-brown-rice-is-the-healthy-choice/>.

(61) "Lentils Nutrition Facts, Benefits and Recipes." *Dr. Axe*. N.p., 30 June 2015. Web. 09 Apr. 2017. <https://draxe.com/lentils-nutrition/>.

SPICES, HERBS, NUTS, AND SEEDS

(1) Fraser, Carly. "17 Incredible Health Benefits of Turmeric." *Live Love Fruit*. N.p., 19 Oct. 2014. Web. 21 Mar. 2017. <http://livelovefruit.com/incredible-health-benefits-of-turmeric/>.

(2) "The Amazing Cancer-Fighting Benefits of Curcumin." *The Truth About Cancer*. N.p., 16 Nov. 2016. Web. 21 Mar. 2017. <https://thetruthaboutcancer.com/cancer-fighting-benefits-of-curcumin/>.

(3) "Turmeric Benefits Superior To 10 Medications At Reversing Disease." *Dr. Axe*. N.p., 27 Feb. 2017. Web. 21 Mar. 2017. <https://draxe.com/turmeric-benefits/>.

(4) "What Is Turmeric Good For?" *Mercola.com*, foodfacts.mercola.com/turmeric.html.

(5) "Turmeric vs. Curcumin - What's the Difference?" *Home: The Difference Between Turmeric and Curcumin : Curcumin For Health*, www.curcuminforhealth.com/the-difference-between-turmeric-and-curcumin/.

(6)"The Amazing Cancer-Fighting Benefits of Curcumin." *The Truth About Cancer*. N.p., 16 Nov. 2016. Web. 21 Mar. 2017. <https://thetruthaboutcancer.com/cancer-fighting-benefits-of-curcumin/>.

(7) N.p., n.d. Web. <http://www.whfoods.com/genpage.php?tname=foodspice&dbid=140>.

(8) "Garlic." *Garlic*. N.p., n.d. Web. 21 Mar. 2017. <http://www.whfoods.com/genpage.php?tname=foodspice&dbid=60>.

(9) Nordqvist, Joseph. "Oregano: Health Benefits, Side Effects." *Medical News Today*. MediLexicon International, n.d. Web. 21 Mar. 2017. <http://www.medicalnewstoday.com/articles/266259.php>.

(10) *Cinnamon, Ground*, www.whfoods.com/genpage.php?dbid=68&tname=foodspice.

(11) "What Is Ginger Good For?" *Mercola.com*. N.p., n.d. Web. 21 Mar. 2017. <http://foodfacts.mercola.com/ginger.html>.

(12) Bode, Ann M. "The Amazing and Mighty Ginger." *Herbal Medicine: Biomolecular and Clinical Aspects. 2nd Edition*. U.S. National Library of Medicine, 01 Jan. 1970. Web. 21 Mar. 2017. <http://www.ncbi.nlm.nih.gov/books/NBK92775/>.

(13) "Peppermint." *University of Maryland Medical Center*. N.p., n.d. Web. 21 Mar. 2017. <http://umm.edu/health/medical/altmed/herb/peppermint>.

(14) *Worldhealthpage.com*. N.p., n.d. Web. 21 Mar. 2017. <http://www.worldhealthpage.com/2016/03/27/curry-powder-health-benefits/>.

(15) "Herbal Information Center - Aloe Vera - Benefits, Usage, Side Effects, Dosage, General Store - Herbs." *Herbal Information Center - Aloe Vera - Benefits, Usage, Side Effects, Dosage, General Store - Herbs*. N.p., n.d. Web. 21 Mar. 2017. <http://www.kcweb.com/herb/aloevera.htm>.

(16) UK, Cancer Research. "Aloe." *Cancer Research UK*. N.p., n.d. Web. 21 Mar. 2017. <http://www.cancerresearchuk.org/about-cancer/cancers-in-general/treatment/complementary-alternative/therapies/aloe-vera>.

(17) "Cumin Seeds." *Cumin Seeds*. N.p., n.d. Web. 21 Mar. 2017. <http://www.whfoods.com/genpage.php?tname=foodspice&dbid=91>.

(18) "Natural Health: 10 Amazing Benefits of Consuming Flax Seed." *Dr. Axe*. N.p., 08 May 2016. Web. 21 Mar. 2017. <https://draxe.com/10-flax-seed-benefits-nutrition-facts/>.

(19) "8 Delicious Ways to Use Chia Seeds." *Mercola.com*. N.p., n.d. Web. 21 Mar. 2017. <http://articles.mercola.com/sites/articles/archive/2015/07/06/chia-seeds-benefits.aspx>.

(20) "9 Amazing Health Benefits of Pumpkin Seeds." *Mercola.com*. N.p., n.d. Web. 21 Mar. 2017. <http://articles.mercola.com/sites/articles/archive/2013/09/30/pumpkin-seed-benefits.aspx>.

(21) "Hemp Seed Benefits and Nutrition Profile." *Dr. Axe*. N.p., 16 June 2015. Web. 21 Mar. 2017. <https://draxe.com/7-hemp-seed-benefits-nutrition-profile/>.

(22) "Sunflower Seeds: Benefits, Nutrition & Recipes." *Dr. Axe*. N.p., 06 Dec. 2016. Web. 21 Mar. 2017. <https://draxe.com/sunflower-seeds/>.

(23) Tan, S. Y., and R. D. Mattes. "Appetitive, Dietary and Health Effects of Almonds Consumed with Meals or as Snacks: A Randomized, Controlled Trial." *Nature News*. Nature Publishing Group, 02 Oct. 2013. Web. 21 Mar. 2017. <http://www.nature.com/ejcn/journal/v67/n11/full/ejcn2013184a.html>.

(24) "9 Surprising Benefits of Brazil Nuts." *Organic Facts*. N.p., 28 Feb. 2017. Web. 09 Apr. 2017. <https://www.organicfacts.net/health-benefits/seed-and-nut/brazil-nuts.html>.

(25) "Cashew Nutrition: Absolute The Best Cure For Depression Without Medication." *NaturalNews Blogs*. N.p., 04 Nov. 2015. Web. 21 Mar. 2017. <http://www.naturalnewsblogs.com/cashew-nutrition-absolute-best-cure-depression-without-medication/>.

(26) Landry, Georgia. "Georgia Landry." *1mhealthtips*. N.p., 18 June 2016. Web. 21 Mar. 2017. <http://www.1mhealthtips.com/7-healthy-reasons-to-snack-on-cashew-nuts/>.

(27) "Hazelnuts Benefit the Heart, Brain & Skin." *Dr. Axe*. N.p., 05 Apr. 2017. Web. 09 Apr. 2017. <https://draxe.com/hazelnuts/>.

(28) Bosch, Laurentine Ten. "10 Fascinating Health Benefits Of Macadamias." *FOOD MATTERS®*. Food Matters, 17 Feb. 2017. Web. 09 Apr. 2017. <http://www.foodmatters.com/article/10-fascinating-health-benefits-of-macadamias>.

(29) "Pecans Nutrition Facts and Health Benefits." *Nutrition And You.com*. N.p., n.d. Web. 09 Apr. 2017. <http://www.nutrition-and-you.com/pecans.html>.

(30) "8 Incredible Health Benefits of Pine Nuts." *8 Incredible Health Benefits Of Pine Nuts | Care2 Healthy Living*. N.p., n.d. Web. 09 Apr. 2017. <http://www.care2.com/greenliving/8-incredible-health-benefits-of-pine-nuts.html>.

(31) "Walnuts: Abundant Disease Prevention Benefits." *LifeExtension.com*. N.p., n.d. Web. 21 Mar. 2017. <http://www.lifeextension.com/magazine/2015/12/walnuts-abundant-disease-prevention-benefits/page-01>.

(32) "What Are the Healthiest Nuts and Seeds?" *Mercola.com*. N.p., n.d. Web. 21 Mar. 2017. <http://articles.mercola.com/sites/articles/archive/2015/10/19/best-nuts-seeds.aspx>.

MEAT,EGGS,AND FISH

(1) "What Are Proteins and What Do They Do? - Genetics Home Reference." *U.S. National Library of Medicine*. National Institutes of Health, n.d. Web. 22 Apr. 2017. <https://ghr.nlm.nih.gov/primer/howgeneswork/protein>.

(2) "Protein." *Diagnosis:Diet*. N.p., n.d. Web. 22 Apr. 2017. <http://www.diagnosisdiet.com/food/protein/>.

(3) "100% Grass Fed Beef: Boneless Rib, Steaks, and Ground Beef." *Mercola.com*. N.p., n.d. Web. 22 Apr. 2017. <http://products.mercola.com/grass-fed-beef/>.

(4) "Where to Find Grass-Fed Beef, Raw Milk, and Pastured Eggs." *Mercola.com*. N.p., n.d. Web. 22 Apr. 2017. <http://www.mercola.com/beef/health_benefits.htm>.

(5) "Grass-Fed vs Grain-Fed Meat: Part 1." *Bulletproof*. N.p., 13 Apr. 2017. Web. 22 Apr. 2017. <https://www.bulletproofexec.com/grass-fed-meat-part-1>.

(6) Daley, Cynthia A., Amber Abbott, Patrick S. Doyle, Glenn A. Nader, and Stephanie Larson. "A Review of Fatty Acid Profiles and Antioxidant Content in Grass-fed and Grain-fed Beef." *Nutrition Journal*. BioMed Central, 2010. Web. 22 Apr. 2017. <https://www.ncbi.nlm.nih.gov/pmc/articles/PMC2846864/>.

(7) "Grass-Fed vs Grain-Fed Beef – What's The Difference?" *Authority Nutrition*. N.p., 18 Aug. 2016. Web. 22 Apr. 2017. <https://authoritynutrition.com/grass-fed-vs-grain-fed-beef/>.

(8) Flower, Frances. "What Makes Organic Chicken Organic?" *Whole Foods Market*. N.p., 04 Aug. 2011. Web. 22 Apr. 2017. <http://www.wholefoodsmarket.com/blog/whole-story/what-makes-organic-chicken-organic>.

(9) Lam, Francis. "What Do "free Range," "organic" and Other Chicken Labels Really Mean?" *Salon*. N.p., n.d. Web. 22 Apr. 2017. <http://www.salon.com/2011/01/20/what_chicken_labels_really_mean/>.

(10) CBSNews. ""Shocking" Reasons to Go Organic." *CBS News*. CBS Interactive, 16 Mar. 2010. Web. 22 Apr. 2017. <http://www.cbsnews.com/news/shocking-reasons-to-go-organic-16-03-2010/>.

(11) Publications, Inc. Ogden. "Meet Real Free-Range Eggs - Real Food." *Mother Earth News*. N.p., 01 Oct. 2007. Web. 22 Apr. 2017. <http://www.motherearthnews.com/real-food/free-range-eggs-zmaz07onzgoe>.

(12) "The Health Benefits of Organic Eggs." *Mercola.com*. N.p., n.d. Web. 22 Apr. 2017. <http://articles.mercola.com/sites/articles/archive/2011/09/02/why-does-this-commonly-vilified-food-actually-prevent-heart-disease-and-cancer.aspx>.

(13) Michaelis, Kristen, About the AuthorKristen Michaelis Is a Passionate Advocate for REAL FOOD -- Food That's Sustainable, Organic, Local, and Traditionally-prepared According to the Wisdom of Our Ancestors. While She Adores Hats & Happy Skirts, Nothing Inspires Her Quite like, Jen Says, Healthylife1 Says, Nutrition_world Says, KristenM Says, Beth @ Hooked on Health Says, Lulu Says, Emily Says, Russkick Says, Tarena Says, Pamelaknits53 Says, Kelly The Kitchen Kop Says, Vin - NaturalBias Says, Heidi From Savory Tv Says, Brie Says, Cajun Chef Ryan Says, Gypsygirl52 Says, Jambutter Says, Rebecca Subbiah Says, Thepinkpeppercorn Says, Sally Says, Ava Says, Fran Levy Says, Reneekatz Says, The Gourmet Grocer Says, Mark Danzig Says, Toni Harrell Says, and Aarati Pawar Says. "Healthy Seafood: What to Buy." *Food Renegade*. N.p., n.d. Web. 22 Apr. 2017. <http://www.foodrenegade.com/healthy-seafood-what-to-buy/>.

ANTIOXIDANTS
(1) Dr. Edward Group DC, NP, DACBN, DCBCN, DABFM. "The Health Benefits of Antioxidants." *Dr. Group's Healthy Living Articles*. Global Healing Center, Inc, 14 Oct. 2015. Web. 10 July 2017.
(2) "These Foods, Herb, Spices & Oils Are Absolutely Bursting with Antioxidants." *Dr. Axe*. N.p., n.d. Web. 10 July 2017.
(3) "Antioxidants and Cancer Prevention." *National Cancer Institute*. N.p., n.d. Web. 10 July 2017.
(4) Lobo, V., A. Patil, A. Phatak, and N. Chandra. "Free Radicals, Antioxidants and Functional Foods: Impact on Human Health." *Pharmacognosy Reviews*. Medknow Publications & Media Pvt Ltd, 2010. Web. 10 July 2017.
(5) *Free Radicals: Effects, Causes, and Defenses*. N.p., n.d. Web. 10 July 2017.
(6) "Antioxidants: What You Need to Know." *HowStuffWorks*. N.p., 26 Nov. 2002. Web. 10 July 2017.
(7) "Does Rich Color in Vegetables Mean More Antioxidants?" *Healthy Eating | SF Gate*. N.p., n.d. Web. 10 July 2017.
(8) "Antioxidants: In Depth." *National Center for Complementary and Integrative Health*. U.S. Department of Health and Human Services, 04 May 2016. Web. 10 July 2017.
(9) "Antioxidants: Beyond the Hype." *The Nutrition Source*. N.p., 12 Apr. 2016. Web. 10 July 2017.

REMOVING TOXINS FROM THE TEMPLE
(1) "Is There Toxic Waste In Your Body?" *Dr. Mark Hyman*. N.p., 18 May 2013. Web. 26 Apr. 2017. <http://drhyman.com/blog/2010/05/19/is-there-toxic-waste-in-your-body-2/>.
(2) *Body Detoxification & The Immune System*. N.p., n.d. Web. 26 Apr. 2017. <http://immunedisorders.homestead.com/detoxification.html>.
(3) "Body Cleanse: 6 Ways to Do a Body Detox." *Dr. Group's Healthy Living Articles*. N.p., 22 Feb. 2017. Web. 26 Apr. 2017. <http://www.globalhealingcenter.com/natural-health/6-ways-to-body-detox/>.
(4) Notes, Lymph. *The Lymphatic System*. N.p., n.d. Web. 26 Apr. 2017. <http://www.lymphnotes.com/article.php/id/151/>.
(5) "Best/Worst Foods for a Detox." *Green Eatz*. N.p., n.d. Web. 26 Apr. 2017. <http://www.greeneatz.com/1/post/2013/07/best-and-worst-foods-for-a-detox-diet.html>.
(6) N.p., n.d. Web. <https://draxe.com/the-best-way-to-detox/.p.,+18+May+2013.+Web.+26+Apr.+2017.+.>.
(7) "11 Probiotic Foods That Are Super Healthy." *Authority Nutrition*. N.p., 18 Aug. 2016. Web. 26 Apr. 2017. <https://authoritynutrition.com/11-super-healthy-probiotic-foods/>.
(8) Marks, Michelle. "7 Liver Cleansing Foods and Herbs." *Natural Health 365*. N.p., 23 Oct. 2013. Web. 26 Apr. 2017. <http://www.naturalhealth365.com/liver_cleansing.html/>.
(9) Chace, Elson M. Haas Daniella. "The New Detox Diet." *Goodreads*. N.p., n.d. Web. 26 Apr. 2017. <https://www.goodreads.com/book/show/755346.The_New_Detox_Diet>.
(10) Baker., Rand Khalil Lina. "Asparagus: Extraordinary Health Benefits." *Pure Inside Out*. N.p., n.d. Web. 30 Apr. 2017. <http://www.pureinsideout.com/asparagus-extraordinary-health-benefits.html>.

MAINTAINING AN ALKALINE DIET
(1) Ströhle, Alexander, and and Andreas Hahn. "Alexander Ströhle." *The American Journal of Clinical Nutrition*, 1 Feb. 2010, ajcn.nutrition.org/content/91/2/406.full.
(2) Schwalfenberg, Gerry K. "The Alkaline Diet: Is There Evidence That an Alkaline PH Diet Benefits Health?" *Journal of Environmental and Public Health*, Hindawi Publishing Corporation, 2012, www.ncbi.nlm.nih.gov/pmc/articles/PMC3195546/.
(3) Babcock, Jillian. "Is an Alkaline Diet the Key to Longevity?" *Dr. Axe*, 6 Oct. 2017, draxe.com/alkaline-diet/.
(4) Smith, S R, et al. "Tumour PH and Response to Chemotherapy: an in Vivo 31P Magnetic Resonance Spectroscopy Study in Non-Hodgkin's Lymphoma." *The British Journal of Radiology.*, U.S. National Library of Medicine, Oct. 1991, www.ncbi.nlm.nih.gov/pubmed/1954534/.

APPLE CIDER VINEGAR
(1) "What the Research Really Says About Apple Cider Vinegar." *Mercola.com*. N.p., n.d. Web. 22 Apr. 2017. <http://articles.mercola.com/sites/articles/archive/2009/06/02/apple-cider-vinegar-hype.aspx>.
(2) Axe, Dr. Josh. "20 Unique #AppleCiderVinegar Uses and Remedies." *Dr. Axe*, 6 Dec. 2017, draxe.com/apple-cider-vinegar-uses/.
(3) Tuttle, Chris. "28 Surprising Ways You Can Benefit From Apple Cider Vinegar." *One Good Thing by Jillee*. N.p., 07 Feb. 2017. Web. 22 Apr. 2017. <http://www.onegoodthingbyjillee.com/2013/09/28-health-and-beauty-benefits-of-apple-cider-vinegar.html>.
(4) Zafar, OCT Jawairia, Gerard, Jackie Wade, Mary Parkin, Phyllis, Ujwala Kamble, Beverly T., Melo, Rimel, Lewisdawson, and Valencia Johnson. "Apple Cider Vinegar Health Benefits." *Home Remedies Web*. Home Remedies Web, 04 Aug. 2016. Web. 22 Apr. 2017. <http://www.homeremediesweb.com/apple_cider_vinegar_health_benefits.php>.
(5) Mypeashealth. "Sixty Health Benefits and Home Remedies of Apple Cider Vinegar." *PEAS Health*. N.p., 10 July 2013. Web. 22 Apr. 2017. <http://www.peashealth.com/sixty-health-benefits-and-home-remedies-of-apple-cider->

HEATING AND COOLING THE TEMPLE
(1) "Is Exercise a Key to Cancer Cure?" *Mercola.com*. N.p., n.d. Web. 28 Apr. 2017. <http://fitness.mercola.com/sites/fitness/archive/2013/05/10/exercise-may-help-cure-cancer.aspx>.
(2) "What Are the Benefits of Exercise during and after Cancer Treatment?" *Memorial Sloan Kettering*. N.p., 02 Jan. 2014. Web. 28 Apr. 2017. <https://www.mskcc.org/blog/what-are-benefits-exercise-during-and-after-treatment>.
(3) *ScienceDaily*. ScienceDaily, n.d. Web. 28 Apr. 2017. <https://www.sciencedaily.com/releases/2012/06/120625065334.htm>.
(4) *American Heart Association Recommendations for Physical Activity in Adults*. N.p., n.d. Web. 17 July 2017. <http://www.heart.org/HEARTORG/HealthyLiving/PhysicalActivity/FitnessBasics/American-Heart-Association-Recommendations-for-Physical-Activity-in-Adults_UCM_307976_Article.jsp#.WWznQ6OZPIF>.
(5) "What We Recommend." *American Diabetes Association*. N.p., n.d. Web. 17 July 2017. <http://www.diabetes.org/food-and-fitness/fitness/types-of-activity/what-we-recommend.html>.
(6) "Exercise Linked to Reduce Cancer Risk." *Mercola.com*. N.p., n.d. Web. 28 Apr. 2017. <http://fitness.mercola.com/sites/fitness/archive/2015/07/31/exercise-reduces-cancer-risk.aspx>.

(7) "Strength Training: Get Stronger, Leaner, Healthier." *Mayo Clinic*, Mayo Foundation for Medical Education and Research, 22 Apr. 2016, www.mayoclinic.org/healthy-lifestyle/fitness/in-depth/strength-training/art-20046670?pg=2.

(8) "Why Strength Training Is so Important for Optimal Health." *Mercola.com*,fitness.mercola.com/sites/fitness/archive/2017/06/30/strength-training-importance.aspx.

(9) Schlinger, Amy. "The Do-It-Anywhere HIIT Workout You Need to Try." *Life by Daily Burn*, 29 Aug. 2017, dailyburn.com/life/fitness/high-intensity-hiit-workout/.

INVITING THE PRESENCE OF THE LORD INTO THE TEMPLE

(1) Amiel, E, et al. "β-Caryophyllene, a Compound Isolated from the Biblical Balm of Gilead (Commiphora Gileadensis), Is a Selective Apoptosis Inducer for Tumor Cell Lines." *Evidence-Based Complementary and Alternative Medicine : ECAM.*, U.S. National Library of Medicine, www.ncbi.nlm.nih.gov/pubmed/22567036.

(2) "12 Healing Oils of the Bible." *DrEricZ.com*, 12 Dec. 2017, drericz.com/12-healing-oils-of-the-bible/.

(3)"What Does the Bible Say About Essential Oils?" *Simple Life Abundant Life*, 12 Mar. 2017, simplelifeabundantlife.com/2013/09/26/biblical-look-use-essential-oils-can-apply-lives/.

(4) Stewart, David. *Healing Oils of the Bible*. Marble Hill, MO: Care Publications, 2007. Print.

(5) "Anointing With Oil." *40 Bible Verses about Anointing With Oil*. N.p., n.d. Web. 09 Apr. 2017. <http://bible.knowing-jesus.com/topics/Anointing-With-Oil>.

HOW TO USE ESSENTIAL OILS

(1) Perez, Sandrine. "Candles." *Nourishing Our Children*. N.p., 17 Oct. 2016. Web. 22 Apr. 2017. <https://nourishingourchildren.org/2011/12/13/candles/>.

(2) "Distilling Quality Essential Oils." *NEATOilEssentials* |, neatoilessentials.com/distilling-quality-essential-oils/.

/.latest_citation_text

(3) "Cinnamon Oil: 10 Proven Benefits and Uses." *Dr. Axe*. N.p., n.d. Web. 22 Apr. 2017. <https://draxe.com/cinnamon-oil/>.

(4) "23 Surprising Benefits of Clove Oil." *Organic Facts*. N.p., 10 Mar. 2017. Web. 22 Apr. 2017. <https://www.organicfacts.net/health-benefits/essential-oils/health-benefits-of-clove-oil.html>.

(5) "Frankincense Oil: A Natural Treatment for Cancer?" *Dr. Axe*. N.p., n.d. Web. 22 Apr. 2017. <https://draxe.com/frankincense-oil-cancer/>.

(6) "Herbal Oil: Frankincense Oil Benefits and Uses." *Mercola.com*. N.p., n.d. Web. 22 Apr. 2017. <http://articles.mercola.com/herbal-oils/frankincense-oil.aspx>.

(7) "10 Wonderful Benefits of Grapefruit Essential Oil." *Organic Facts*. N.p., 01 Mar. 2017. Web. 22 Apr. 2017. <https://www.organicfacts.net/health-benefits/essential-oils/grapefruit-essential-oil.html>.

(8) "10 Amazing Benefits of Lemon Oil." *Organic Facts*. N.p., 01 Mar. 2017. Web. 22 Apr. 2017. <https://www.organicfacts.net/health-benefits/essential-oils/health-benefits-of-lemon-oil.html>.

(9) "10 Essential Oils For Healing ." *DrEricZ.com*. N.p., 05 Apr. 2017. Web. 22 Apr. 2017. <http://drericz.com/10-essential-oils-for-healing/>.Apr. 2017. <https://thetruthaboutcancer.com/rosemary-essential-oil/>

(10) "Treating Infections Naturally." *Dr. Theresa Ramsey*. N.p., n.d. Web. 22 Apr. 2017. <http://www.drramsey.com/treating-infections-naturally-2/>.

(11) Deckard, Angela. "11 Proven Peppermint Essential Oil Benefits." *Healthy Focus*. N.p., 28 May 2016. Web. 22 Apr. 2017.

(12) "10 Health Benefits of Roman Chamomile Essential Oil." *Daily Free Health Articles and Natural Health Advice*. N.p., 12 Apr. 2017. Web. 22 Apr. 2017. <http://www.doctorshealthpress.com/general-health-articles/roman-chamomile-essential-oil-uses-benefits>.

(13) Fernández, L. F., O. M. Palomino, and G. Frutos. "Effectiveness of Rosmarinus Officinalis Essential Oil as Antihypotensive Agent in Primary Hypotensive Patients and Its Influence on Health-related Quality of Life." *Journal of Ethnopharmacology*. U.S. National Library of Medicine, n.d. Web. 22 Apr. 2017. <http://www.ncbi.nlm.nih.gov/pubmed/24269249>.

(14) "Do You Know These 6 Health Benefits & Uses for Rosemary Essential Oil?" *The Truth About Cancer*. N.p., 16 Nov. 2016. Web. 22

(15) "15 Amazing Benefits of Sandalwood Essential Oil." *Organic Facts*. N.p., 01 Mar. 2017. Web. 22 Apr. 2017. <https://www.organicfacts.net/health-benefits/essential-oils/sandalwood-essential-oil.html>./.latest_citation_text

(16)"14 Benefits and Uses for Tea Tree Oil." *Authority Nutrition*. N.p., 21 Apr. 2017. Web. 22 Apr. 2017. <https://authoritynutrition.com/tea-tree-oil/>.

REMOVING THE CHEMICALS FROM THE TEMPLE

(1) Earth, Down To. "Your Skin: It Absorbs!" *Down to Earth Organic and Natural*. N.p., 09 July 2016. Web. 29 Apr. 2017. <http://www.downtoearth.org/health/general-health/your-skin-it-absorbs>.

Cleaning the Temple

(1) God's Not Dead. Dir. Harold Cronk. Perf. Kevin Sorbo, Shane Harper, Dean Cane, David A.R. White, Willie Robertson. Pure Flix Entertainment. 2014. DVD

(2)N.p.,n.d.Web.<http://www.bing.com/cr?IG=D52E971F85F5423685B3F165C66560EA&CID=004A57299D8963DA1A805D5A9C1962FA&rd=1&h=ZgVX
UA311m-dvTFPON1MlKBfHPBwW2PGo24-
hfKkbeQ&v=1&r=http%3a%2f%2flindaswellness.yolasite.com%2fresources%2ffragranced%2520consumer%2520products.PDF&p=DevEx,5038.1>.

(3) "How Toxic Are Your Household Cleaning Supplies?" *Organic Consumers Association*. N.p., n.d. Web. 29 Apr. 2017. <https://www.organicconsumers.org/news/how-toxic-are-your-household-cleaning>.

(4) "Cleaning at Home and at Work in Relation to Lung Function Decline and Airway Obstruction." *American Journal of Respiratory and Critical Care Medicine*, www.atsjournals.org/doi/abs/10.1164/rccm.201706-1311OC.

(5) Dovey, Dana. "Common Cleaning Products May Increase Your Risk of Chronic Lung Diseases, Study Shows." *Newsweek*, 11 Sept. 2017, www.newsweek.com/cleaning-products-increase-risk-chronic-lung-disease-asthma-663175.

Resources I have found helpful and Recommend if you want to delve deeper into a subject you find interesting and want to learn more.

Diet: Recommended reading and viewings:

The Daniel Plan: 40 Days to a Healthier Life by Rick Warren, Dr. Daniel Amen, Mark Hyman · Foods to Fight Cancer: Essential Foods to Help Prevent Cancer By Richard Beliveau

Forks Over Knives A documentary, Director: Lee Fulkerson

Food Inc. A documentary, A Robert Kennar Film

The World's Healthiest Foods: Essential Guide for the Healthiest Way of Eating by George Mateljan

Whole Foods: The World's Healthiest Foods: Essential Guide for the Healthiest Way of Eating... by George Mateljan

Fight Back with Food December 30, 2002 by Editors of Reader's Digest
Superfood Kitchen: Cooking with Nature's Most Amazing Foods by Julie Morris
1-degree of change by Standard Process (a free resource found online)

Juicing And Smoothies:
The Juicing Bible
The Big Book of Juices: More Than 400 Natural Blends for Health and Vitality Every Day

Detoxing:
Recommendations:
The 10- Day Detox Diet by Dr. Mark Hyman

The New Detox Diet The Complete Guide for Lifelong Vitality with Recipes, Menus & Detox Plans by Elson M. Haas, M.D.

Websites to help determine if your cleaning supplies are toxic:
https://experiencelife.com/article/8-hidden-toxins-whats-lurking-in-your-cleaning-products/
https://www.organicconsumers.org/news/how-toxic-are-your-household-cleaning-supplies
https://wellnessmama.com/4733/cleaning-checklist/